THE ULTIMATE
EVERYTHING KIDS'
GROSS
Out Book

Nasty and Nauseating Recipes, Jokes, and Activities

Beth L. Blair, Jennifer A. Ericsson, Melinda Sell Frank, Colleen Sell, and Aileen Weintraub

An Everything® Series Book.
Everything® and everything.com® are registered trademarks of F+W Media, Inc.

Contains materials adopted and abridged from *The Everything Kids' Gross Jokes Book*, by Aileen Weintraub, copyright © 2005, F+W Media; *The Everything Kids' Gross Cookbook*, by Colleen Sell and Melinda Sell Frank, copyright ©2007, F+W Media; and *The Everything Kids' Gross Puzzle & Activity Book,* by Beth L. Blair and Jennifer Ericsson, copyright © 2005, F+W Media.

Published by Adams Media, a division of F+W Media, Inc.
57 Littlefield Street, Avon, MA 02322. U.S.A.
www.adamsmedia.com

ISBN: 10: 1-4405-0490-3
ISBN 13: 978-1-4405-0490-7

Printed by R. R. Donnelley, Owensville, MO, US.

10   9   8   7   6   5   4   3   2   1
November 2009

This publication is designed to provide accurate and authoritative information with regard to the subject matter covered. It is sold with the understanding that the publisher is not engaged in rendering legal, accounting, or other professional advice. If legal advice or other expert assistance is required, the services of a competent professional person should be sought.

—From a *Declaration of Principles* jointly adopted by a Committee of the American Bar Association and a Committee of Publishers and Associations

Many of the designations used by manufacturers and sellers to distinguish their products are claimed as trademarks. When those designations appear in this book and Adams Media was aware of a trademark claim, the designations have been printed with initial capital letters.

Cover and Interior illustrations by Kurt Dolber.
Puzzles by Beth L. Blair.

This book is available at quantity discounts for bulk purchases.
For information, please call 1-800-872-5627.

See the entire Everything® series at *www.everything.com.*

Contents

Introduction

Get ready to get grossed out!

This book is totally GROSS!

Gross?

Yes, Gross. You know . . . disgusting, vulgar, possibly even shocking. Parts of it will certainly make you scrunch up your face and yell "EEEW! THAT'S GROSS!"

Are you still reading?

Then you must find gross things fascinating. Maybe you think snot is swell. Perhaps you find tarantulas tasty. You may even think that maggots are marvelous! Well, if grossness is your thing, then you'll definitely love this book.

We've created 28 chapters of great puzzles, jokes, and recipes. We know there is something here to happily gross out every kind of kid!

Also, as you puzzle your way through the book, you might be surprised to find that many of the gross topics included are, in fact, historical, comical, or even useful!

So get ready, get set, get GROSS!

Vowel Scramble

Knick, Knick.
Whi's thara?
Wutsin.
Wutsin whi?
**Wutsin yior nisa?
Et liiks leka u beg
ild biigar!!**

PART 1:
Gross Puzzles

What do you get when you cross a skunk, an owl, and a mountain?

To find the answer to this riddle, think of a word that best fits each of the descriptions below. Write the words on the numbered lines, and then transfer each letter into the numbered grid. The black boxes are the spaces between words.

A. Says "BOO"

G H O S T
42 47 48 1 50

B. To cast a ballot

v o t e
44 49 5 4

C. A small clue

H i n t
22 23 31 41

D. To push hard

S h o v e
19 25 37 29 27

E. Opposite of fat

T h i n
10 6 43 40

F. To put up a picture

H a n g
11 12 17 24

G. A precious jewel

G e m
9 30 3

H. Cousin of a frog

T o a d
13 2 46 35

I. Bugs at a picnic

A n t s
28 8 15 14

J. Do, Re, or Me

N o t e
34 21 20 45

K. Past tense of SAY

s a i d
32 33 7 36

L. Long walks

H i k e s
26 16 18 38 39

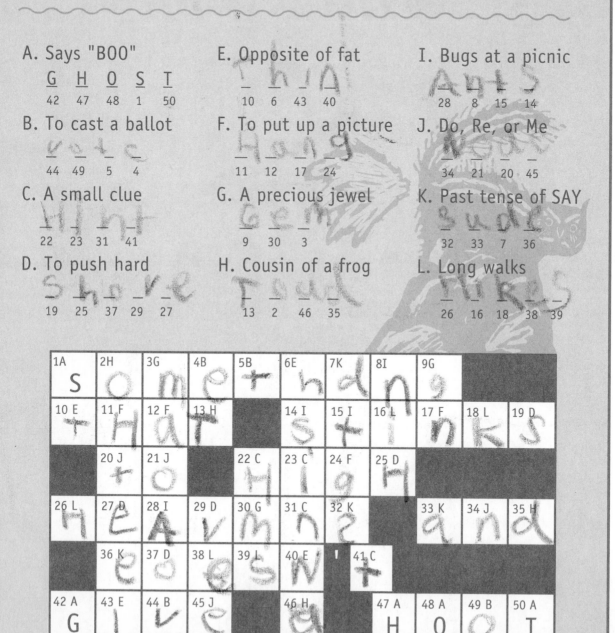

1A S	2H o	3G m	4B e	5B t	6E h	7K i	8I n	9G g		
10E t	11F H	12F a	13H t		14I s	15I t	16L i	17F n	18L k	19D s
	20J t	21J o		22C H	23C i	24F g	25D H			
26L H	27D E	28I A	29D V	30G m	31C n	32K s		33K a	34J n	35H d
	36K e	37D o	38L s	39L n	40E t	41C t				
42A G	43E i	44B v	45J e		46H a		47A H	48A O	49B O	50A T

4

Pillow P.U.

What do you call a tiny, magical being who farts under your pillow?

To find out, connect the dots. Then, put a penny on each of the two dots without numbers. Trace around them to complete the picture.

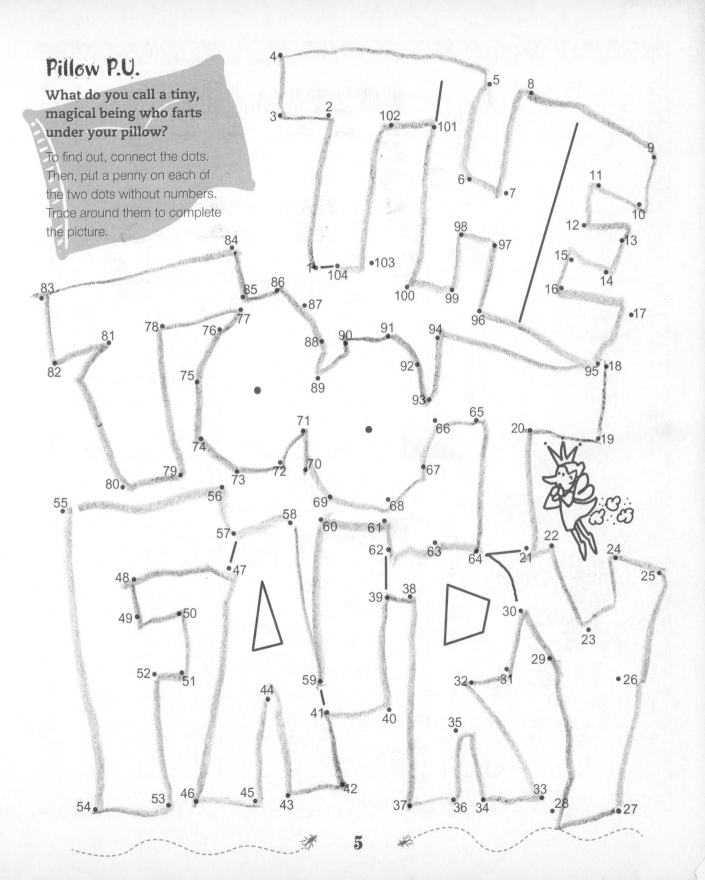

What did the mad scientist say when he finally created a smelly monster?

To find out what the scientist said, use a dark color marker or pencil to color in all the boxes with the letters S-M-E-L-L-Y.

```
▓ B C A ▓ ▓ ▓ ▓ ▓ ▓ ▓ ▓ ▓ ▓ ▓ ▓ C B
A ▓ H F ▓ A ▓ C ▓ B ▓ C ▓ ▓ B ▓ H G
F ▓ W J ▓ F B H D G H A H A G ▓ W K
J G ▓ O ▓ J G ▓ I K W F ▓ F K ▓ Q
O K Q T ▓ O K ▓ P Q ▓ J ▓ ▓ V P
T P V ▓ T P ▓ U V ▓ O U F ▓ U
▓ M D ▓ A X U W N Z A J W T ▓ A ▓ Z
X U I ▓ ▓ Z Q R ▓ O Q ▓ Z ▓ A
B Z N X L B ▓ V W A F T ▓ X C L D F
G E E B Y G C D S L M L V B H Y I G
K L R G F S Y I A F J X A S E F L O
P L W K J K H Y M L E Y E G W C L T
S B C D S A B D S A C L X Q A D I S
A G H S D F G M M F H L S W E M N M
F K W I W J K I E S S E A R G E R A
M P S N M S M N A J W Z F T O L E J
E U M R E A E R L O Q S J D T I Y G
L S E W L F L W L T V M O I X N W E
J M G A L J S A Y X B E T N X R A G
O E K F Y M E B S M E L P R T W B O
T Z P G Q A B C B D H Z P W O D C T
L L S O E M G E S I L W M Q A S E L
Y C M T L F K L C N L N E A G M Q L
S L A X L E P L S R M L N ▓ E Y S
M H L Q S J U Y D W Y B S B W L Z Y
S W E R M L Z E L Q E G E C Q L Q E
```

Officially Bad Breath

Believe it or not, scientists have a special word for stinky breath! To learn what it is, unscramble the words to the right. They are all things that can give you a smelly mouth. Write the unscrambled words on the dotted lines, and read the shaded letters from top to bottom.

LIHIC c h i l i

STIVACIE c A v i t e _ _

QUELAP _ _ _ _ _ _

CLIRAG _ _ _ _ _ _

RATRAT _ _ _ _ _ _

FEEFOC _ _ _ _ _ _

SNIOON _ _ _ _ _ _

FINSECTION _ _ _ _ _ _ _ _ _

MOGINKS _ _ _ _ _ _ _

Do what?!?

Everyone knows that brushing and flossing are good ways to get rid of bad breath. There's something unexpected that also helps! Work your way through the maze picking up letters as you go. Write the letters down in order to reveal another way to clean up a messy mouth.

GROSS, BUT TRUE!

Ancient Egyptians used a toothpaste made from ox hooves and eggshells (first burned, and then ground up), mixed with myrrh (a spice), and pumice (grit).

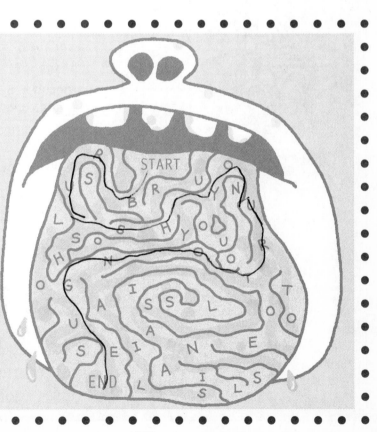

FRANK

FREDD

Fart Foods

Frank and Fredd want to have a farting contest. They have each chosen foods known to make people get tooting. Use the Fart Foods list, below, to see who has the highest score, and will toot more!

Apple Pie *(with cheese)*
Grilled Cheese
Baked Beans
Radishes

Cheese Pizza
Cauliflower
   (with cheese sauce)
Large Cola
Steamed Broccoli
Bean Soup

milk = 1
apples = 2
cheese = 3
onions = 4
radishes = 5
soda = 6
beans = 7
broccoli = 8
cabbage = 9

brussels
sprouts = 10

cauliflower
= 11

Onion Rings

Coleslaw

Milkshake

GROSS, BUT TRUE!

A fart is not a burp that went the wrong way. The chemicals that make up a fart are different than those that make up a burp!

Mon.	
Tues.	
Wed.	
Thurs.	
Fri.	
Sat.	
Sun.	

Fart Chart

Most people fart about 14 times a day. Keep track of the number of times you fart each day for a whole week. Add up all the farts, then divide that number by 7 to find the average number of farts per day.

How do you rate? Are you a "Tiny Tooter" or a "Gale Force"?

GROSS, BUT TRUE!

If you hold in a fart, it doesn't just disappear. It bubbles back up into your intestines, and comes out again later!

_____ ÷ 7 = _____
total farts   *farts per day*

1-3   Tiny Tooter
4-7   Big Wind
8-10   Thunderstorm
11-14 Gale Force
15+   Class 5 Hurricane

Stink Pinks

The answers to Stink Pinks are two rhyming words that each have one syllable. Use the clues to figure these out!

An intelligent toot

_ _ _ _ _ _ _ _ _

Seven days of smelliness

_ _ _ _ _ _ _ _

A fish fart

_ _ _ _ _ _ _ _

A hard, quick sniff

_ _ _ _ _ _ _ _ _

Smell from a moldy camping shelter

_ _ _ _ _ _ _ _ _

An apple passing gas

_ _ _ _ _ _ _ _ _

Smelly odor from a liquid you might swallow

_ _ _ _ _ _ _ _ _

Disgusting Dump

It doesn't take much to make a whole can-full of trash smell pretty putrid. Can you find a used diaper, a slimy banana peel, a rotten egg, a half-eaten chicken leg, a bunch of stinky fish bones, moldy wheel of cheese, moldy slice of bread, a dirty sock, and an old onion? For extra "fun," how many cartons of sour chocolate milk can you count?

Funky Fertilizer

These two farmers are having quite a conversation about their cows' stinky manure. To see what they are saying to each other, figure out where each puzzle piece goes in the empty grids. Then, write the letters in their proper places.

Smelling Sweet?

Change the word SWEET into the word SMELL one letter at a time. For each step, definitions have been provided as clues to the new word.

HINT: Letters might change position from step to step, but only one of the letters will be new.

SWEET	tastes like sugar
	salty body fluid
	to say curse words
	sharp, pointy weapon
	to utter words
	to slap on the butt
	past tense of stink
	main stem of a plant
	horse's room in a barn
	formal form of "will"
	hard outer covering
SMELL	to use your nose

Smell vs. Smell

A certain item has been used throughout history to cover up the smell of unwashed bodies, dirty clothes, and rank rooms. What is it? Place the words in alphabetical order from top to bottom. Read the answer down the shaded boxes.

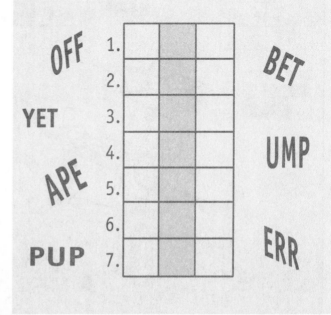

OFF   YET   APE   PUP

1.
2.
3.
4.
5.
6.
7.

BET   UMP   ERR

Super Sweat

Do you know what part of your body sweats the most? To find out, circle the letters that appear only once.

GROSS, BUT TRUE!

On a hot day, your body can make up to four cups of sweat!

It Was the Dog!

START

Travel from START to FART to find out which innocent-looking character really passed the gas.

fart

fart

Ode to Odor

Choose words from the list to complete this rancid rhyme in praise of dirty socks!

_____ socks, they never get _____.

The _____ you _____ them,

the _____ they get!

_____ falls, you _____

of the _____ , but

_____ inside you

says, "Don't _____ them yet!"

LAUNDRY
DIRTY
BLACK
WASH
WEAR
BLACKER
DREAM
LONGER
NIGHT
SOMETHING

EXTRA FUN:
Try filling in this poem using totally different words. Or, try changing the lyrics of a favorite song to make them smellier!

Stinky Socks

Which socks smell the worst? To find out, use the pattern code to count up the points.

GROSS, BUT TRUE!
The Guinness Book of Records lists a researcher who has sniffed over 5,600 pairs of feet!

thin stripes = 2 pts. each
polka dots = 3 pts. each

diamonds = 4 pts. each
fat stripes = 5 pts. each

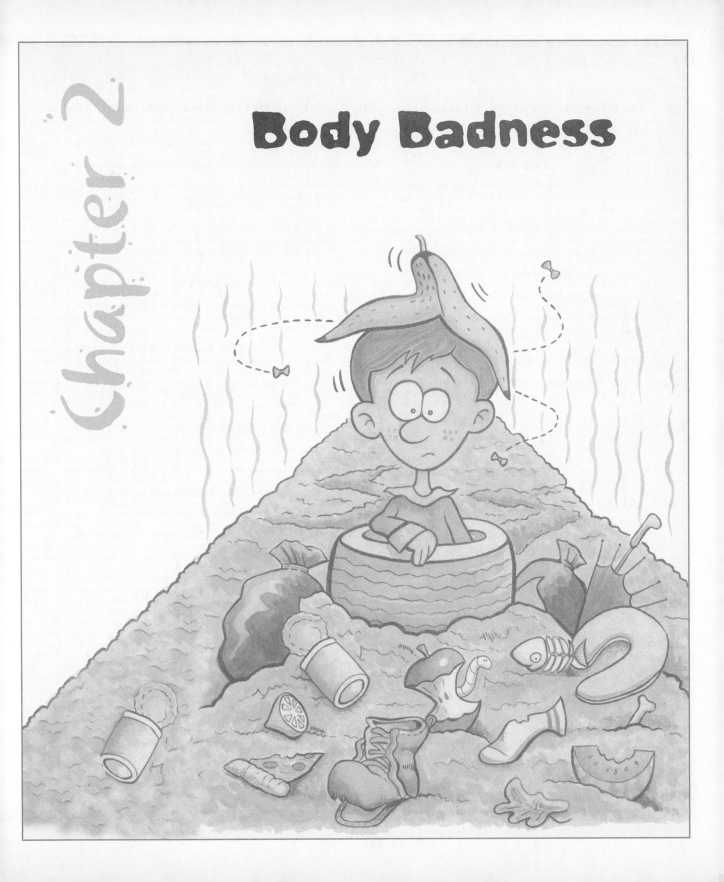

X-tremely Gross

Our bodies can be really gross! Figure out the words suggested by the clues below, and fit them into the grid on the next page. We left a few I-C-K-Y F-A-T B-O-O-G-E-R-S to help.

ACROSS

2. Sound your body makes after a big meal or a fizzy drink.
5. Itchy skin bumps caused by an allergy.
7. When you have the flu, you feel really _____.
10. Crusty covering for a cut.
12. Red, itchy spots all over your skin.
14. Drinking water or holding your breath will sometimes stop these.
15. Another word for GROSS.
16. A hot, red swelling under the skin filled with pus.
18. Another word for "dirt."
19. A brown spot on your skin. Sometimes it's hairy.
20. Most people fart approximately 14 times a _____.
25. Dry flakes of skin from your scalp.
26. Sometimes when your mouth waters, it's a _____ that you're about to throw up.
28. Sweaty hollow under your arm.
30. Another word for GROSS.
32. It is impossible to keep your eyes open when your body does this!
34. A short way to say "That hurt!"
35. More common word for "saliva."
41. Your mouth is where a burp _____ from your body.
42. Another word for "booger."

43. Salty fluid that squirts from your eyes when you smell onions.
44. Wet and sticky, like your eyeball.
45. On a really hot day, your skin _____.
46. Another word that means someone is "smelly."

DOWN

1. A body part that often gets bruised against furniture.
3. Nasty, blood-sucking bugs that can make your scalp all itchy.
4. Another name for a germ that can make you feel gross.
6. The proper word for "hurl."
8. The official name for the slimy fluid in your mouth, nose, and throat.
9. Broken, leaky blood vessels under your skin makes one of these purple blotches.
11. The lump of nerves, blood vessels, body fluid, and tissue inside your skull.
13. The skin on your palms is hairless, but the skin on your head is _____.
16. What gushes out of a nasty cut.
17. Common name for the gunk between your toes. You don't want this on toast!
21. Squishy bubble of liquid on the skin.
22. Believe it or not, this is the strongest muscle in your body!
23. Bumpy growth on your skin caused by a virus, not a toad.
24. Another word for GROSS.

27. When your mom says "You have potatoes in your ears!", she's really talking about this stuff.

29. Yellowish-white liquid that oozes from an infection.

31. Another way to say "smells really bad."

33. Another word for GROSS.

36. Short way of saying "That stinks!"

37. What every kid calls "pimples."

38. In some parts of the world, people eat a kind of _____ made with vegetables, broth, and jelly-fish. Gross!

39. This is your body's largest organ. Hint: It sweats a lot!

40. When you have a really bad cold, snot may _____ out of your nose.

41. A cyclops has only one _____.

Slop Talk

Yuck! Can you grab the slippery letters and fit them into the blanks to create five words? All these words will rhyme with each other, and one of them is a common name for "saliva"!

1. _ _ _ _ _

2. _ _ _ _ _

3. _ _ _ _ _

4. _ _ _ _

5. _ _ _ _ _

Ah-Zoom!

How many miles-per-hour can a sneeze explode out of your nose? To find out, unscramble the eight sneeze-causing words below. Fit the answers into the grid and read down the shaded column. We left a bit of S-N-O-T to help you out!

7. NEOPLL

6. YRELALG

3. TILGH

5. DOCL

8. LOMD

1. EOSMK

2. EREPPP

4. TUDS

1. S
S N O T
2.

3. T
4. T
S N O T
5. O
6.
7. O N
8. O

Dust and Decay

Most of the dust in your house is made up of one particular part of your body. To find out what that is, start at the number one in each of the three sections of this puzzle, and and connect the dots in order.

HINT: Connect the dots with swooping, curved lines—as if you were writing cursive!

-K + F

H +  -C

Vomit Vocab

Everybody vomits, but not everyone calls it the same thing! See if you can figure out the following picture puzzles and word equations. Each one will either spell or act out some familiar vomit vocabulary. How many of these phrases do you use?

EXTRA FUN: See if you can find the answers hidden in the word search!

CHUCK

GROSS
#1 + OPPOSITE OF ME + -Y

SNAKE NOISE + GROSS #1 + FEMALE SHEEP

cHUNK

O	S	T	O	B	S	S	R	F	A	B	T	R
S	P	H	B	L	O	C	H	U	N	K	O	I
M	W	R	O	O	H	F	R	U	H	C	P	D
I	E	P	U	W	O	R	H	T	L	U	S	E
S	P	O	C	C	U	A	B	P	K	H	S	T
S	U	W	H	H	R	B	L	E	U	C	C	H
O	E	L	R	U	H	A	O	W	K	P	O	E
R	K	U	U	N	L	R	W	B	E	U	O	P
G	S	P	Y	K	O	O	C	L	B	P	K	O
B	T	O	S	S	C	O	O	K	I	E	S	R

True or False

Read the following statements about your body. Some of them are True and some of them are False. Circle your answer, then check in the back of the book to see if you're right!

? ? ? ?

1. You have as many hairs on your body as a gorilla.
   TRUE or FALSE
2. Your skull protects your brain so it can't be bruised.
   TRUE or FALSE
3. Cracking your knuckles can lead to arthritis.
   TRUE or FALSE
4. If you hold in a burp, it will become a fart.
   TRUE or FALSE
5. Boogers are very clean.
   TRUE or FALSE
6. Fresh spit is cleaner than fresh pee.
   TRUE or FALSE
7. The scientific name for snot is mucus.
   TRUE or FALSE
8. You will shed 40 pounds of skin in your lifetime.
   TRUE or FALSE

Grossly Gifted

The Guinness Book of Records lists a guy who can blow spaghetti out his nose! How many inches did he shoot a spaghetti strand to earn this honor? Complete the equations below to find out.

$$4 + 6 - 5\frac{1}{2} = \underline{\hspace{2cm}}$$

$$7 - 6 + \frac{1}{2} - 2 = \underline{\hspace{2cm}}$$

$$3 + 1\frac{1}{2} - 4\frac{1}{2} = \underline{\hspace{2cm}}$$

$$6 - 4\frac{1}{2} + 1 = \underline{\hspace{2cm}}$$

$$9\frac{1}{2} - 8 - \frac{1}{2} = \underline{\hspace{2cm}}$$

Total inches = \underline{\hspace{2cm}}

Edible Earwax

Here's an easy way to make a gross-out treat for your next party. Don't wait for Halloween—earwax is good to eat any time of year!

You will need:
An adult to help with the oven
1 tube ready-bake sugar cookie dough
1 small jar of apricot preserves
½ cup golden (not brown) raisins
dinner knife
teaspoon
spatula
oven-mitts

1. Read the directions on the tube of sugar cookie dough, and ask your adult helper to preheat the oven to 350°.

2. Together with your helper, slice the cookie dough into slices about ¼ inch thick. Cut each circular slice in half, and place on an ungreased cookie sheet, about 2 inches apart. Take a pinch of dough and roll it into a ball the size of a marble. Stick a dough ball on the bottom edge of each half circle.

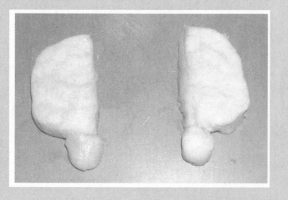

3. Poke your fingertip into each "ear" to make a hole for the earwax.

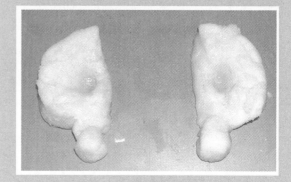

4. Fill the hole with a very small scoop of apricot preserves, about ¼ teaspoon. Stick one or two raisins in the preserves.

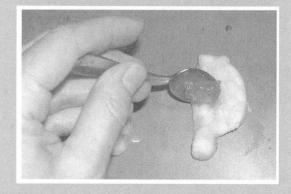

5. Bake ears for 11 minutes, until golden brown all over and puffy.

6. Have your helper take the cookies out of the oven. While the cookies are still on the cookie sheet, and still hot, take a metal teaspoon and gently press the tip into the cookie to make the shape of the ridges in the ear. We think it looks best to make two ridges, one close to the edge of the ear, and a smaller ridge in close to the earwax.

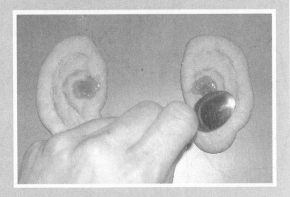

7. Use a spatula to slide the ears off the cookie sheet. Cool on a wire rack. This recipe will make at least 18 pairs of ears with wax. YUM!

What Smells?

You can almost read the joke below, but something isn't quite right! Figure out which letters have been switched to see what these two stinkers are really talking about.

Stenky: Thasa pells E git ti gat red if B.I. din't wirk.

Penky: Why nit?

Stenky: Thay kaap fulleng iot frim ondar my urms!

Acne Art

Artie has a horrible case of zits! But if you connect them all in order by number, the end result is rather cool.

GROSS, BUT TRUE!

Scientists in England were happy to discover a pile of fossilized vomit estimated to be 160 million years old! The vomit gave them information about what ichthyosaurs (ancient marine reptiles) ate.

Pus-itively Putrid

You get a cut, it gets dirty, it gets hot and red and suddenly there's a lot of icky, yellowish-white pus gooshing around in there. This is a sure sign that your body is fighting off an infection, but what is that gross and goopy pus made of? Use a reverse letter substitution code (A=Z, B=Y, C=X, etc.) to find out!

WVZW YZXGVIRZ, WVZW DSRGV

YOLLW XVOOH, ZMW WVZW YLWB

XVOOH UOLZGRMT RM YLWB UOFRW

How did the teen with acne leave the jail?

To get the answer to this riddle, figure out which letters are described by each fraction. Print the letters, in order, in the boxes from left to right.

1. First ⅔ of HEAVED
2. Middle ⅓ of DEBRIS
3. Last ⅗ of CHOKE
4. Last ½ of SPROUT

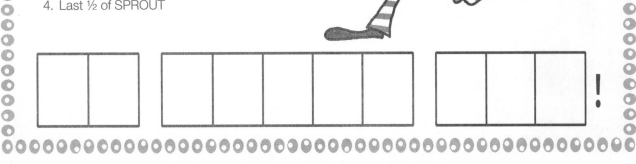

!

Nasty Rashes

Most of the time your skin is smooth, unbroken, and skin colored. But once in a while it gets itchy, oozy, bumpy, and yucky! Figure out the word and letter puzzles to find the name of six nasty rashes that can make you want to scratch your skin off!

GROSS, BUT TRUE!
"Scabies" is a nasty rash caused by a teeny tiny mite, or bug, that digs into the skin. The female mite lays her eggs, and the burrowing, growing, chomping baby mites make your skin itch like crazy. You can often see the zigzag tunnels they make as they move around. GROSS!

1. Places where bees live

2. Popular poultry + saucepan − 20th letter + letter 3rd from end

3. Killer chemical + 9th letter + letter 5th from end

4. Finger jewelry + wiggly bait

5. A little stick from a needle + LY + 8th letter + consume food

Hurry Up!

Someone has really gotta go! Quickly collect all the words with the same number from the grid and write them in their numbered bathroom door. Rearrange the words to get the answer to each door's desperate plea.

1	4	3	2	4
Ben	**the**	**done**	**will**	**NOW!**
3	2	5	3	1
you'll	**be**	**up**	**Hope**	**long**
4	5	1	4	3
RIGHT	**there!**	**a**	**toilet**	**soon!**
1	2	3	5	2
waiting	**Gwen**	**be**	**in**	**you**
2	1	5	1	4
done?	**really**	**Harriet**	**time!**	**Anita**

1

Knock, knock.
Who's there?
Ben.
Ben who?

2

Knock, knock.
Who's there?
Gwen.
Gwen who?

3

Knock, knock.
Who's there?
Hope.
Hope who?

4

Knock, knock.
Who's there?
Anita.
Anita who?

5

Knock, knock.
Who's there?
Harriet.
Harriet who?

The answers to Stink Pinks are two rhyming words that each have one syllable. Use the clues to figure these out!

A bunch of Boy Scouts all going #2 at the same time

_ _ _ _ _   _ _ _ _

Tiny tinkle

_ _ _   _ _ _

Long time you sat when constipated

_ _ _ _ _   _ _ _ _ _

Fast press of the toilet handle

_ _ _ _   _ _ _ _ _

Line of poop on the toilet paper

_ _ _ _   _ _ _ _ _

When you accidentally throw up on your mom's fancy clothes

_ _ _ _ _   _ _ _ _

What kind of nasty nuts and vulgar vegetables can you find in a toilet bowl?

Color in all the letters that appear more than three times. Read the remaining letters from left to right, and top to bottom to get the answer.

B P F E H J E H
N H U F B O T
M B H F M R S
G V A M R J G
O V M C J V N
F H D M J R R
G F C O R V L F
M E C V O G J
A G B C F H K
G C H S B V O

CONSTIPATION

Sometimes you just can't poop! Take this puzzle with you into the bathroom while you are waiting for "something" to happen. OK, are you sitting comfortably? Now, see how many three-letter words you can make from the letters C-O-N-S-T-I-P-A-T-I-O-N. Try to make fifteen.

Nothing yet? OK, try a little harder to make twelve words with four letters each!

Still nothing?? First, go eat some prunes. Then see if you can squeeze out five words with five letters each.

Give yourself a bonus "poop-point" for each six-letter word!

Why did the toilet paper roll down the hill?

To find out, start at the top of the hill. Pick up every other letter as you follow the roll down to the bottom of the page. The trick is to pick the correct letter to start with!

Write the correct letters on the dotted lines provided.

T T H O I G S E I T S T N O O T T H E C B O E R O R T E C O T

_ _
_ _ _
_ _
_ _ _ _
_ _ _ _ _ _ !

GROSS, BUT TRUE!
On Earth, gravity makes poops plop into the toilet. But in outer space there is no gravity! That's why NASA developed a high-tech toilet that uses a vacuum to suck poop down into a special container. Otherwise, smelly "asteroids" would be floating all over the inside of the space shuttles!

Silly Sentences

Each sentence can be completed by picking one letter of the alphabet to fill in the blanks.
Can you say each sentence three times fast?

__ reddy __ arted __ ifty __ ast __ umes.

__ eter __ ooped __ artly __ ointy __ ieces.

__ ictor __ omited __ ery __ iolet __ itamins.

__ herese __ inkled __ welve __ iny __ imes.

__ illy __ lew __ lue __ oogers __ ackwards.

__ teven __ pit __ oggy __ unflower __ eeds.

GROSS, BUT TRUE! You might think that a fancy castle would have fancy bathrooms, too. Nope! The bathrooms, or "garderobes" were usually hollowed out of the wall in a tower. Some garderobes had a chute that went down into a sewer pit; others just dumped into the moat!

How do two pieces of "number 2" greet one another?

The answer to this rancid riddle has been put in a grid, and cut into pieces. Figure out where each piece fits, and fill the letters into the empty grid.

Be careful: Some of the pieces have been turned around!

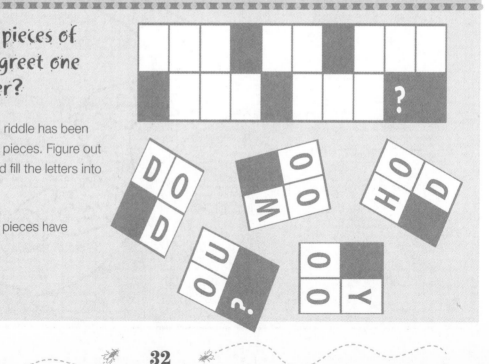

Anti-Gross

While it may be fun to read about gross stuff, no one really likes to smell it. But we all know that the air in the bathroom can get wicked gross! Here's a recipe for a homemade air freshener that's sure to get the stink out.

You will need:
small spray bottle that holds 2-4 oz. (available at local drug store)
essential oils (available at local health food store or craft store)
bottled water, either plain or distilled
rubbing alcohol

1. To sterilize the spray bottle: Place 1 tablespoon of rubbing alcohol in the bottle, screw the lid on and shake vigorously. Dump out the alcohol and let the bottle air dry upside down. Fill the bottle with ¼ cup bottled water and add a combination of up to three different essential oils to total 15-20 drops.

2. Here are some good combinations:
8 drops LEMON, 6 drops LAVENDER, 6 drops ROSEMARY
5 drops CLOVE, 9 drops ORANGE, 6 drops VANILLA
5 drops LEMON, 5 drops ORANGE, 5 drops PEPPERMINT

3. Essential oils evaporate rapidly, so don't mix batches larger than ¼ cup at a time—it will lose its scent if it sits around too long. Shake the bottle well before each use to mix the oil with the water.

EXTRA FUN: Make a special label for your bottle of super smell buster!

Clue	Answer pattern
A step on a ladder	**R U N** __
Smallest one in a litter	**R U N** __
What a model walks down	**R U N** __ __ __
Someone who likes to run	**R U N** __ __ __
Breakfast and lunch combo	__ **R U N** __ __
Past tense of drink	__ **R U N** __
Dirty and messy	__ **R U N** __ __
A noisy, crackling chew	__ **R U N** __ __
A fruit that helps you poop	__ **R U N** __
Main stem of a tree	__ **R U N** __
Short, deep sound	__ **R U N** __
To play again	__ __ **R U N**

Run! Run! Run!

When you have diarrhea, you are constantly running to the bathroom. See how quickly you can complete all these words that contain the letters R-U-N.

What is white, full of poop, and can be found in a playroom?

Hold this puzzle up to the bathroom mirror and see if you can figure out how to read it!

Target Practice

Pete, Pablo, and Perry are each shooting "liquid ammunition" at this familiar target! Can you figure out who has made which puddles?

Count the points each marksman has scored using these rules:

Add the value of each ring a puddle is in

Subtract 10 points for each puddle on the bathroom floor

A direct hit in the toilet is worth 15 extra points

If a boy hasn't left any puddles on the floor, he gets 20 extra points

Pete

Pablo

Perry

20 30 40 50 40 30 20

Why did that guy . . .

To find the answer to this riddle, think of a word that best fits each of the descriptions at right. Write the words on the numbered lines, and then transfer each letter into the numbered grid.

Why did that guy bring toilet paper to a birthday party?

1D	2D	3A	4A	5C	6C	7B
8D	9E	10E		11B		
12B	13E	14B	15D	16E		
17C	18C	19D	20A	21A	22D	

A. Robe worn by superheroes

___ ___ ___ ___
3   4   20   21

B. Autumn fruit

___ ___ ___ ___
12   7   11   14

C. Meat or veggies cooked in broth

___ ___ ___ ___
6   18   5   17

D. To annoy

___ ___ ___ ___ ___ ___
1   19   15   8   2   22

E. Not hard

___ ___ ___ ___
9   13   10   16

Gotta Go

There are many ways to say you have to go to the bathroom.
Match up the floating words to make seven different phrases.

LEAK

NATURE WHIZ

THE THE TO HEAD

TAKE

GO

CALLS CAN FILL TAKE THE

A PEE HIT A GOT

TO JOHN

HINT:
Cross off words as you use them to be sure you use them all.

1. _____ _____
2. _____ _ _____
3. _____ _ _____
4. _____ _ _____

5. ____ ____ _____
6. ____ ____ ____ _____
7. ____ ____ _____

J EPO'U TXJN

JO ZPVS

UPJMFU,

TP EPO'U

QFF JO

NZ QPPM!

It's the Rule!

Figure out this letter substitution code (A=B, B=C, C=D, etc.) to find out what the lifeguard is yelling about!

Bathroom Pass

These kids all have their hands raised to go and use the bathroom. Who needs to go the most? Add all the numbers "1" and "2" hidden on each student and their desk. Whoever has the highest score gets to go first!

GROSS, BUT TRUE!
In Ancient Rome there was no toilet paper. In a public bathroom you would have to use a sponge soaked in saltwater on a stick!

The Putrid Painter

Gomer's grandpa is a famous painter, but he only uses disgusting colors! Can you figure out his favorites? The label on each tube of paint is missing letters that can be found in the word R-E-V-O-L-T-I-N-G.

S_CK
S_NNA

M_ _DY
G_ _D

S_ _ _KY
P_ _K

G_U_GY
G_E_ _

_OM_ _ _
_I_LE_

BU_ P
B_U_

U_I_E
YE_ _OW

P_MP_ _
PU_P_ _

BA_F
B_ _GE

GROSS, BUT TRUE!

Hundreds of years ago, painters used to mix colored pigments with eggs to make a smooth and long-lasting paint called "egg tempera." Sometimes they would also add earwax to the mix to help get rid of tiny bubbles!

What is long and pointy and runs in a family?

Color in all the shapes that have the letters P-O-I-N-T-Y inside.

Baby Brother B.O.

One of Luis's little brothers has a load in his diaper. Using the logic clues below, can you sniff out which one it is?

He has curly hair
He is wearing a shirt and a diaper
He is sitting between Lance and Larry
He is not sucking his thumb

Lance

Luke

Leo

Larry

Lenny

How can you tell if
your brother is upside down?

Solve as many clues below as you can and put the letters in their proper place in the grid. Work back and forth between the grid and the clues until you can read the answer to this gross riddle.

A. A good time

‾‾ ‾‾ ‾‾
18   9   4

B. Happy faces have these

‾‾ ‾‾ ‾‾ ‾‾ ‾‾ ‾‾
6   23 16 25   7 11

C. To make better

‾‾ ‾‾ ‾‾ ‾‾ ‾‾
1   19 12 26 17

D. Number after eight

‾‾ ‾‾ ‾‾ ‾‾
10   2 13 20

E. Decays

‾‾ ‾‾ ‾‾ ‾‾
8   5 21 22

F. Small storage building

‾‾ ‾‾ ‾‾ ‾‾
3   15 24 14

1C	2D	3F		4A	5E	6B	7B
8E	9A	10D	11B		12C	13D	14F
15F	16B	17C		18A	19C	20D	21E
22E	23B	24F	25B	26C			
					!		

Juicy Jobs?

Some jobs just have to be done, but that doesn't mean you would want to do them! Look at the picture clues to help you unscramble each job title. Could they pay you enough to do these things?

TROPA-TOPTY NEALCER
_____

EPT DOOF STERAT
_____

OPOP YALSTAN
_____

REWES VIRED
_____

IRAMPT RFISNFE
_____

GROSS, BUT TRUE!

The poop, pee, and everything else from 20 million people all flows into the ancient sewer system of Mexico City, Mexico. The liquid that sloshes through the more than 800 miles of pipes is so murky and full of "stuff," even a spotlight can't cut through it. That's why the special divers sent to unplug pipes and repair leaks have to feel their way around!

Uncle Leon's Lovely Leg

NOT! Uncle Leon's leg is anything but lovely. Start at his knee and see if you can find a path all the way down through his big bunion. Watch out for the varicose veins, rashes, scabs, hair, and athlete's foot along the way—eeeew!

START

END

Just Joking!

Use the names from the list, right, to answer the following questions.

Careful: There are extra names!

What would be a good name for a relative with no arms and no legs who . . .

1. ...sits in the butter dish?
2. ...sits in the mailbox?
3. ...hangs on the wall?
4. ...holds up your car?
5. ...lives in the bushes?
6. ...lies by the door?

1. _____

2. _____

3. _____

4. _____

5. _____

6. _____

PAT MATT
RUSSELL
NEAL
BILL BOB
MARK ART
JACK EILEEN

44

Scritch Scratch

Uncle Steve is always scratching! The names of 12 of his itchiest places are hidden in the grid below. To find them, put a different letter of the alphabet into each of the empty boxes. You might be adding the letter at the beginning, middle, or end of a word. Each letter on the list will be used only once. Circle each word as you find it.

C E G H K L
M N O R S T

1.	F	A	R		P	I	T
2.	S	C	A		P	O	P
3.	E	N	O		E	A	T
4.	B	E	L		H	I	N
5.	L	U	O		E	C	K
6.	B	A	C		S	I	D
7.	E	R	C		E	S	T
8.	O	B	U		T	E	N
9.	T	H	A		M	E	T
10.	S	L	E		I	G	E
11.	E	S	T		E	N	O
12.	R	U	B		L	L	Y

Bob's Bad Body Noises

One day Brenda counted her brother Bob making eight different disgusting noises! Can you find how many times Bob made each one? Use a light-colored marker to run a single line of color through each word you find. Make a mark in the box next to a word each time you find it.

EXTRA FUN: Use a dark marker to color all the letters X. What do you see when you're done?

BELCH	
FART	
GAG	
GRUNT	
GULP	
RETCH	
SNIFF	
SNORT	

```
W F A R T G A G W G R U N T W G
T R A F X X X X X X X X K W T U
S K W X G A G B E L C H X R K L
N W X T R O N S R G A G A X W P
O X G S K X W F E K X F W T X K
R X A N X K X A T X K X W R X S
T X G I X X X R C X X X G O X N
W X F F X X X T H X X X R N X I
K X A F W F G A G W G G U S X F
S X R W A W X X X X A A N W X F
N X T R W T N U R G G G T K X B
I X T X X X X X X X X X X W X E
F X R E T C H X G G X W K T X L
F X G A G G G X A A X K R T X C
K G X W K A A X B G G X O R X G H
G U W X W G G W X X N A X W A G
A L K W X G U L P S F X W K G A
G P G A G X X X X X X T R A F G
B E L C H W K P L U G S N I F F
```

Very Funny, Grandpa!

Greg's Gramps lives in a cabin without indoor plumbing. When Greg visits, he has to use the outhouse! Help him find it by making compound words through the grid. You can move left, right, up, down, but not diagonally.

START GRAND	CHILD	LIKE	WISE	MEN
MOTHER	BIRTH	DOWN	RIGHT	HORSE
HOOD	DAY	BREAK	HAND	CLOTH
ON	TIME	TABLE	OUT	HOUSE END

After visiting the outhouse, see if you can decipher this Grandpa joke.

Hint: A mirror will help!

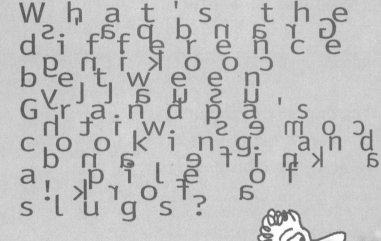

What's the difference between Grandpa's cooking and a pile of slugs?

JUST FOLLOW YOUR NOSE...

GROSS, BUT TRUE!

Before indoor bathrooms were available, people were frequently bitten by spiders that lived in their outhouses. That's enough to make your skin crawl!

Family Photos

Can you find the 10 differences between these two photos? Which one would you send to Grandma?

What do you call your cousin who never uses a tissue to wipe his nose?

To get the answer to this joke, figure out which letters are described by each fraction. Print the letters, in order, in the boxes from left to right.

1. First 3/6 of GREASE
2. Last 1/3 of DAMPEN
3. First 1/2 of SLOP
4. Middle 1/3 of WET
5. Middle 3/5 of SEVEN
6. First 1/4 of SPIT

Relatively Gross

The next time you get together with your family, and especially a bunch of cousins your age, why not have a contest to see who can make the best gross noise? Or let everyone make a different noise, but all at the same time! Here are a few suggestions:

The Classic Armpit Fart

Put the open palm of your right hand under your left armpit. Cup the hand slightly. Now flap your left arm up and down, and squeeze the air, and fart noises, out from under your palm. This works best if your palm is moist. You can wait till you're sweaty, wet your hand in the sink, or lick your palm! You can also make fart noises by cupping your two damp hands across each other and squeezing the palms together.

Sick Elephant

You'll Need: toilet paper tube, rubber band, tape, paper punch, scissors, waxed paper

Take the tube and punch a hole in the side, about an inch from one end. Cut a circle of waxed paper bigger than the end of the tube. Use the rubber band to hold the waxed paper over the same end of tube where you punched the hole, making sure not to cover the hole. To make sick elephant sounds, put your mouth over the open end of the tube and hum, moan, sing, or talk funny.

Shriekers

Blow up a balloon and hold it closed, but not tied. Let the air out very slowly, stretching the neck of the balloon to change the sound.

Barking Belcher

You'll Need: waxed paper cup, wooden toothpick, yarn, scissors, sharp pencil

Cut a piece of yarn about 6 inches long. Soak the yarn in water until it is really wet. Tie one end around the toothpick. Use a pencil to poke a hole in the middle of the bottom of the paper cup. Push the end of the wet yarn through the hole so the yarn is hanging out of the cup and the toothpick is lying flat inside. You might have to break a bit off the toothpick to make it fit. Wet your thumb and forefinger and pinch the yarn just below the cup. Pull down hard.

HINT: If you don't get a sound, wet your fingers more. Also, a longer piece of yarn will give you a deeper belch!

What did the monster mama say to her son?

Add straight and diagonal lines to find the answer.

STOP PICKING YOUR NOSES!

EXTRA FUN: Can you tell which shadow exactly matches the picture, above?

Losing Lunch

Have a friend help you finish this story. Don't show them the story first! Ask your helper for the kind of word needed for each blank line (a description is written underneath). Write in the words your helper chooses, then read the story out loud.

EXTRA FUN: Use a pencil, then you can erase the words and try again!

(_____) I had a (_____) stomach
   day of the week   _awful adjective_

ache. I don't know why! At lunch I only ate (_____)
                                              big number

(_____) and (_____)(_____).
   food item, plural   _big number_   _different food item, plural_

For dessert I had (_____) (_____). By the time I
                    number   _food item, plural_

got home, I felt (_____). My stomach started
                   awful adjective

(_____) and my face turned (_____). I ran for the
 action word   _color_

bathroom, but my (_____) brother, (_____),
                   awful adjective   _boy's name_

was in there. Sometimes he stays

in there for (_____) hours.
              big number

Oh no! So I ran into the

(_____), instead,
 room in your house, not the bathroom

and threw up in a (_____).
                    container

I felt much better after that!

Yum! Bugs!

How would you like scorpion soup for dinner? Perhaps grasshopper tacos or spaghetti with mealworms? Believe it or not, bugs are a tasty and nutritious food! See if you can find all the edible bugs hidden in the word search.

grub
scorpion
tarantula
beetle
grasshopper
worm
termite
dragonfly
stink bug
spider
caterpillar
ant
silkworm
waterbug
cricket
cicada

```
W E Y L F N O G A R D H G
A T E K C I R C T D O Y U
O I U C I C A D A G E T B
I M F A N T B Y O U N C K
G R R T O S E S M R O W N
U E A E T E E R M I I T I
B T A R A N T U L A P G T
R E W P I T L H A B R O S
E O K I A N E I N U O S P
T E C L T T H A B T C E I
A S I L K W O R M A S T D
W S I A T S O W N W O R E
D S G R A S S H O P P E R
```

EXTRA FUN: After you have found all the bugs, collect the leftover letters from left to right and top to bottom and write them in order on the lines below.

_ _ _ _ _ _ _ _ _ _ _ _ _ _ _ _ _ _ _ _ _ _

_ _ _ _ _ _ _ _ _ _ _ _ ? _ _ _ _ _ _ _

_ _ _ _ _ _ _ _ _ _ _ _ _ !

Waiter! There's a fly in my soup!

This man does not eat bugs. He is not pleased to find a fly in his soup! Collect all the words with the same number from the grid and write them in the numbered soup bowl. Rearrange the words to get the answers that four different waiters gave to this unhappy diner.

2 That's	3 like	2 of	3 they	1 everyone
4 has	1 quiet,	4 Oops!	2 There's	4 a
2 enough	4 Today's	3 rotten	1 will	4 yesterday's
4 soup	2 you!	1 Be	4 That's	2 for
1 want	3 Yes,	4 soup.	2 OK!	1 one!
3 food!	1 or	2 both	3 really	4 beetle.

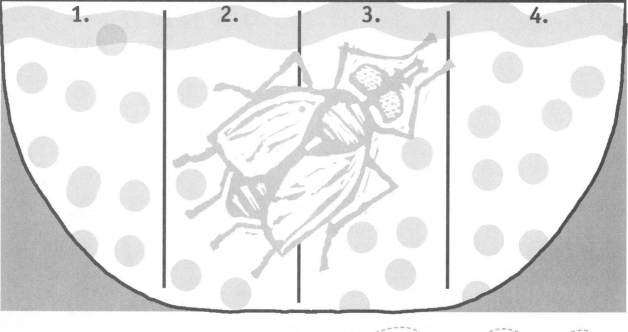

1.

2.

3.

4.

Clean the Fridge!

Know how leftovers get when they have been in the fridge a reeeeeeally long time? Fit the eighteen words that describe how gross they look (and smell) into the grid, right. When you are done, read down the shaded column to find the answer to the riddle. We left you a few L-E-F-T-O-V-E-R-S to help!

SLIMY	**TOXIC**
STINKY	**ROTTEN**
MOLDY	**OOZING**
SCARY	**CRUSTY**
PUTRID	**SMELLY**
GREEN	**YUCKY**
RANCID	**FETID**
NASTY	**WEIRD**
FIZZY	**VOMITOUS**

What do leftovers turn into if you leave them in the fridge too long?

Peanut Butter and . . . ?

You may like peanut butter sandwiches with jelly or marshmallow. But some people like peanut butter with more unusual foods! Complete each of the food items below with letters from the word PEANUT BUTTER.

_ O L O G N _

_ O _ _ _ O CHI _ S

CHOCOL _ _ _

B _ CO _

CH _ _ S _

_ ICKL _ S

M _ S _ _ _ D

_ _ _ SL _ Y

M _ YO _ _ _ IS _

O _ IO _

_ . _ . Q. _ S _ _ C _

START

END

EXTRA FUN: Munch your way through this unusual sandwich from START to END. Find any strange ingredients?

Poll your friends—which P.B. combo is their favorite?

Gag Man, Glad Man

Gag Man has to eat some-thing slimy and gross. He will be glad when he is done! Can you help? Get through the maze alter-nating from Gag Man to Glad Man. You can move up and down and side to side, but not diagonally. If Gag Man throws up, you are going the wrong way!

Broccoli, Turnip, and Liver Casserole

Suppose you are served something really gross for dinner—what would you do? Ask your friends and families which of the following would be their way to deal with an awful meal (they can only pick one answer). Write their name in the square next to their choice. Your graph will show if one answer is the most popular!

Roll your eyes, but try it anyway.							
Hide it under other food on your plate.							
Slip it in your napkin to throw away later.							
Feed it to the dog.							

Lose Your Appetite

Have you ever been so grossed out watching someone eat that you just don't feel like eating your own meal anymore? While you're watching this disgusting diner, see if you can find the 15 items hidden in the mess.

Look for: cat's face, cow, key, face of a king, sock, teacup, flying bird, daisy, spoon, ghost, needle, gingerbread man, tic tac toe grid, caterpillar, witch hat.

Bug Eater

There is a special term for the practice of eating bugs. Use the clues to fill in the rows from top to bottom. When you are done, read down the shaded column.

Clue			
You sleep in this at night			
The number before two			
Past tense of eat			
Opposite of cold			
Referee at a ballgame			
Man's best friend			
Relative of a monkey			
Not "he"			
Very angry			
Years you have lived			
You wink with this			

Delicious Delicacies

A "delicacy" is something to eat that is considered rare or luxurious. Using the clues, figure out these six delicacies that some people really enjoy eating. Would you try any of them?

GROSS, BUT TRUE!

Natives of Iceland celebrate their Viking heritage at a Thorrablot feast. The menu might include sheep's blood pudding, boiled lamb's heads, and rotten shark meat—dug up after being buried for months!

Milk-giver's smart parts

_ _ _   _ _ _ _ _ _

Cud chewer's mouth muscle

_ _ _   _ _ _ _ _ _

Hopper's essential parts

_ _ _ _   _ _ _ _

Baa baa's tum tum

_ _ _ _ _   _ _ _ _ _ _

Ape's kissing equipment

_ _ _ _ _ _   _ _ _ _

Porker's walkers

_ _ _   _ _ _

Make a Mold Factory

Molds are a kind of fungi that grow on food and in damp places. There are thousands of different kinds. Although you don't really want them in your house, molds are good natural recyclers outside. They break down foods and return nutrients to the soil. If you would like to see some molds at work, try making this "Mold Factory."

Here's what you'll need:
Permission from an adult.
1 clean, empty mayo jar with lid
Masking tape
Water
Small pieces (approx 1 inch) of food like bread, fruit, vegetables or cheese.

NOTE: Avoid meat as it will rot and smell before it grows mold.

Here's what you do:

1. Open the jar and lay it on its side.

2. Dip each piece of food in the water and place it in your container. Space the pieces so they are not all on top of each other.

3. Carefully, screw the lid on the jar and seal it with masking tape.

4. Make a label for your "Mold Factory" and attach it.

5. Put your Factory in a safe place where you can watch it.

6. Look at your Mold Factory every day. You won't see much for 2-3 days, but then molds will start to grow on the food. Answer these questions:

What colors of mold grew?
What texture were they?
What food got moldy first?
Did all the foods get moldy?

7. As the days pass, the food in your factory will start to look really gross. The mold is breaking the food down and causing it to rot.

8. Watch the changes for about two weeks. After that, not much else will happen.

9. Do not remove the lid from your Mold Factory. After two weeks, throw your factory out!

GROSS, BUT TRUE!

The mushrooms that many people like to eat on pizza or in spaghetti sauce are one kind of fungus. Athlete's Foot and Ringworm (both itchy, oozy skin conditions) are caused by two other kinds of fungus!

To Market

In many countries, going to the market is quite an adventure. If you were sent to get food for dinner, you might not want to eat anything! Use written and picture clues to see if you can decipher this unusual shopping list. Write the items you are shopping for in the spaces provided.

1 P.H. (with big ears)

4 D.F. (clean webbing)

3 F. (good jumpers)

4 T. (with all 8 legs)

1 S. (watch stinger)

15 W. (wiggly)

2 G. (necks 9 inches)

The Barf Buffet

What's on the menu today? Figure out which code is used for each answer. Break the codes to find out what "goodies" are being served!

1. Sore Throat Drink
2. Smells Bad Snack Food
3. Bad Hair Breakfast Food
4. Foam-at-the-Mouth Dessert

Simple Letter Shift
(A=B, B=C, C=D, etc.)

Reverse Simple Letter Shift
(A=Z, B=A, C=B, etc.)

First-to-Last Letter Shift
(BOOK becomes OOKB)

Reverse Letter Substitution
(A=Z, B=Y, C=X, etc.)

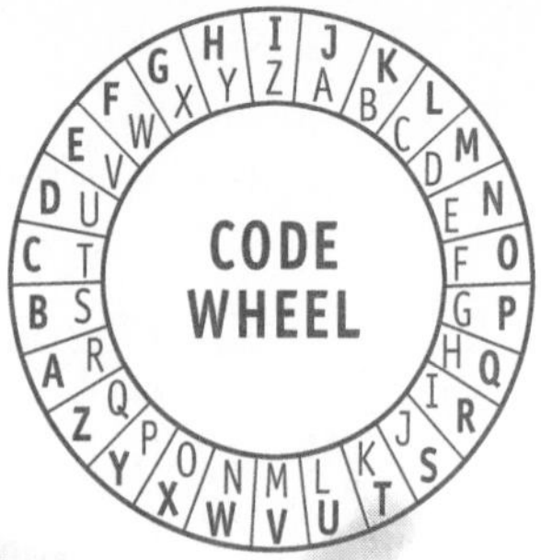

CODE WHEEL

XLFTS-VV

EBOESVGG
GMZLFT

RSDMBG EQHDR

AKEC FO
OAPS

White stuff from the sky?

Remember that there are many disgusting things that can drop on you from out of the blue. Think of a word that best fits each of the clues on the next page. Write the words on the numbered lines, and then transfer each letter into the numbered grid. Work back and forth until you can read this good advice. It might just keep you from getting a whole mouthful of gross!

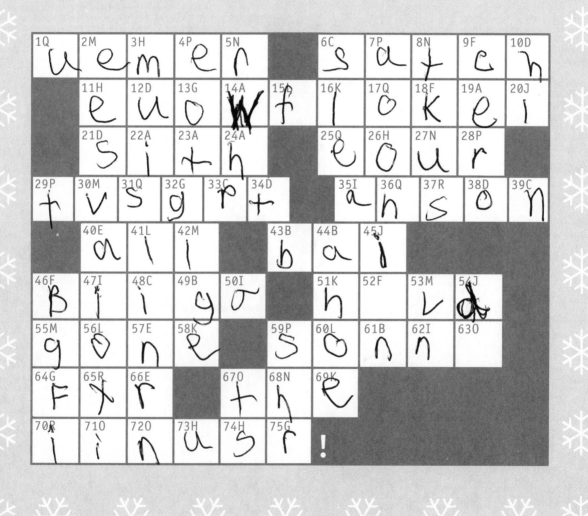

1Q	2M	3H	4P	5N		6C	7P	8N	9F	10D
u	e	m	e	r		s	a	t	c	h

	11H	12D	13G	14A	15Q	16K	17Q	18F	19A	20J
	e	u	o	w	f	l	o	k	e	i

	21D	22A	23A	24A		25Q	26H	27N	28P	
	s	i	t	h		e	o	u	r	

29P	30M	31Q	32G	33C	34D		35I	36Q	37R	38D	39C
t	v	s	g	r	t		a	h	s	o	n

	40E	41L	42M		43B	44B	45J				
	a	l	l		b	a	j				

46F	47I	48C	49B	50I		51K	52F	53M	54J		
B	l	i	g	a		h		v	d		

55M	56L	57E	58K		59P	60L	61B	62I	63O		
g	o	n	e		s	o	n	n			

64G	65R	66E		67O	68N	69K					
F	r	r		t	h	e					

70R	71O	72O	73H	74H	75G						
i	i	n	u	s	r	!					

A. Opposite of black

white
14 24 22 23 19

B. A heavy, dropping sound

bang
43 44 61 49

C. To wind around

spin
6 33 48 39

D. High, complaining voice

shout
21 10 38 12 34

E. Past tense of run

ran
66 40 57

F. Opposite of front

back
46 52 9 18

G. Toad's relative

frog
64 75 13 32

H. Casts a ballot

mouse
3 26 73 74 11

I. Pants and jacket combo

Jain
50 35 47 62

J. Take in with the eyes

lid
20 45 54

K. Rear part of a foot

heel
51 58 69 16

L. To trick

fool
15 56 60 41

M. Winter hand covering

glove
55 42 30 53 2

N. To injure

hurt
68 27 5 8

O. Not fat

thin
67 63 71 72

P. Look at for a long time

stare
59 29 7 28 4

Q. Live-in babysitter

house
36 17 1 31 25

R. Number before three

six
37 70 65

A Creature's Gotta Eat

It's hard to eat politely if you don't have hands to use a knife and fork. The creatures hiding in the sentences below use some pretty gross means to get a meal! Collect the capital letters in each sentence and unscramble them to see who is eating what, and how.

i Shove my StomAcH out thRough my mouth and surround what i'm eaTing. i pull It back in when i'm Full.

_____

i tHrow up On Food, and thE acid turns mY meaL to soUp. then i Slurp it up!

_____

i liVe by eating animals thaT are alReady dead. the eye-balLs are easy to get to, so it is not UnusUal that i Eat them first.

_____

i attaCh to my dinnEr's skin and suck bLood up to ninE times my weigHt.

_____

i crush an animal uNtil it stoPs breathing. then i unHook my jaws and stretch mY mouth exTra wide. this lets me swallow my dinner whOle!

_____

Doo They, or Don't They?

Some animals eat poop. Others don't. Circle YES next to the animals you think might be dung munchers. Circle NO next to those animals that aren't. Then check your answers in the back.

Rabbits	YES	NO
Cats	YES	NO
Dogs	YES	NO
Koalas	YES	NO

Those Dang Beetles

There is a small creature who is big in the gross department! To learn this critter's name, look carefully at the rings below. Some look like they are linked through each other. Others look like two rings that overlap, but are not linked. Color the linked rings and read the letters inside them from left to right and top to bottom.

To get really grossed out, break the FIRST TO LAST CODE, below, and see how this creature spends its time!

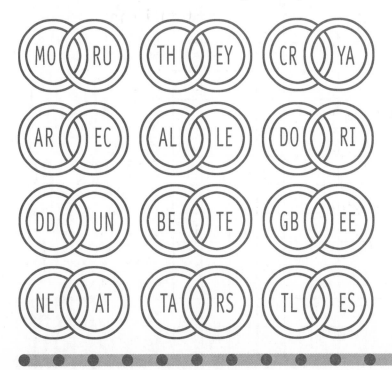

MO RU   TH EY   CR YA

AR EC   AL LE   DO RI

DD UN   BE TE   GB EE

NE AT   TA RS   TL ES

heseT eetlesb
ollectc nda
ollr allsb fo
ungd, ro
oopp, ni
hichw ot ayl
heirt ggse.
heyT lsoa ate
ungd orf
innerd!

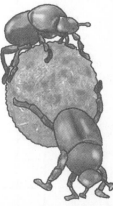

ICK! That's what makes me sneeze?!?

Are you allergic to dust? Well, it's not actually the dust that makes you sneeze. Color in the boxes with a dot in the upper right-hand corner to learn what really gets in your nose and makes you blow! Crack the MIRROR CODE to find out more.

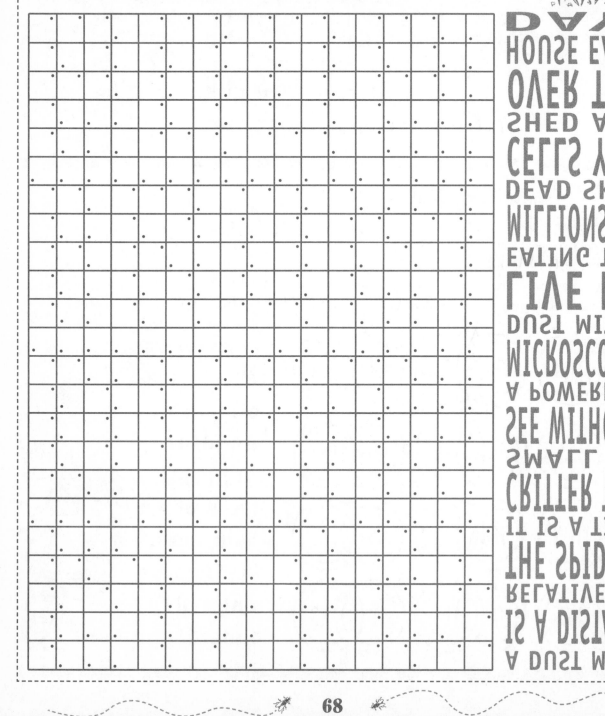

Open Wide

Many snakes swallow their prey whole, and sometimes still alive! The victim slowly digests inside the snake. Can you tell what animal each of these snakes has eaten today? Choose from the list, but be careful—there are a few extra meals included!

WEASEL

FROG

BIRD

MOUSE

TOAD

WORM

RABBIT

OWL

GATOR

TURTLE

FISH

SPIDER

DEER

SNAKE

LIZARD

Nice Cow?

Picture this: a sunny day, blue sky, fluffy clouds, and a herd of peaceful cows lying in a field chewing . . . what is that stuff they're chewing anyway? Figure out the code pattern and cross out the extra words to find out!

Cows chew have chew trouble chew digesting chew the chew grass chew they chew eat chew. They chew chew chew and chew swallow chew grass chew in chew the chew field chew. Later chew, they chew upchuck chew the chew partially chew digested chew grass chew and chew rechew chew it chew — for chew up chew to chew 9 chew hours chew a chew day chew!

URPS

CHOMP

Shark Bite

There is a nasty species of shark that uses a suction cup mouth to clamp onto dinner as it swims by. Then it spins around, and with sawlike teeth cuts a hole in the side of the victim. After slurping the plug of flesh out of the animal, this cutter goes looking for more! Check out these sorry swimmers to find the letters that spell the descriptive name of these sharks.

C ☐ ☐ ☐ ☐ ☐ C ☐ ☐ ☐ ☐ ☐ S ☐ ☐ ☐ ☐ ☐ ☐

Big Monkeys

Fill in the letters that appear in the grid less than three times. Write the letters in order (left to right, and top to bottom) on the dotted lines to get the answer to this riddle:

What do you get when you cross big monkeys with dynamite?

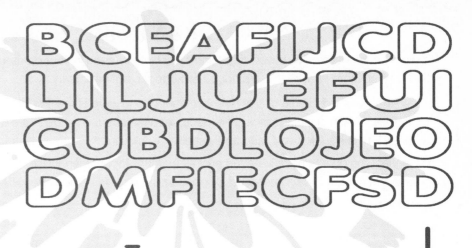

B C E A F I J C D
L I L J U E F U I
C U B D L O J E O
D M F I E C F S D

_ _ _ - _ _ _ _ _ _ !

Elephant Nose Pick

Each of the letters in a column belongs in one of the boxes directly below it, but not always in the same order! After you put each letter into the correct space, you will have the answer to this riddle:

Why don't elephants pick their nose?

		T O	O				N					K O	N		
	B	E E	E Y	R	D	R	T	T			K	I N	O	N	G
T	W	O	H	O	E	O	O	O	T			I	D	E	W
A	H	H	W	G	E	F	O	O	H			L		O	

(grid with shaded cells and an apostrophe and exclamation point)

It's Not Snot

If you live on the Pacific coast, you might find something strange in your garden. It's ten inches long, bright yellow, and covered in slime. No, it's not a living booger, but what is it?

1. Use the clues to fill in the circles. The last letter of one word is the first letter of the next. Only one letter goes in each circle. When you are done, read the shaded letters in order to learn this slimy critter's name. **HINT:** It's OK if you seem to be spelling backwards!

2. Connect the dots to get a life-sized portrait of your slippery friend! Use markers or crayons to color him yellow with a few brown spots, just like the familiar fruit it's named after. **HINT:** Use curving, not straight, lines to connect the dots.

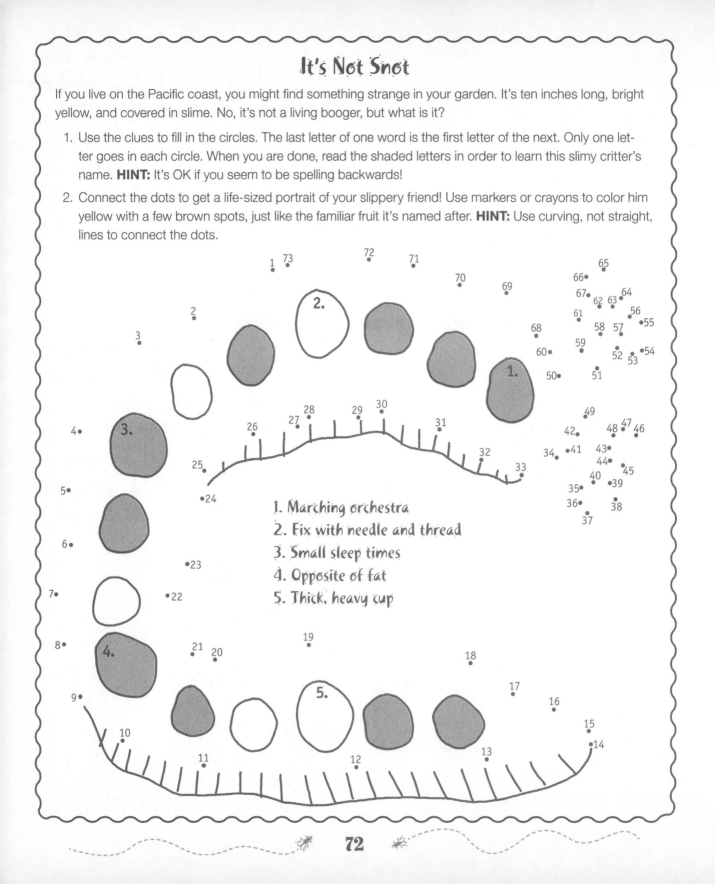

1. Marching orchestra
2. Fix with needle and thread
3. Small sleep times
4. Opposite of fat
5. Thick, heavy cup

Homemade Banana Slime

Caution: Slime is very messy, so do this activity in or near the kitchen sink!

You will need:
1 cup of cornstarch
½ cup of lukewarm water
yellow food coloring
banana extract
vegetable oil

1. Place the cornstarch into a bowl. Add one or two drops of food coloring, one or two drops of banana extract, and ¼ teaspoon of oil to the water.

2. SLOWLY pour the water mixture into the cornstarch and moosh it together with your fingers. Mix until the slime is goopy through and through.

3. Enjoy some gross and gooshy fun playing with the slime in the bowl. **EXTRA GROSS:** Carefully pour the slime into a shallow pan and add a homemade slug!

● ● ● ● ● ● ● ● ●

Homemade Banana Slug

Fill a thin, yellow water balloon a little less than full with water. It should not be so full that it's ready to burst. Rub your hands with a little bit of vegetable oil and grease up the "slug" before you nestle it into a pan of slime. See how it moves!

Giraffe

Break the VOWEL SCRAMBLE CODE to find the answer to this riddle:

Why do giraffes have such long necks?

BACUOSA GERUFFA FURTS SMALL SI BUD!

Slobber = ?

The human tongue is used for tasting, drinking, and making noises. A dog's tongue does these things, too. But when a dog pants on a broiling summer day, his tongue is being used to do something totally different! To find the damp and sticky answer to what a hot dog is doing, fill in the five grids using the following directions:

Fill in all the squares across the top of 1, 3, 4 and 5.
Fill in all the squares across the bottom of 1 and 3.
Fill in all the squares across the middle of 1, 3, and 4.
Fill in all the squares down the left side of 2, 3 and 4.
Fill in the squares down the right side of 2 and 4.
Fill in the squares down the center of 2 and 5.

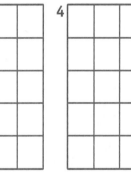

On a hot day, a dog uses its tongue to...

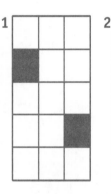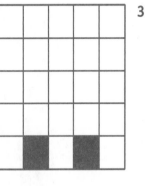

1 2 3 4 5

GROSS, BUT TRUE!

Jellyfish are such simple creatures that they have a digestive system with only one opening. That means they use their "mouth" for both eating and pooping!

Your breath is awful!

Sorry!

A. Not a special one
$\overline{10}\ \overline{11}\ \overline{9}$

B. Cow noise
$\overline{13}\ \overline{17}\ \overline{18}$

C. Opposite of work
$\overline{19}\ \overline{15}\ \overline{14}\ \overline{4}$

D. Center of a peach
$\overline{16}\ \overline{12}\ \overline{6}$

E. Opposite of she
$\overline{2}\ \overline{3}$

F. Tiny bits of dirt
$\overline{8}\ \overline{7}\ \overline{5}\ \overline{1}$

Watch Your Step

Scatologists are scientists with a very specialized job. They study a lot of one particular thing that is found all over nature. To find out what it is, think of a word that best fits each of the clues. Write the words on the numbered lines, and then transfer each letter into the numbered grid.

What do SCATOLOGISTS do?

	1F	2E	3E	4C	
5F	6D	7F	8F	9A	
10A	11A	12D	13B	14C	15C
	16D	17B	18B	19C	

Hey, Hippo!

If two male hippos meet at the border of their territories, they have a particularly gross way of telling each other to "STAY AWAY!" What is it? Break the FIRST TO LAST Code to find out.

Hint: Hippos use their paddle-shaped tails like propellers to help spread this messy message around.

ALEM IPPOSH ILLW URNT UTTB OT
UTTB NDA PRAYS ACHE THERO ITHW A
LOPPYG IXTUREM FO OOPP NDA RINEU!

Feed Me

I am a plant that eats flesh. I like ants, spiders, and juicy bugs. When an insect lands in my open mouth—SNAP! I slam shut and trap the bug inside where it is slowly digested. Use a dark color to fill in the shapes that have the letters F-E-E-D M-E. The leftover white shapes will show what kind of predatory plant I am.

Yucky Yucky

The Loa loa is an African worm that likes to travel. It starts out as a tiny larvae being carried in a fly, but makes its way to someplace a lot more cozy. Follow the directions to see where it ends up.

EXTRA GROSS: As an adult, the Loa loa can grow to be over one and a half inches long!

1. Find puzzle piece 1A (on facing page) and copy it into square 1A of the grid.
2. Find piece 2A and copy it into square 2A.
3. Continue until you have copied all the puzzle pieces into the grid.
4. Crack the VOWEL SCRAMBLE CODE to read the answer across the bottom of the puzzle.

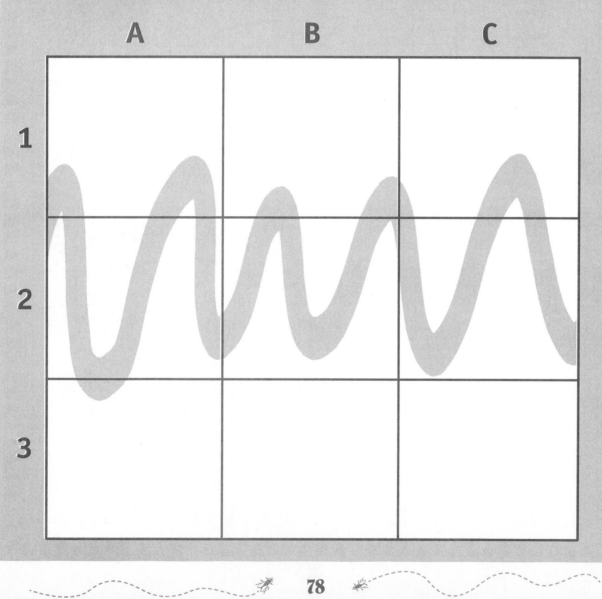

2B

3B
HOMU

1B

3C
N AYA

1C

3A
THA H

2C

1A

2A

Monster Eyes

Break the EXTRA LETTER Code to find the answer to this gory story:

Where did the mad scientist get eyes for his monster?

PIAIRIIISI, BIEICIAIUISIEI TIHIEI EIYIEI-FIUILILI TIOIWIEIRI IISI TIHIEIRIEI!

Attack Plant

There is a mean bunch of green that might be lurking in your backyard. This common plant is covered with an oily chemical that causes skin to go haywire. The chemical is so strong that it can cause nasty rashes even if the plant has been dead for five years! It is so powerful, that just a teensy bit carried in the smoke from a brushfire can cause an awful and oozy rash up your nose, down your throat, and even into your lungs! What is the name of this perilous plant?

Answer each clue on this page with a three-letter word.

Write the middle letter from each word in the numbered grid.

5. What a ghost says

— — —

9. Monkey relative

— — —

7. Opposite of lose

— — —

4. Number before two

— — —

3. Fake hair

— — —

8. Mama pig

— — —

1. Opposite of "Hi!"

— — —

2. Night before

— — —

6. To request

— — —

1.	2.	3.		4.	5.	6.	7.	8.	9.

Smelly Letters

What are the four smelliest letters in the alphabet?

Color in the letters that appear only one time. Then read the dark letters from left to right and top to bottom to get the answer!

QBISXCSOJ
LTCAMTCXY
RWEIRYNZJ
ZTJDQTEIM
SPIEXULWCI

How Many Farts

See if you can find the nine letters that make up the answer to this riddle. Write them in the correct order on the dotted lines.

How many farts does it take to fill a school bus? ___ ___ ___ ___ ___ ___ ___ ___ ___!

Where's the Gross?

Can you underline the eight gross words hiding in these sentences? The words you're looking for are in the list, but careful — there are a few extras!

soiled   retch
rotten   spit
gore   snot
scab   nasty
foul   gag
slime   grimy
gross   slug

1. The kids lugged four cans of garbage.
2. The slim earthworm poops in the dirt.
3. While belching, Ross can also chant.
4. Joe's pit bull was chewing a greasy bone.
5. The secret chain opens the dirty drain.
6. Does anyone eat warthog or electric eel?
7. Bob's note was dumb and disgusting.

That's great!

Why was the pig farmer thankful when a bird pooped on his head?

Use the directions to cross out words in the grid. Read the remaining words and you will get the answer. Cross out all words . . .

. . . that rhyme with PEE and have three letters
. . . that end in NK
. . . that start with FO

HE	FOE	WAS	THINK
TANK	THANKFUL	SEA	FOG
THAT	FORGETFUL	PIGS	RANK
TEA	CAN'T	FEE	FLY

Add one letter to each
of the blanks in the
sentences to the right.
Each sentence will use
a different letter.

_even _limy _lugs _lid _oftly _ideways.

_ary's _reasy _uts _rew _reen _arbage.

_ig _lack _ugs _leed _lack _lood.

_oul _eces _lopped _rom _ive _latworms.

_any _aggots _ake _oist _eals _essy.

B-U-T-T Spells . . .

Play this game in teams like charades, but instead
of trying to mime or spell a word out with your
hands, face, or body language, use your rear end
to spell out the word! The first team to shout out
the correct word wins the point.

Scaggy Scavenger Hunt

How many gross things can you find lurking in your house? Keep a copy of the list below for yourself, and make a copy for a sibling or parent. Then search your house from top to bottom. Each item is worth 3 points. Whoever gets the most gross points wins!

___ **pet poop**

___ **hairball**

___ **dust bunny**

___ **smelly sock**

___ **sour milk**

___ **toenail clipping**

___ **used cotton swab**

___ **used bandage**

___ **moldy leftover**

___ **dried booger**

___ **chewed gum**

___ **dead insect**

___ **other** _____

Here's a few rules:

Don't pick up the gross stuff you find. Just check it off your list and add up the points.

If you want to play with a friend, let him search his house while you search your own house. Get together later to compare results.

Gross Gulps

Your body makes between four and six cups of this stuff each day. You get rid of most of it without a thought. What is it? Where does it go? The answer is hidden in the letter grid. Start in one of the four corners, and read the letters in a logical order. You have to figure out in which direction to read!

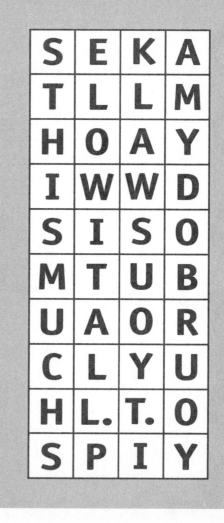

S	E	K	A
T	L	L	M
H	O	A	Y
I	W	W	D
S	I	S	O
M	T	U	B
U	A	O	R
C	L	Y	U
H	L.	T.	O
S	P	I	Y

ET

ED

SU

NU

JU

ER

RO

BA

ED

EST

LE

Y

FO

LE

BI

E

GI

WI

DRA

HU

AGE

LL

LER

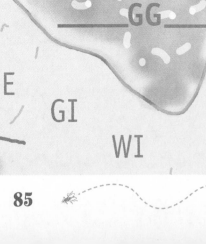

_____ **GG** _____

_____ **GG** _____

_____ **GG** _____

_____ **GG** _____

_____ **GG** _____

_____ **GG** _____

_____ **GG** _____

_____ **GG** _____

_____ **GG** _____

_____ **GG** _____

_____ **GG** _____

Got Maggots?

The larvae of a Blowfly can be placed in a deep wound where they eat dead tissue and kill harmful bacteria. The maggots in this wound have eaten away all the letters except for the GGs. Use the letters and letter pairs scattered around the page to fix the words.

HINT: Some letters make sense in more than one word, but there is only one way that uses all the letters.

Terribly Tiny

A mite is a teensy, tiny creature related to a spider. Even though you have never seen them, there are bunches of mites living very close to you. Up to 25 mites at a time can cram themselves head-first into this very small space. They eat during the day, and at night wiggle out to mate and lay their eggs. Use the decoder to learn where these common mites like to hide. Be careful—do you really want to know?

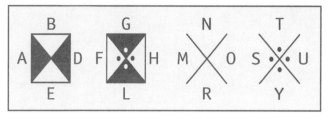

CHAPTER 8

Medical Madness

Ouch!

In 1848, Phineas Gage had an awful accident with the iron "tamping rod" he used to set explosive charges. The blasting powder Phineas was working with went off too soon, and there was no time to get out of the way. Doctors were amazed that after the accident Phineas could walk, talk, and make jokes! Even though Phineas recovered, his personality changed quite a bit. Why do you think that might be? Connect the numbered dots to show a picture of Phineas, and you will see why!

CAREFUL: There are two different sets of numbers for the dots! One set is regular (1-35), and the second set is underlined (1-38).

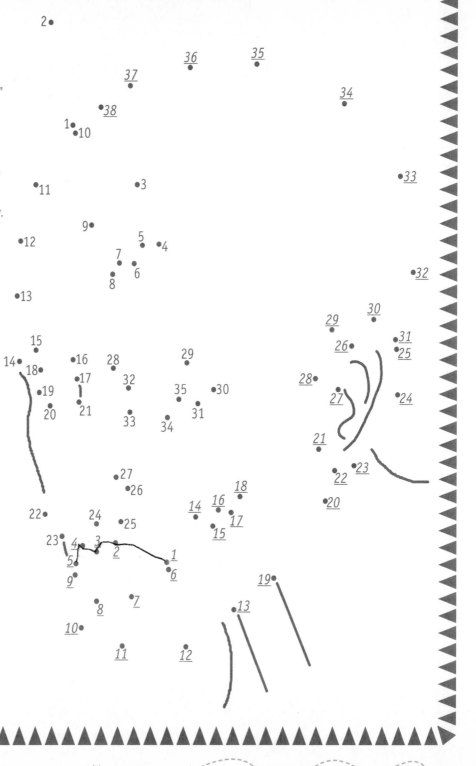

Awfully Ancient

For more than 3,000 years humanity has been plagued by an infectious disease called "leprosy" which attacks the nerves of the hands, feet, and face. Doctors only found a way to treat it about 50 years ago. However, if left untreated, leprosy can have some awful results!

In each row, cross out the letters that appear more than three times. The remaining letters will spell out the answers.

R N T U R T M T T B N T E R T S S R

B R B O P T P E B N B N P O P S E

Y E T L T L O T W T B T U T M P T S

L T M H I L C M K L E M A R M S L M

S R T I R F F R E R Y E R L I R D S

N M O M F M R O M N T M E M E T H

L D E L F O R L M E L D T O L E S L

L O T S T S O T F F T I N G T E R S

Nail Biter

Use this hint to break the coded answer.

Flip Flop

*Doctor, Doctor! How can
I stop biting my nails?*

WEAR YOUR SHOES!

Seriously Surgical

The *Guinness Book of World Records* lists a man who has had the most operations ever! Most of the surgeries were to remove tumors on his face. To see how many operations he's had, fill in each blank with a number from the clue. Then add them up. Be ready for a BIG answer!

A decade is ? years ____

Cards in a deck ____

A score is ? years ____

Twelve pairs of shoes ____

Fingers on two hands ____

A gross equals ? items ____

Eighty quarters is ? dollars ____

An egg carton holds ? eggs ____

Two cups of butter is ? sticks ____

There are ? days in a year ____

There are ? keys on the piano ____

Number of pennies in a dollar ____

Ten gallons of milk is ? quarts ____

An octogenarian is ? years old ____

Number of pits in an avocado ____

TOTAL ____

Awful Smell

Use this hint to break the coded answer:

Picture Words

Doctor, Doctor! I want something to make my awful smell go away!

  !

Almost Everybody Gets It

A huge number of people use creams, powders, and sprays to treat this skin infection. In fact, about 70% of the world's population will get this infection at least once in their life! To find out what it is, figure out a word that fits each description below. Write it on the dotted lines. Then, read the circled letters from top to bottom.

If you are under 12, you probably have not had your first case of this skin infection!

A little hot = _ _ _ _
Foot digit = _ _ _
Stand-up bath = _ _ _ _ _ _
Body dryer = _ _ _ _ _
Opposite of dry = _ _ _
Scratch this = _ _ _ _
To perspire = _ _ _ _ _
Foot bottom = _ _ _ _
No foot cover = _ _ _ _ _ _ _ _
Soft foot cover = _ _ _ _
Hard foot cover = _ _ _ _
Barely wet = _ _ _ _

Had it?	
yes	no

Poll your grown-up family and friends.

What percentage have had this infection before?

Swallowed Pen

Use this hint to break the coded answer:

B=C
C=B

Doctor, Doctor! I swallowed a pen! What should I do?

VTF B QFODJM UJM J HFU UIFSF!

Sticky Solution

Acupuncture is a healing art that has been used in China for thousands of years. It is hard to imagine that this treatment makes you feel better, but it can! What does an acupuncturist do? Cross out words using the following rules. The remaining words are the answer.

CROSS OUT words that . . .

. . . are two letters and start with an A

. . . have a U in the exact middle

. . . end in a vowel

BODY
BODE
BUD
ARE
YOUR
ACE
BE
BUS
OVER
RUM
ALE
ALL
AS

SKUNK
STICK
AN
LOUNGE
LONG
AT
LOVE
THIN
THINE
AN
APE
NEEDLES
NOODLE
TUNE
PUN
IN
DUDE
PANE
YOUR
SCONE
SKIN

Run Down

Use this hint to break the coded answer:

First to Last

Doctor, Doctor! What should I take if I feel run down?

heT icensel latep umbern fo het arc hatt ith ouy!

92

Rhinowhat?

There are complicated medical words to describe the most common, and gross, things! To figure out what Doctor Doofus is talking about, first unscramble each definition. Then draw a line to match it to the correct medical term.

the a look deep inside nose close

and yellow the nose of liquid from flow green

picking constant nose

You must stop that
RHINOTILLEXOMANIA

while I do a
RHINOSCOPY

to look more closely at your
RHINORRHEA!

GROSS, BUT TRUE!

"Rhinorrhea" shares a word-part with a common ailment that causes you to run to the bathroom in a hurry. Can you think of this other word? How would you like that coming out your nose??

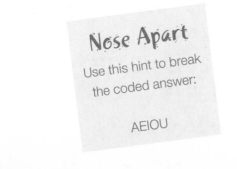

Nose Apart

Use this hint to break the coded answer:

AEIOU

Doctor, Doctor! Why did you take the patient's nose apart?

_ W _ NT _ D T _ S _ _

WH _ T M _ D _ _ T R _ N!

Body Sculpting

Some people will do anything to get a slimmer body. Doctors use a procedure called LIPOSUCTION to help these people, but you won't believe what it is! Write letters from the puzzle pieces in the correct spaces of the grid to find out.

Brain Surgeon

Use this hint to break the coded answer:

A=1
Z=26

Doctor, Doctor! How did you become a brain surgeon?

9   23-1-19   1   4-5-14-20-9-19-20
21-14-20-9-12   13-25
4-18-9-12-12   19-12-9-16-16-5-4!

Slimy Helpers

A doctor who is trying to reattach a finger or an ear onto an accident victim needs all the help he can get. It is very important to get fresh blood flowing through the part that is being sewn back on. Doctors have started to use a little "helper" that was popular as long as 2,000 years ago. While this pump is beautifully designed by nature to keep blood moving, it sure isn't pretty to look at. In fact, it's downright disgusting! Fill in the shapes that contain the letters B-L-O-O-D S-U-C-K-E-R to find out what doctors might stick on a newly attached body part.

Biting Insects

Use this hint to break the coded answer:

Missing Lines

Doctor, Doctor! How can I stop catching diseases caused by biting insects?

STOP BITING THEM!

Where does Mrs. Doctor keep spare body parts?

To find the answer to this riddle, think of a word that best fits each of the clues. Write the words on the numbered lines, and then transfer each letter into the numbered grid.

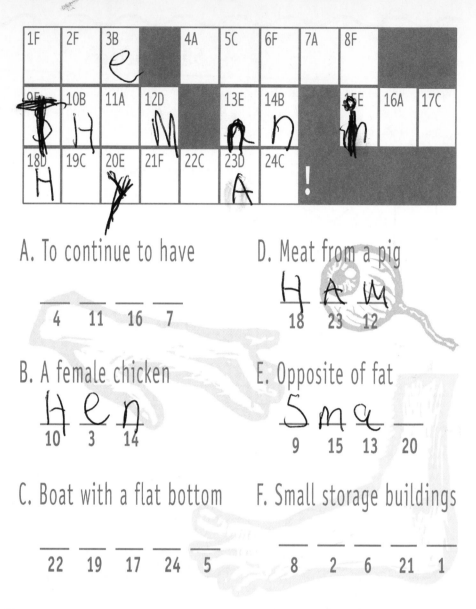

1F	2F	3B e		4A	5C	6F	7A	8F		
9E T	10B H	11A	12D M		13E a	14B n		15E h	16A	17C
18D H	19C	20E X	21F	22C	23D A	24C	!			

A. To continue to have

___ ___ ___ ___
4 11 16 7

B. A female chicken

H e n
10 3 14

C. Boat with a flat bottom

___ ___ ___ ___ ___
22 19 17 24 5

D. Meat from a pig

H A M
18 23 12

E. Opposite of fat

S m a ___
9 15 13 20

F. Small storage buildings

___ ___ ___ ___ ___
8 2 6 21 1

First Surgery

Use this hint to break the coded answer:

Mirror, Mirror

Doctor, Doctor! I'm scared! This is the first time I've had surgery!

Surgeon: I know just how you feel. This is the first time I've done any!

"I don't feel very good . . ."

What's making you feel so gross? The doctor has left a few possibilities, and a few germs, in the puzzle grid. Now you have to figure out a word or two that fits each description below. Write them in the grid, too.

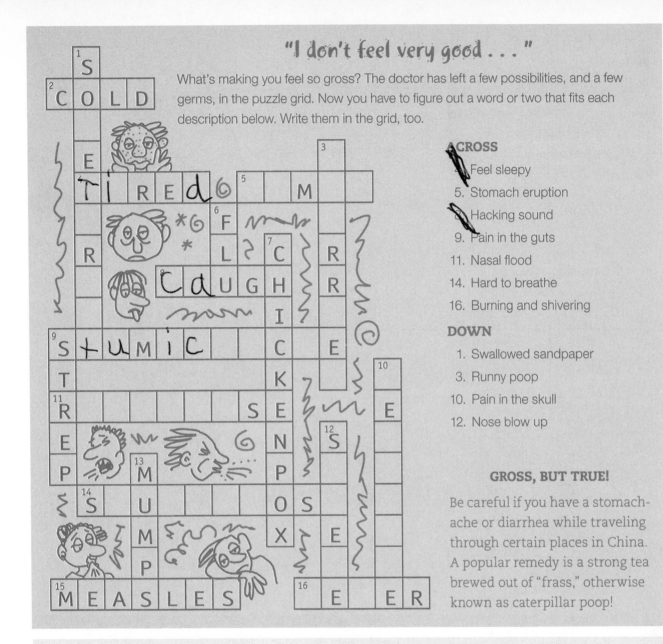

ACROSS

4. Feel sleepy
5. Stomach eruption
8. Hacking sound
9. Pain in the guts
11. Nasal flood
14. Hard to breathe
16. Burning and shivering

DOWN

1. Swallowed sandpaper
3. Runny poop
10. Pain in the skull
12. Nose blow up

GROSS, BUT TRUE!

Be careful if you have a stomach-ache or diarrhea while traveling through certain places in China. A popular remedy is a strong tea brewed out of "frass," otherwise known as caterpillar poop!

Double Vision

Use this hint to break the coded answer:

Sounds Like

Doctor, Doctor! Can you fix my double vision?

Ee her vee shun iz phu eye n. Thuh purr ah blem eez yoo haa vuh tew heh duz!

Really Rotten

Doctors never like to see this condition, because it means that part of their patient has started to rot! The body part that's in trouble turns black, and the smell can be awful. To find out what this creepy condition is called, use the clues to fill in the blanks. The last letter of one word is the first letter of the next. When you are done, write the numbered letters in the spaces provided.

1. A pet _____ pig
2. End of a prayer
3. Xmas Spice
4. Male goose

5. To lift up
6. Opposite of odd
7. Letter after eight
8. Not difficult

1	2	3	4	5	6	7	8

Headache

Use this hint to break the coded answer:

Vowel Mix

Doctor, Doctor! Can you cure this terrible headache?

Yas! Crush yior haud thriogh thut wendiw und tha puna well ba gina!

98

Dead End

Chapter 9

Zombie Newspaper Article

Break the REVERSE WORD Code to read the latest news.

THE DAILY POOP

TOILET
NEWS
PAPER

EIBMOZ SESOL NOHTARAM YB EDIW NIGRAM

retfA etiuq a ylevil trats, eibmoz etelhta, retseF .N ttoR, saw deyamsid ot hsinif eht ecar daed tsal.

What's the last thing to go through a bug's mind as he hits a car windshield?

Collect the letters along the path from START to END.

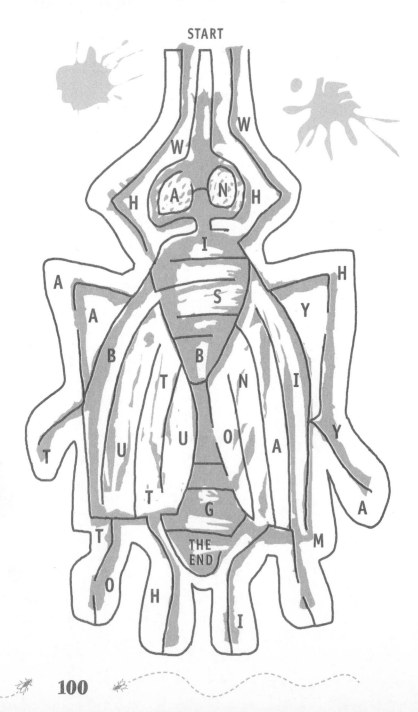

START

THE END

From the fourteenth to the seventeenth century there was a medicine popular in Europe called "mummy." It was made from—you guessed it—ground-up mummies. When the supply of real mummies ran low, untrustworthy medicine makers used any old, dried out bodies they could find. Or make.

Dead on My Feet

These two zombies are both out for a midnight stroll. At first glance, they look gruesomely the same. Can you find the 13 differences between these two pictures?

Cannibal King Newspaper Article

Break the AEIOU/12345
Code to read the latest news.

THE DAILY POOP

TOILET
NEWS
PAPER

44PS!

Th3s r2p4rt
j5st 3n fr4m
L41 L41 3sl1nd.
3nf1m45s
C1nn3b1l K3ng,
W1nn1 21tch1,
1cc3d2nt1lly
p5t h3s f1ls2
t22th 3n
b1ckw1rds 1nd
1t2 h3ms2lf.

Chop Chop

What is a guillotine (gill-uh-teen)? It is a very tall cutting machine with a heavy blade that drops down between two posts. It was designed a long time ago for just one awful purpose. Add straight lines to see what.

To find out what else a guillotine is, copy the pattern in each numbered square into the empty grid.

ZOMBIE HEADS

You will need:
several apples, with stems
vegetable peeler
small metal teaspoon
variety of dried materials for making features
    (such as twine, cloves, dried beans, rice,
      dried corn kernels, pasta, etc.)
wooden skewer
string

1. Peel the apples. Leave the stems in!

2. With the blunt end of the peeler or the metal teaspoon, carefully gouge out eyes, nose, mouth, and ears into each peeled apple. The carving doesn't have to be perfect. Also, since the apple will shrink a lot, making features bigger and thicker is better.

2. Poke beads, rice, beans, etc., into the apple to make eyes and teeth. Black-eyed peas or cloves make especially good eyes. Raw rice, dried corn, or broken noodles make good teeth.

3. Knot the end of the string around the stem. Hang the apple in a warm and dry place. Make sure the apple is not touching anything. Or, you can set the heads on a metal cookie cooling rack out of the sun.

4. Visit your zombie heads every few days. When the apples begin to turn leathery, you can change their expressions by pinching and twisting the features. In a few weeks you'll have some amazing shrunken faces. YUCK!

Break the FIRST TO LAST Code
to read the latest news.

THE DAILY POOP

TOILET
NEWS
PAPER

YNAMICD UOD ITH YB TEAMS OLLERR

atmanB nda obinR rea xpectede ot ecoverr, utb ska hatt het ublicp own eferr ot hemt sa "latmanF nda ibbonR."

Dead Poet's Society

Can you dig the rotten rhyme out of the cemetery? To find it, color in the following kinds of words, and read the remains from top to bottom, left to right. You must put the punctuation in the correct places.

SHOES
ODD NUMBERS
GROSS BODY STUFF
BODY PARTS WITH FOUR LETTERS

SEVEN SNEAKER DEAD
VOMIT MAN ON THE
BRIDGE ONE LAST
NIGHT POOP HIS CLOG
BONES WERE THREE
ALL EARWAX AQUIVER
HE SPIT GAVE A FART
COUGH HIS BOOT LEG
FOOT FELL YUCK OFF
SANDAL AND FLOATED
FIVE DOWN POOP THE
'BUTT HEAD RIVER

I — tightly wrapped

H — body cavity is stuffed with

given a salt bath

A

G

are removed and put in jars

B — painted with resin

Mummy Mia!

Mummies look pretty cool, but do you know what happened to those bodies before they were all neatly boxed in a sarcophagus? It is not pretty! Finish each sentence by choosing one phrase from the edge of the page. Write the letter from the phrase on the empty line. When you're finished, you'll know how ancient Egyptians preserved their mummies (and their daddies, too!)

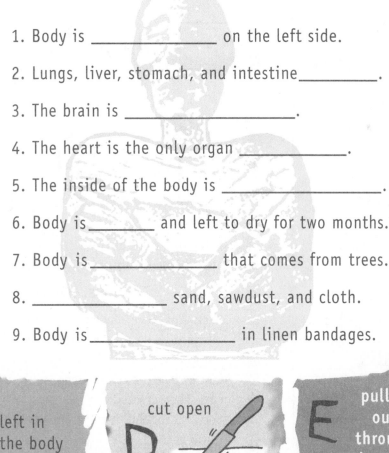

1. Body is _____ on the left side.

2. Lungs, liver, stomach, and intestine_____.

3. The brain is _____.

4. The heart is the only organ _____.

5. The inside of the body is _____.

6. Body is_____ and left to dry for two months.

7. Body is_____ that comes from trees.

8. _____ sand, sawdust, and cloth.

9. Body is_____ in linen bandages.

F — cleaned with wine

C — left in the body

D — cut open

E — pulled out through the nose

Karate Newspaper Article

Break the EXTRA WORD Code
to read the latest news.

THE DAILY POOP
TOILET
NEWS
PAPER

**KAROUCHATE
EXPOUCHERT
KNOOUCHCKED
OOUCHUT
FIROUCHST
DAOUCHY
IOUCHN
AROUCHMY**

Priouchvate
Bouch. Beouchlt
wouchas
practouchicing
hoouchw toucho
salouchute.

Hangman's Holiday

Can you match the following riddles with their answer?
Write the correct number in front of each picture puzzle.

1. **What do hangmen like to read?**
2. **Where do hangmen like to swim?**
3. **What's a hangman's favorite fruit?**

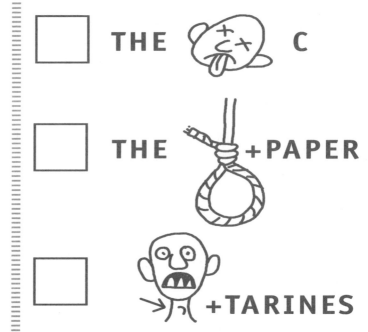

THE ⬜ C

THE ⬜ +PAPER

⬜ +TARINES

GROSS, BUT TRUE!

Beck Weathers was left for dead during a terrible blizzard on Mt. Everest. He survived the storm, but lost his nose to frostbite. Doctors made him a new nose out of cartilage from his ears and ribs. They created the nose upside-down on Beck's forehead, using a flap of skin with healthy blood vessels. When the nose was "finished," they flipped it around to the proper place.

Hangman

It's pretty gross to think that this fun and familiar game is really based on a gruesome form of execution! So to make sure no one accidentally gets "stretched," get rid of all the ropes, and grab a pencil and piece of paper instead.

To play:

1. Find a partner to play with you. One of you will think up the word (the drawer) and the other will try to guess it (the guesser).
2. The drawer thinks up a word and tells the guesser how many letters it has.
3. The guesser guesses one letter at a time. If the letter is in the word, the drawer writes it in the proper space or spaces. If not, the drawer writes the used letter next to the gallows and draws the head on the hangman.
4. Play continues and a new body part is (head, stick body, arms, legs, eyes, nose, frown) added to the hangman each time a wrong letter is guessed.

TO WIN: Either the guesser or the drawer can win. If the guesser figures out the word before the hangman is completely drawn, then he wins. But if he doesn't, then the drawer wins. The guesser can also try to solve the word at any time, but automatically loses the game if he or she is wrong.

Example

The guesser in this game did not guess the word "slippery" before the hangman was completely drawn. The guesser loses. Too bad!

GALLOWS

F O U
M T A
H C B
G

_ L I _ _ E R _

Try playing this game with only gross words! Here's a list:

STINKY

OOZING

CRUSTY

MOLDY

PUTRID

ROTTEN

REPULSIVE

HORRIBLE

DECAYING

CREEPING

SKELETAL

HIDEOUS

Break the ALL MIXED UP Code
to read the latest news.

THE DAILY POOP

TOILET
NEWS
PAPER

INDIAN CHIEF DIES IN STRANGE ACCIDENT

Chief Hot Wug reportedly drank fifteen cups of tea before going to bed last night. He was found this morning, drowned in his own tea-pee.

What does the headstone say for the man who struck a match by the leaky gas tank?

Collect the letters blown around and write them in the correct order on these lines. We left some hints.

H _ R _ _ _ _ _

I _ P _ _ _ _ _ _

Can you put the scattered scatterbrain back together? Circle the four pieces that make a whole man. We left you a "before" picture!

THE DAILY POOP

TOILET
NEWS
PAPER

MUD SCEANTEST TORNS ENTI FRIG

Dictir Graanbliid's mithar wus qoitad us suyeng "E tild hem navar ti leck tha spiin uftar mexeng u naw pitein!"

Dead End

A dead end means there is nowhere else to go. You are finished! You must stop! Our final puzzle in this book is to figure out all these words that contain the word E-N-D. Use the letters and letter pairs scattered around the page. Each one is used only once. Goodbye, gross friENDs!

SS

LE

PR

B

SP

S

L

FRI

REC

OFF

ER

BL

OMM

ABLE

ET

Rotten bananas are very _ <u>E N D</u> _ _ _ _.

Would you really eat a bug, or just _ _ _ _ _ <u>E N D</u> to?

A true _ _ _ <u>E N D</u> will _ <u>E N D</u> you his whoopie cushion.

Would you _ _ <u>E N D</u> your money on garlic gum or earwax candy?

A boring monster movie seems <u>E N D</u> _ _ _ _.

A really gross joke might _ _ _ <u>E N D</u> your grandma.

Some things should <u>not</u> go in a _ _ <u>E N D</u> _ _.

The gross cook _ _ _ _ _ _ <u>E N D</u> _ the scorpion soup.

Look Again!

Just when you thought the gross was all gone, there's more! See if you can find each of these picture pieces somewhere in this book. Write the name of the puzzle each piece is from in the space under each box. **HINT:** There is only one picture piece from each chapter.

1.

2.

3.

4.

5.

6.

7.

8.

9.

References

If you haven't had enough of gross stuff, there are plenty of books you can read or Web sites you can visit. Below are listed a few of our favorites.

Books

Oh Yuck! The Encyclopedia of Everything Nasty

By Joy Masoff (2000). If you want to know "all the best stuff about some of the worst stuff on earth," then this is the book for you. From acne to eye gunk, fleas to feet, parasites to puking, it is all here.

Gross Universe: Your Guide to All Disgusting Things Under the Sun

By Jeff Szpirglas (2004). A guide to many of the disgusting, yet amazing, things in our world—be it animal, plant—or human.

Phineas Gage: a Gruesome But True Story About Brain Science

By John Fleischman (2002). The fascinatingly true story about how one man's horrible accident has helped doctors understand the workings of the human brain.

Grossology series (1995–2004)

By Sylvia Branzei. A best-selling book series including the titles *Grossology and You, Animal Grossology, Hands-On Grossology* and others. Lots of information on all things gross and disgusting, combined with hands-on activities.

Nature's Yucky

By Lee Ann Landstrom (2003). Explores icky, but interesting, facts about the behavior of some animals—and the good reasons they have for what they do.

Revolting Recipes (1997); Even More Revolting Recipes (2001)

By Roald Dahl. Based on foods from his famous children's books, these fun, simple recipes sound worse than they really are. Anyone for a stink bug egg?

Web Sites

www.guinnessworldrecords.com

Get lost here looking at the world records for strange diseases, incredible body parts and medical marvels. Whether it is the champion eyeball-popper, the longest sneezing bout, or the person-who-can-spit-a dead-cricket-the-farthest, we guarantee you will be fascinated!

http://yucky.kids.discovery.com

This site declares itself the "Yuckiest Site on the Internet"! It contains lots of information on gross and cool body stuff, and has whole sections on worms and roaches. It also has a great fun and games area that is divided into things like creepy crafts, revolting recipes, and icky experiments.

www.grossology.org

The Web site of Sylvia Branzei and Jack Keely, author and illustrator of the Grossology series (see books to the left). Information on both individuals, a grossology store, and recipes for fake blood, barf, snot—and more!

PUZZLE ANSWERS

page vi • **Vowel Scramble**

Knock, Knock.
Who's there?
Watson.
Watson who?
Watson your nose?
It looks like a big
old booger!!

page 4 • **What do you get . . .**

A. Says "BOO"
<u>G</u> <u>H</u> <u>O</u> <u>S</u> <u>T</u>
42 47 48 1 50

B. To cast a ballot
<u>V</u> <u>O</u> <u>T</u> <u>E</u>
44 49 5 4

C. A small clue
<u>H</u> <u>I</u> <u>N</u> <u>T</u>
22 23 31 41

D. To push hard
<u>S</u> <u>H</u> <u>O</u> <u>V</u> <u>E</u>
19 25 37 29 27

E. Opposite of fat
<u>T</u> <u>H</u> <u>I</u> <u>N</u>
10 6 43 40

F. To put up a picture
<u>H</u> <u>A</u> <u>N</u> <u>G</u>
11 12 17 24

G. A precious jewel
<u>G</u> <u>E</u> <u>M</u>
9 30 3

H. Cousin of a frog
<u>T</u> <u>O</u> <u>A</u> <u>D</u>
13 2 46 35

I. Bugs at a picnic
<u>A</u> <u>N</u> <u>T</u> <u>S</u>
28 8 15 14

J. Do, Re, or Me
<u>N</u> <u>O</u> <u>T</u> <u>E</u>
34 21 20 45

K. Past tense of SAY
<u>S</u> <u>A</u> <u>I</u> <u>D</u>
32 33 7 36

L. Long walks
<u>H</u> <u>I</u> <u>K</u> <u>E</u> <u>S</u>
26 16 18 38 39

1A S	2H O	3G M	4B E	5B T	6E H	7K I	8I N	9G G	
10E T	11F H	12F A	13H T		14I S	15I T	16L I	17F N	18L K	19D S
	20J T	21J O		22C H	23C I	24F G	25D H			
26L H	27F E	28I A	29D V	30G E	31C N	32K S		33K A	34J N	35H D
	36K D	37D O	38L E	39L S	40E N	41C ' T				
42A G	43E I	44B V	45J E		46H A		47A H	48A O	49B O	50A T

(Crossword reads: SOMETHING THAT STINKS TO HIGH HEAVENS AND DOESN'T GIVE A HOOT)

page 5 • **Pillow P.U.**

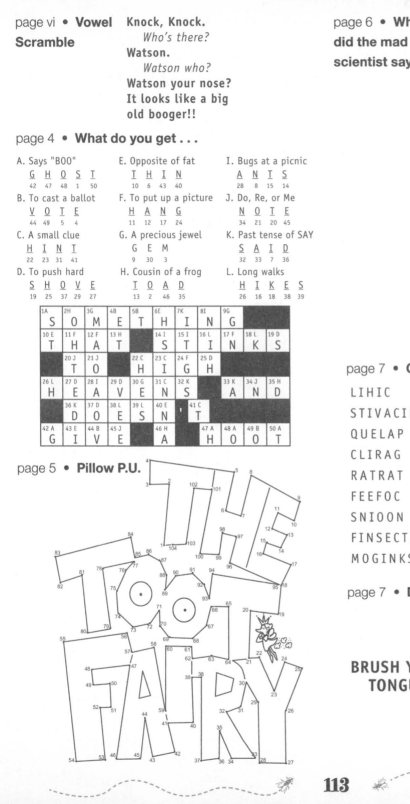

THE TOOTH FAIRY

page 6 • **What did the mad scientist say . . .**

YOU REEK-A! (EUREKA!)

page 7 • **Officially Bad Breath**

LIHIC — <u>C H I L I</u>
STIVACIE — <u>C A V I T I E S</u>
QUELAP — <u>P L A Q U E</u>
CLIRAG — <u>G A R L I C</u>
RATRAT — <u>T A R T A R</u>
FEEFOC — <u>C O F F E E</u>
SNIOON — <u>O N I O N S</u>
FINSECTION — <u>I N F E C T I O N S</u>
MOGINKS — <u>S M O K I N G</u>

page 7 • **Do What?**

BRUSH YOUR
TONGUE

PUZZLE ANSWERS

page 8 • Fart Foods

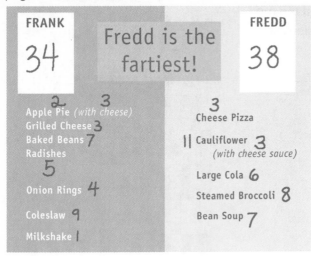

FRANK
34

Fredd is the fartiest!

FREDD
38

Apple Pie *(with cheese)* 2
Grilled Cheese 3
Baked Beans 7
Radishes 5
Onion Rings 4
Coleslaw 9
Milkshake 1

Cheese Pizza 3
Cauliflower (with cheese sauce) 3
Large Cola 6
Steamed Broccoli 8
Bean Soup 7

page 10 • Stink Pinks

An intelligent toot
S M A R T   F A R T

Seven days of smelliness
R E E K   W E E K

A fish fart
B A S S   G A S

A hard, quick sniff
S T I F F   W H I F F

Smell from a moldy camping shelter
T E N T   S C E N T

An apple passing gas
F R U I T   T O O T

Smelly odor from a liquid you might swallow
D R I N K   S T I N K

page 10 • Disgusting Dump

five cartons of sour milk

page 11 • Funky Fertilizer

WHAT ARE YOU DOING WITH ALL THAT MANURE?

I'M PUTTING IT ON MY CORN.

YUCK! I PUT BUTTER AND SALT ON MINE!

page 12 • Smelling Sweet?

SWEET	tastes like sugar
SWEAT	salty body fluid
SWEAR	to say curse words
SPEAR	sharp, pointy weapon
SPEAK	to utter words
SPANK	to slap on the butt
STANK	past tense of stink
STALK	main stem of a plant
STALL	horse's room in a barn
SHALL	formal form of "will"
SHELL	hard outer covering
SMELL	to use your nose

page 12 • Smell vs. Smell

1.	A	P	E
2.	B	E	T
3.	E	R	R
4.	O	F	F
5.	P	U	P
6.	U	M	P
7.	Y	E	T

page 13 • Super Sweat

PUZZLE ANSWERS

page 13 • It Was the Dog!

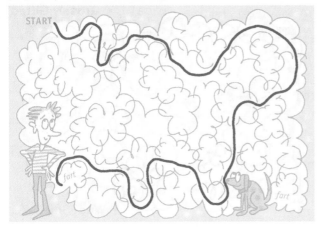

page 14 • Ode to Odor

Black socks, they never get _dirty_.

The _longer_ you _wear_ them,

the _blacker_ they get!

Night falls, you _dream_

of the _laundry_, but

Something inside you

says, "Don't _wash_ them yet!"

page 14 • Stinky Socks

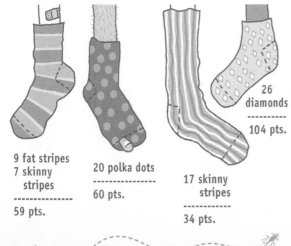

9 fat stripes
7 skinny
stripes
----
59 pts.

20 polka dots
----
60 pts.

17 skinny
stripes
----
34 pts.

26
diamonds
----
104 pts.

page 17 • X-tremely Gross

page 18 • Slop Talk

1. S P I T
2. F L I T
3. K N I T
4. Q U I T
5. G R I T

page 18 • Ah-Zoom!

1. S M O K E
   S N O T
2. P E P P E R

3. L I G H T
4. D U S T
   S N O T
5. C O L D
6. A L L E R G Y
7. P O L L E N
8. M O L D

PUZZLE ANSWERS

page 19 • **Dust and Decay**

page 20 • **Vomit Vocab**

THROW UP

BARF

TOSS COOKIES

HURL

PUKE

UPCHUCK

SPEW

BLOW CHUNKS

O	S	T	O	B	S	S	R	F	A	B	T	R
S	P	H	B	L	O	C	H	U	N	K	O	I
M	W	R	O	O	H	F	R	U	H	C	P	D
I	E	P	U	W	O	R	H	T	L	U	S	E
S	P	O	C	C	U	A	B	P	K	H	S	T
S	U	W	H	H	R	B	L	E	U	C	C	H
O	E	L	R	U	H	A	O	W	K	P	O	E
R	K	U	U	N	L	R	W	B	E	U	O	P
G	S	P	Y	K	O	O	C	L	B	P	K	O
B	T	O	S	S	C	O	O	K	I	E	S	R

page 21 • **True or False**

1. You have as many hairs on your body as a gorilla.
   TRUE or FALSE

2. Your skull protects your brain so it can't be bruised.
   TRUE or **FALSE**

3. Cracking your knuckles can lead to arthritis.
   TRUE or FALSE

4. If you hold in a burp, it will become a fart.
   TRUE or **FALSE**

5. Boogers are very clean.
   TRUE or **FALSE**

6. Fresh spit is cleaner than fresh pee.
   TRUE or **FALSE**

7. The scientific name for snot is mucus.
   TRUE or FALSE

8. You will shed 40 pounds of skin in your lifetime.
   TRUE or FALSE

page 21 • **Grossly Gifted**

$4 + 6 - 5\frac{1}{2} =$ ___ $4\frac{1}{2}$

$7 - 6 + \frac{1}{2} - 2 =$ ___ $-\frac{1}{2}$

$3 + 1\frac{1}{2} - 4\frac{1}{2} =$ ___ 0

$6 - 4\frac{1}{2} + 1 =$ ___ $2\frac{1}{2}$

$9\frac{1}{2} - 8 - \frac{1}{2} =$ ___ 1

Total inches = ___ $7\frac{1}{2}$

page 23 • **What Smells?**

Stinky: These pills I got to get rid of B.O. don't work.

Pinky: Why not?

Stinky: They keep falling out from under my arms!

page 24 • **Acne Art**

PUZZLE ANSWERS

page 25 • **Pus-itively Putrid**

WVZW — **DEAD** YZXGVIRZ — **BACTERIA,** WVZW — **DEAD** DSRGV — **WHITE**

YOLLW — **BLOOD** XVOOH — **CELLS,** ZMW — **AND** WVZW — **DEAD** YLWB — **BODY**

XVOOH — **CELLS** UOLZGRMT — **FLOATING** RM — **IN** YLWB — **BODY** UOFRW — **FLUID**

page 25 • **How did the teen with acne . . .**

HE BROKE OUT!

page 26 • **Nasty Rashes**

1. Places where bees live

HIVES

2. Popular poultry + saucepan
   - 20th letter + letter 3rd from end

CHICKEN POX

3. Killer chemical + 9th letter
   + letter 5th from end

POISON I V (ivy)

4. Finger jewelry + wiggly bait

RING WORM

5. A little stick from a needle + LY
   + 8th letter + consume food

PRICKLY HEAT

page 28 • **Hurry Up!**

1	2	3	4	5
Knock, knock. *Who's there?* Ben. *Ben who?*	Knock, knock. *Who's there?* Gwen. *Gwen who?*	Knock, knock. *Who's there?* Hope. *Hope who?*	Knock, knock. *Who's there?* Anita. *Anita who?*	Knock, knock. *Who's there?* Harriet. *Harriet who?*
Ben waiting a really long time!	Gwen will you be done?	Hope you'll be done soon!	Anita the toilet RIGHT NOW!	Harriet up in there!

page 29 • **More Stink Pinks**

A bunch of boy scouts all
going #2 at the same time

TROOP POOP

Tiny tinkle

WEE PEE

Long time you sat
when constipated

GREAT WAIT

Fast press of the
toilet handle

RUSH FLUSH

Line of poop on
the toilet paper

WIPE STRIPE

When you accidentally
throw up on your
mom's fancy clothes

DRESS MESS

page 29 • **What kind of
Nasty Nuts . . .**

B P F E H J E H
N H U F B O T
M B H F M R S
G V A M R J G
O V M C J V N
F H D M J R R
G F C O R V L F
M E C V O G J
A G B C F H K
G C H S B V O

PEENUTS AND LEAKS!
(PEANUTS AND LEEKS)

page 30 • Constipation

3 LETTERS: can, tan, pan, pat, tap, nap, cap, cat, pin, nip, pit, tip, tin, sin, ton, son, top, pot, cot, cop

4 LETTERS: coat, coin, stop, pant, cost, post, past, cast, snip, spin, snap, span, pain

5 LETTERS: paint, stain, patio, point, onion, stoop

6 LETTERS: notion, potion, nation, station

page 31 • Why did the toilet paper . . .

You start with the second letter "T" from the end of the roll.

T O
G E T
T O
T H E
B O T T O M!

page 32 • Silly Sentences

F reddy f arted f ifty f ast f umes.

P eter p ooped p artly p ointy p ieces.

V ictor v omited v ery v iolet v itamins.

T herese t inkled t welve t iny t imes.

B illy b lew b lue b oogers b ackwards.

S teven s pit s oggy s unflower s eeds.

page 32 • How do two pieces of "number 2" . . .

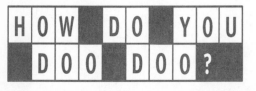

H O W   D O   Y O U

D O O   D O O ?

page 34 • Run! Run! Run!

A step on a ladder	R U N **G**
Smallest one in a litter	R U N **T**
What a model walks down	R U N **W A Y**
Someone who likes to run	R U N N **E R**
Breakfast and lunch combo	**B** R U N **C H**
Past tense of drink	**D** R U N K
Dirty and messy	**G** R U N **G Y**
A noisy, crackling chew	**C** R U N **C H**
A fruit that helps you poop	**P** R U N **E**
Main stem of a tree	**T** R U N K
Short, deep sound	**G** R U N **T**
To play again	**R E** R U N

page 34 • What is white, full of poop, . . .

Turn the book on its side when you hold it up to the mirror, and tip the top edge slight back toward you. Then you should be clearly able to read the answer "A TOY-LET"!

page 35 • Target Practice

The puddle each guy makes matches the shape on his head. So each of Pete's puddles has four blobby "arms," Pablo's puddles have five, and Perry's puddles have three.

Pete
$70 - 10 = 60$
1 puddle on floor

Pablo
$80 + 15 - 20 = 75$
direct hit
2 puddles on floor

Perry
$60 + 20 = 80$
bonus for no puddles on floor

PUZZLE ANSWERS

page 36 • **Why did that guy . . .**

A. Robe worn by superheroes
C A P E
3 4 20 21

B. Autumn fruit
P E A R
12 7 11 14

C. Meat or veggies cooked in broth
S O U P
6 18 5 17

D. To annoy
B O T H E R
1 19 15 8 2 22

E. Not hard
E A S Y
9 13 10 16

page 37 • **Gotta Go**

1. NATURE CALLS
2. TAKE A LEAK
3. GOT TO PEE
4. TAKE A WHIZ
5. FILL THE CAN
6. GO TO THE JOHN
7. HIT THE HEAD

page 37 • **It's the Rule!**

I DON'T SWIM

IN YOUR

TOILET,

SO DON'T

PEE IN

MY POOL!

page 38 • **Bathroom Pass**

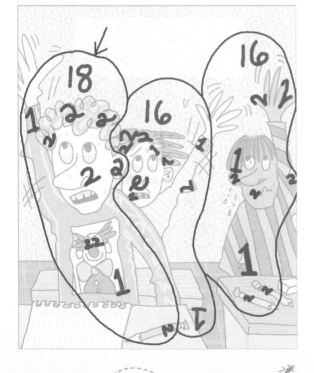

page 40 • **The Putrid Painter**

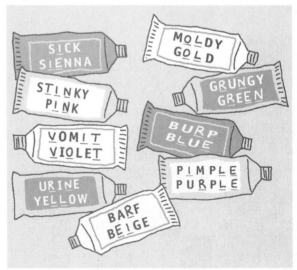

page 41 • **What is long and pointy . . .**

page 41 • **Baby Brother B.O.**

Lance Luke Leo Larry Lenny

page 42 • **How can you tell if . . .**

A. A good time
F U N
18 9 4

B. Happy faces have these
S M I L E S
6 23 16 25 7 11

C. To make better
H E A L S
1 19 12 26 17

D. Number after eight
N I N E
10 2 13 20

E. Decays
R O T S
8 5 21 22

F. Small storage building
S H E D
3 15 24 14

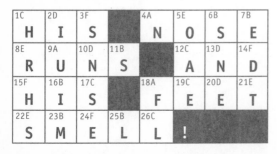

1C	2D	3F		4A	5E	6B	7B
H	I	S		N	O	S	E
8E	9A	10D	11B		12C	13D	14F
R	U	N	S		A	N	D
15F	16B	17C		18A	19C	20D	21E
H	I	S		F	E	E	T
22E	23B	24F	25B	26C			
S	M	E	L	L	!		

page 43 • **Juicy Jobs?**

TROPA-TOPTY NEALCER	PORTA-POTTY CLEANER
EPT DOOF STERAT	PET FOOD TASTER
OPOP YALSTAN	POOP ANALYST
REWES VIRED	SEWER DIVER
IRAMPT RFISNFE	ARMPIT SNIFFER

page 44 •
Uncle Leon's Lovely Leg

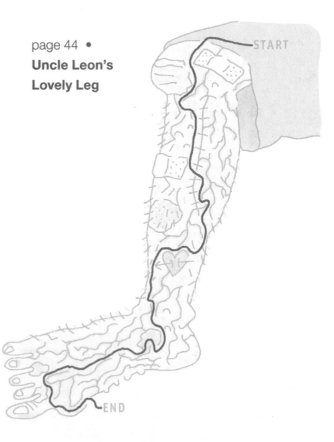

START

END

PUZZLE ANSWERS

page 44 •
Just Joking!

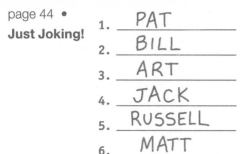

1. PAT
2. BILL
3. ART
4. JACK
5. RUSSELL
6. MATT

page 45 •
Scritch Scratch

1. F A R M P I T
2. S C A L P O P
3. E N O S E A T
4. B E L C H I N
5. L U O N E C K
6. B A C K S I D
7. E R C H E S T
8. O B U T T E N
9. T H A R M E T
10. S L E G I G E
11. E S T O E N O
12. R U B E L L Y

page 46 • **Bob's Bad Body Noises**

BELCH	3
FART	8
GAG	16
GRUNT	3
GULP	4
RETCH	2
SNIFF	4
SNORT	4

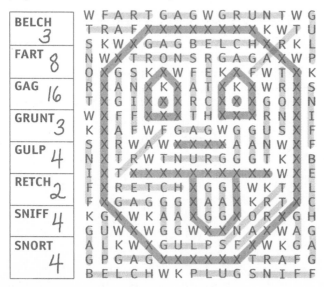

page 47 • **Very Funny, Grandpa!**

START GRAND	CHILD	LIKE	WISE	MEN
MOTHER	BIRTH	DOWN	RIGHT	HORSE
HOOD	DAY	BREAK	HAND	CLOTH
ON	TIME	TABLE	OUT	HOUSE END

Answer to "Grandpa's Cooking": The joke reads normally from left to right "What's the difference between Grandpa's cooking and a pile of slugs?" The answer to the joke is written between the lines. It is backwards and can be read if you hold the book up to a mirror. "Grandpa's cooking usually comes with a knife and a fork!"

page 48 • **Family Photos**

page 48 • **What do you call your cousin . . .**

G	R	E	E	N	S	L	E	E	V	E	S

PUZZLE ANSWERS

page 50 • **What did the monster mama say . . .**

STOP PICKING YOUR NOSES!

page 52 • **Losing Lunch**

Everyone's story will be different. Here's a sample:

(MONDAY) I had a (GOOEY) stomach
  day of the week   awful adjective
ache. I don't know why! At lunch I only ate (47)
                                           big number
(PIZZAS) and (312)(TWINKIES).
  food item, plural   big number   different food item, plural
For dessert I had (1,201)(RAISINS). By the time I
                    number   food item, plural
got home, I felt (MOLDY). My stomach started
                  awful adjective
(JUMPING) and my face turned (AQUA). I ran for the
  action word   color
bathroom, but my (STICKY) brother, (ALFRED),
                   awful adjective   boy's name
was in there. Sometimes he stays
in there for (32) hours.
             big number
Oh no! So I ran into the
(LAUNDRY ROOM), instead,
  room in your house, not the bathroom
and threw up in a (PENCIL HOLDER).
                        container
I felt much better after that!

page 53 • **Yum! Bugs!**

```
W E Y L F N O G A R D H G
A T E K C I R C T D O Y U
O I U C I C A D A G E T B
I M F A N T B Y O U N C K
G R R T O S E S M R O W N
U E A E T E E R M I I T I
B T A R A N T U L A P G T
R E W P I T L H A B R O S
E O K I A N E I N U O S P
T E C L T T H A B T C E I
A S I L K W O R M A S T D
W S I A T S O W N W O R E
D S G R A S S H O P P E R
```

WHAT DO YOU GET IF YOU CROSS A
TERMITE WITH A BOOK? AN INSECT
THAT EATS ITS OWN WORDS!

page 54 • **Waiter! There's a fly in my soup!**

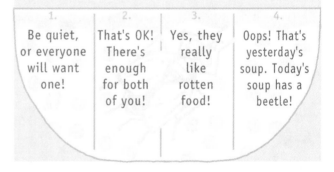

1.	2.	3.	4.
Be quiet, or everyone will want one!	That's OK! There's enough for both of you!	Yes, they really like rotten food!	Oops! That's yesterday's soup. Today's soup has a beetle!

page 55 • Clean the Fridge!

```
C R U S T Y
Y U C K Y
    F I Z Z Y
S M E L L Y
    N A S T Y
R A N C I D
    F E T I D

  G R E E N
  T O X I C
      P U T R I D
R O T T E N
S C A R Y
O O Z I N G
    M O L D Y
    W E I R D
S T I N K Y
V O M I T O U S
    S L I M Y
```

page 56 • Peanut Butter and . . .?

BOLOGNA

POTATO CHIPS

CHOCOLATE

BACON

CHEESE

PICKLES

MUSTARD

PARSLEY

MAYONNAISE

ONION

B.B.Q. SAUCE

START

END

page 57 • Gag Man, Glad Man

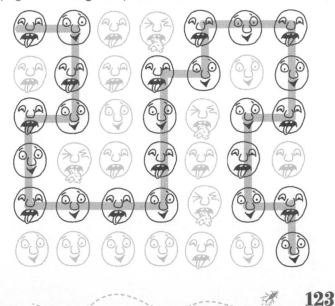

PUZZLE ANSWERS

page 58 • Lose Your Appetite

page 61 • To Market

1 P.H. (with big ears)
PIG HEAD
4 D.F. (clean webbing)
DUCK FEET
3 F. (good jumpers)
FROGS
4 T. (with all 8 legs)
TARANTULAS
1 S. (watch stinger)
SCORPION
15 W. (wiggly)
WORMS
2 G. (necks 9 inches)
GEESE

page 59 •
Bug Eater

B	E	D
O	N	E
A	T	E
H	O	T
U	M	P
D	O	G
A	P	E
S	H	E
M	A	D
A	G	E
E	Y	E

page 59 • Delicious Delicacies

Milk-giver's smart parts
COW BRAINS

Cud chewer's mouth muscle
COW TONGUE

Hopper's essential parts
FROG LEGS

Baa baa's tum tum
SHEEP STOMACH

Ape's kissing equipment
MONKEY LIPS

Porker's walkers
PIG FEET

page 62 • The Barf Buffet

XLFTS-VV
COUGH-EE

RSDMBG EQHDR
STENCH FRIES

EBOESVGG
DANDRUFF
GMZLFT
FLAKES

AKEC FO
CAKE OF
OAPS
SOAP

page 64 • White stuff from the sky?

1Q N	2M E	3H V	4P E	5N R		6C C	7P A	8N T	9F C	10D H
11H S	12D N	13G O	14A W	15L F	16K L	17Q A	18F K	19A E	20J S
21D W	22A I	23A T	24A H		25Q Y	26H O	27N U	28P R	
29P T	30M O	31Q N	32G G	33C U	34D E		35I U	36Q N	37R T	38D I	39C L
	40E A	41L L	42M L		43B T	44B H	45J E	
46F B	47I I	48C R	49B D	50I S		51K H	52F A	53M V	54J E
55M G	56L O	57E N	58K E		59P S	60L O	61B U	62I T	63O H
64G F	65R O	66E R		67O T	68N H	69K E	
70R W	71O I	72O N	73H T	74H E	75G R	!

Reading: NEVER CATCH SNOWFLAKES WITH YOUR TONGUE UNTIL ALL THE BIRDS HAVE GONE SOUTH FOR THE WINTER!

A. Opposite of black
W H I T E
14 24 22 23 19

B. A heavy, dropping sound
T H U D
43 44 61 49

C. To wind around
C U R L
6 33 48 39

D. High, complaining voice
W H I N E
21 10 38 12 34

E. Past tense of run
R A N
66 40 57

F. Opposite of front
B A C K
46 52 9 18

G. Toad's relative
F R O G
64 75 13 32

H. Casts a ballot
V O T E S
3 26 73 74 11

I. Pants and jacket combo
S U I T
50 35 47 62

J. Take in with the eyes
S E E
20 45 54

K. Rear part of a foot
H E E L
51 58 69 16

L. To trick
F O O L
15 56 60 41

M. Winter hand covering
G L O V E
55 42 30 53 2

N. To injure
H U R T
68 27 5 8

O. Not fat
T H I N
67 63 71 72

P. Look at for a long time
S T A R E
59 29 7 28 4

Q. Live-in babysitter
N A N N Y
36 17 1 31 25

R. Number before three
T W O
37 70 65

page 66 • A Creature's Gotta Eat

i Shove my StomAcH out thRough my mouth and surround what i'm eaTing. i pull It back in when i'm Full.

STARFISH

i tHrow up On Food, and thE acid turns mY meaL to soUp. then i Slurp it up!

HOUSEFLY

i liVe by eating animals thaT are alReady dead. the eye-baLls are easy to get to, so it is not UnusUal that i Eat them first.

VULTURE

i attaCh to my dinnEr's skin and suck bLood up to ninE times my weigHt.

LEECH

i crush an animal uNtil it stoPs breathing. then i unHook my jaws and stretch mY mouth exTra wide. this lets me swallow my dinner whOle!

PYTHON

page 67 • Doo They, or Don't They?

Rabbits (YES) NO
Cats YES (NO)
Dogs (YES) NO
Koalas (YES) NO

page 67 • Those Dang Beetles

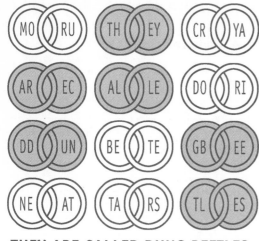

MO RU	TH EY	CR YA
AR EC	AL LE	DO RI
DD UN	BE TE	GB EE
NE AT	TA RS	TL ES

These beetles collect and roll balls of **dung,** or **poop,** in which to lay their eggs. They also eat **dung** for **dinner!**

THEY ARE CALLED DUNG BEETLES

page 68 • ICK! That's what makes me sneeze?!?

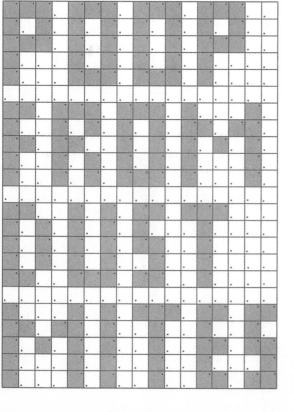

A DUST MITE IS A DISTANT RELATIVE OF THE SPIDER. IT IS A TINY CRITTER TOO SMALL TO SEE WITHOUT A POWERFUL MICROSCOPE. DUST MITES LIVE BY EATING THE MILLIONS OF DEAD SKIN CELLS YOU SHED ALL OVER THE HOUSE EACH DAY.

page 69 • Open Wide

TURTLE

DEER

TOAD

OWL

FISH

MOUSE

page 69 • Nice Cow?

Cows ~~chew~~ have ~~chew~~ trouble ~~chew~~ digesting ~~chew~~ the ~~chew~~ grass ~~chew~~ they ~~chew~~ eat ~~chew~~. They ~~chew~~ chew ~~chew~~ and ~~chew~~ swallow ~~chew~~ grass ~~chew~~ in ~~chew~~ the ~~chew~~ field ~~chew~~. Later ~~chew~~, they ~~chew~~ upchuck ~~chew~~ the ~~chew~~ partially ~~chew~~ digested ~~chew~~ grass ~~chew~~ and ~~chew~~ rechew ~~chew~~ it ~~chew~~ — for ~~chew~~ up ~~chew~~ to ~~chew~~ 9 ~~chew~~ hours ~~chew~~ a ~~chew~~ day ~~chew~~!

PUZZLE ANSWERS

page 70 • **Shark Bite**

COOKIE CUTTER SHARKS

page 71 • **Big Monkeys**

BCEAFIJCD
LILJUEFUI
CUBDLOJEO
DMFIECFSD

B A - B O O M S !

page 71 • **Elephant Nose Pick**

T	H	E	Y		D	O	N	'	T		K	N	O	W
	W	H	E	R	E		T	O		H	I	D	E	
A		T	W	O		F	O	O	T		L	O	N	G
	B	O	O	G	E	R	!							

page 72 • **It's Not Snot**

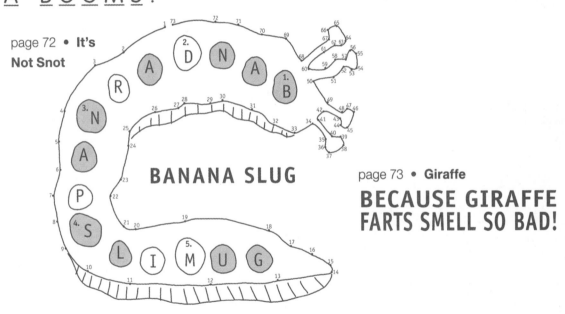

BANANA SLUG

page 73 • **Giraffe**

BECAUSE GIRAFFE
FARTS SMELL SO BAD!

page 74 • **Slobber = ?**

On a hot day, a dog uses its tongue to...

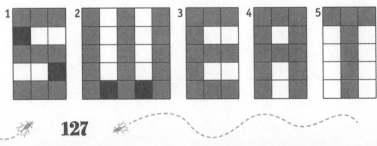

PUZZLE ANSWERS

page 76 • **Watch Your Step**

A. Not a special one
$\underset{10}{A}\ \underset{11}{N}\ \underset{9}{Y}$

B. Cow noise
$\underset{13}{M}\ \underset{17}{O}\ \underset{18}{O}$

C. Opposite of work
$\underset{19}{P}\ \underset{15}{L}\ \underset{14}{A}\ \underset{4}{Y}$

D. Center of a peach
$\underset{16}{P}\ \underset{12}{I}\ \underset{6}{T}$

E. Opposite of she
$\underset{2}{H}\ \underset{3}{E}$

F. Tiny bits of dirt
$\underset{8}{D}\ \underset{7}{U}\ \underset{5}{S}\ \underset{1}{T}$

page 76 • **Hey, Hippo!**

MALE HIPPOS WILL TURN BUTT TO BUTT AND SPRAY EACH OTHER WITH A GLOPPY MIXTURE OF POOP AND URINE!

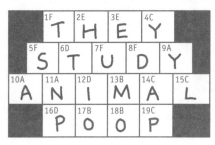

THEY STUDY ANIMAL POOP

page 77 • **Feed Me**

VENUS FLY TRAP

page 78 • **Yucky Yucky**

THA HOMUN AYA
THE HUMAN EYE

page 79 • **Monster Eyes**

PARIS, BECAUSE THE EYE-FULL TOWER IS THERE!

PUZZLE ANSWERS

page 80 • **Attack Plant**

1. Opposite of "Hi!"
B Y E

2. Night before
E V E

3. Fake hair
W I G

4. Number before two
O N E

5. What a ghost says
B O O

6. To request
A S K

7. Opposite of lose
W I N

8. Mama pig
S O W

9. Monkey relative
A P E

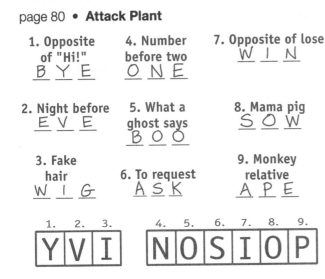

1.	2.	3.
Y	V	I

4.	5.	6.	7.	8.	9.
N	O	S	I	O	P

If you read the answer the correct way, it's POISON IVY.

page 81 • **Smelly Letters**

QBISXCSOJ
LTCAMTCXY
RWEIRYNZJ
ZTJDQTEIM
SPIEXULWCI

B.O. AND P.U.

page 82 • **Where's the Gross?**

1. The kid(s lug)ged four cans of garbage.
2. The (slim e)arthworm poops in the dirt.
3. While belchin(g, Ross) can also chant.
4. Joe'(s pit) bull was chewin(g a g)reasy bone.
5. The sec(ret ch)ain opens the dirty drain.
6. Does anyone eat wartho(g or e)lectric eel?
7. Bob'(s not)e was dumb and disgusting.

page 82 • **Why was the pig farmer . . .**

HE	~~FOE~~	WAS	~~THINK~~
~~TANK~~	THANKFUL	~~SEA~~	~~FOG~~
THAT	~~FORGETFUL~~	PIGS	~~RANK~~
~~TEA~~	CAN'T	~~FEE~~	FLY

He was thankful that pigs can't fly!

page 81 • **How Many Farts**

J U S T   A   P H E W!

PUZZLE ANSWERS

page 83 • Sloppy Sentences

Seven slimy slugs slid softly sideways.

Gary's greasy guts grew green garbage.

Big black bugs bleed black blood.

Foul feces flopped from five flatworms.

Many maggots make moist meals messy.

page 84 • Gross Gulps

S	E	K	A
T	L	L	M
H	O	A	Y
I	W	W	D
S	I	S	O
M	T	U	B
U	A	O	R
C	L	Y	U
H	L.	T.	O
S	P	I	Y

Your body makes this much spit. You swallow it all.

page 85 • Got Maggots?

JUGGLER
FOGGY
DRAGGED
EGGROLL
HUGGED
BIGGER
GIGGLE
BAGGAGE
WIGGLE
SUGGEST
NUGGET

page 86 • Terribly Tiny

AROUND THE

ROOTS OF YOUR

EYELASHES.

YES, YOURS!

page 88 • Ouch!

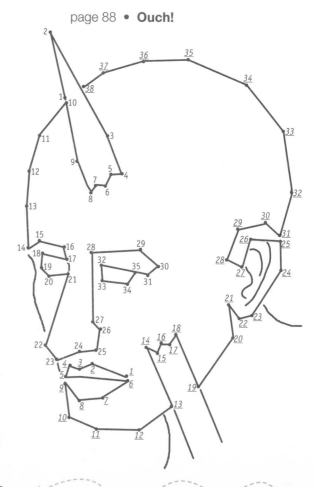

page 89 • Awfully Ancient

N	U	M		B N	E		S S	
R B O	T	T E	B N	B N	O	SE
Y E L	L O	W	B	U	M P	S
T M H I	C M K	E	A R M S	
S T I	F F	E Y E	L I	D S
N O M	F R O M N T M T E	E T H
D E	F O R	M E	D T O	E S
L O S	S O F F	I N G	E R S

page 89 • Nail Biter

WEAR YOUR SHOES!

page 90 • Seriously Surgical

A decade is ? years	10
Cards in a deck	52
A score is ? years	20
Twelve pairs of shoes	24
Fingers on two hands	10
A gross equals ? items	144
Eighty quarters is ? dollars	20
An egg carton holds ? eggs	12
Two cups of butter is ? sticks	4
There are ? days in a year	365
There are ? keys on the piano	88
Number of pennies in a dollar	100
Ten gallons of milk is ? quarts	40
An octogenarian is ? years old	80
Number of pits in an avocado	1

TOTAL 970

page 90 • Awful Smell

So would I!
(Sew wood eye!)

page 91 • Almost Everybody Gets It

A little hot = W A R M
Foot digit = T O E
Stand-up bath = S H O W E R
Body dryer = T O W E L
Opposite of dry = W E T
Scratch this = I T C H
To perspire = S W E A T
Foot bottom = S O L E
No foot cover = B A R E F O O T
Soft foot cover = S O C K
Hard foot cover = S H O E
Barely wet = M O I S T

page 91 • Swallowed Pen

USE A PENCIL TIL I GET THERE!

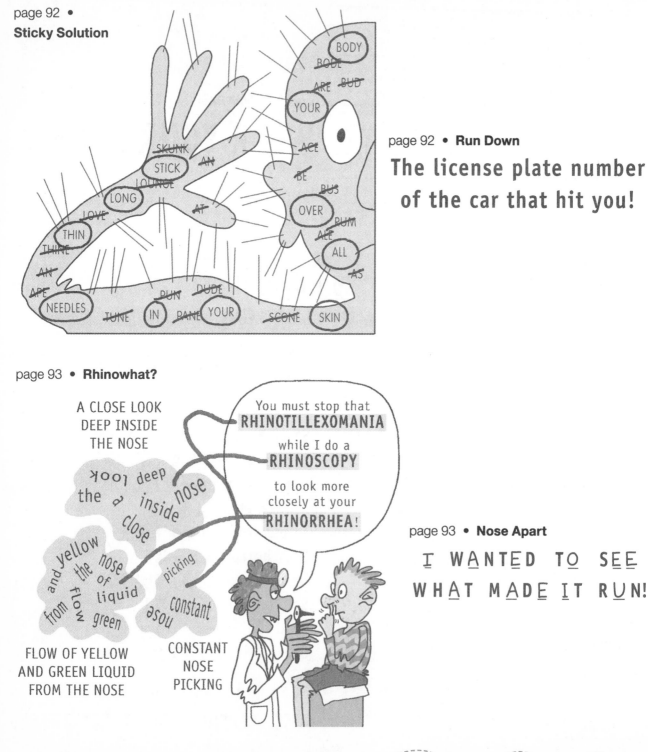

page 92 •
Sticky Solution

page 92 • **Run Down**

The license plate number of the car that hit you!

page 93 • **Rhinowhat?**

A CLOSE LOOK
DEEP INSIDE
THE NOSE

You must stop that
RHINOTILLEXOMANIA
while I do a
RHINOSCOPY
to look more
closely at your
RHINORRHEA!

page 93 • **Nose Apart**

I WANTED TO SEE WHAT MADE IT RUN!

FLOW OF YELLOW
AND GREEN LIQUID
FROM THE NOSE

CONSTANT
NOSE
PICKING

page 94 • Body Sculpting

A		L	O	N	G		M	E	T	A	L	
	T	U	B	E		I	S		S	T	U	C	K
		U	N	D	E	R		T	H	E		
S	K	I	N		A	N	D		F	A	T	
	I	S		S	U	C	K	E	D		O	U	T

page 94 • Brain Surgeon

I was a dentist until my drill slipped!

page 95 • Slimy Helpers

page 95 • Biting Insects

STOP BITING THEM!

page 96 • Where does Mrs. Doctor keep . . .

1F S	2F H	3B E		4A	5C K	6F E	7A E	8F P	S	
9E T	10B H	11A E	12D M		13E I	14B N		15E H	16A E	17C R
18D H	19C A	20E N	21F D	22C B	23D A	24C G	!			

A. To continue to have
K E E P
4 11 16 7

B. A female chicken
H E N
10 3 14

C. Boat with a flat bottom
B A R G E
22 19 17 24 5

D. Meat from a pig
H A M
18 23 12

E. Opposite of fat
T H I N
9 15 13 20

F. Small storage buildings
S H E D S
8 2 6 21 1

page 96 • First Surgery

Surgeon: I know just how you feel. This is the first time I've done any!

page 97 • "I don't feel very good . . ."

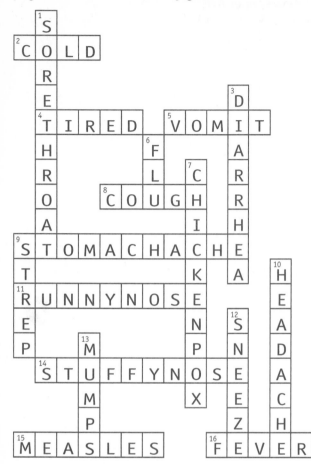

Crossword answers:
- 1 SORETHROAT (down)
- 2 COLD
- 3 DIARRHEA (down)
- 4 TIRED
- 5 VOMIT
- 6 FLU
- 7 CHICKENPOX (down)
- 8 COUGH
- 9 STOMACHACHE
- 10 HEADACHE (down)
- 11 RUNNYNOSE
- 12 SNEEZE (down)
- 13 MUMPS (down)
- 14 STUFFYNOSE
- 15 MEASLES
- 16 FEVER

STREP

page 98 • Really Rotten

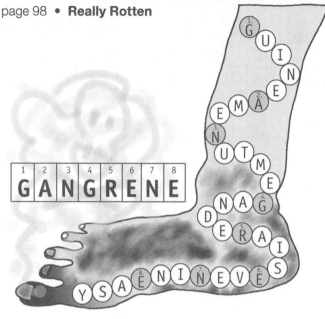

GANGRENE

1 2 3 4 5 6 7 8
G A N G R E N E

GUINEA MANGER NUTMEG DERAIS... SEVEN...

page 97 • Double Vision

Your vision is fine. The problem is you have two heads!

page 98 • Headache

Yes! Crash your head through that window and the pane will be gone!

page 100 • Zombie Newspaper Article

THE DAILY POOP

TOILET
NEWS
PAPER

ZOMBIE LOSES MARATHON BY WIDE MARGIN

After quite a lively start, zombie athlete, Fester N. Rott, was dismayed to finish the race dead last.

PUZZLE ANSWERS

page 100 • **What's the last thing . . .**

HIS BUTT!

page 101 • **Dead on My Feet**

page 102 • **Cannibal King Newspaper Article**

THE DAILY POOP
TOILET
NEWS
PAPER

OOPS!

This report just in from Loa Loa Island. Infamous Cannibal King, Wanna Eatcha, accidentally put his false teeth in backwards and ate himself.

page 102 • **Chop Chop**

TO CUT SOMEONE'S HEAD OFF

A BIG PAIN IN THE NECK

page 104 • **Batman Newspaper Article**

THE DAILY POOP
TOILET
NEWS
PAPER

DYNAMIC DUO HIT BY STEAM ROLLER

Batman and Robin are expected to recover, but ask that the public now refer to them as "Flatman and Ribbon."

PUZZLE ANSWERS

page 104 • Dead Poet's Society

SEVEN SNEAKER DEAD VOMIT MAN ON THE BRIDGE ONE LAST NIGHT, POOP HIS CLOG BONES WERE THREE ALL EARWAX AQUIVER. HE SPIT GAVE A FART COUGH, HIS BOOT LEG FOOT FELL YUCK OFF, SANDAL AND FLOATED FIVE DOWN POOP THE BUTT HEAD RIVER!

page 105 • Mummy Mia!

1. Body is _____D_____ on the left side.

2. Lungs, liver, stomach, and intestine_____G_____.

3. The brain is _____E_____.

4. The heart is the only organ _____C_____.

5. The inside of the body is _____F_____.

6. Body is_____A_____ and left to dry for two months.

7. Body is_____B_____ that comes from trees.

8. _____H_____ sand, sawdust, and cloth.

9. Body is_____I_____ in linen bandages.

page 106 • Karate Newspaper Article

THE DAILY POOP

TOILET NEWS **PAPER**

KAR**OUCH**ATE
EXP**OUCH**ERT
KNO**OUCH**CKED
O**OUCH**UT
FIR**OUCH**ST
DA**OUCH**Y
I**OUCH**N
AR**OUCH**MY

Pri**ouch**vate B**ouch**. Be**ouch**lt w**ouch**as pract**ouch**icing ho**ouch**w t**ouch**o sal**ouch**ute.

page 106 • Hangman's Holiday

[2] THE 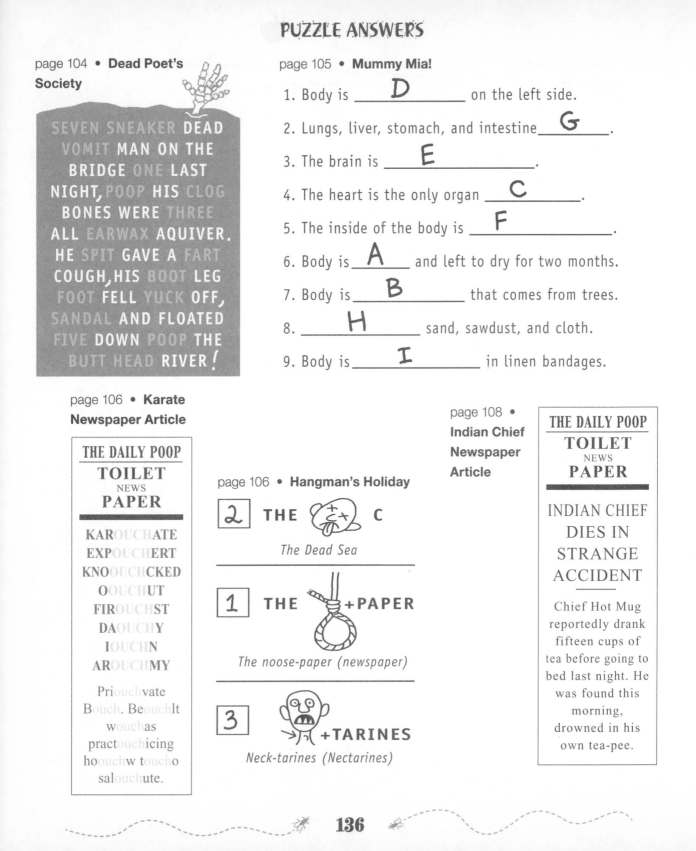 C

The Dead Sea

[1] THE +PAPER

The noose-paper (newspaper)

[3] +TARINES

Neck-tarines (Nectarines)

page 108 • Indian Chief Newspaper Article

THE DAILY POOP

TOILET NEWS **PAPER**

INDIAN CHIEF DIES IN STRANGE ACCIDENT

Chief Hot Mug reportedly drank fifteen cups of tea before going to bed last night. He was found this morning, drowned in his own tea-pee.

PUZZLE ANSWERS

page 108 • What does the headstone say . . .

HE RESTS
IN PIECES

page 110 • Dead End

Rotten bananas are very B E N D A B L E.

Would you really eat a bug, or just P R E T E N D to?

A true F R I E N D will L E N D you his whoopie cushion.

Would you S P E N D your money on garlic gum or earwax candy?

A boring monster movie seems E N D L E S S.

A really gross joke might O F F E N D your grandma.

Some things should <u>not</u> go in a B L E N D E R.

The gross cook R E C O M M E N D S the scorpion soup.

page 109 •
Mad Scientist
Newspaper
Article

THE DAILY POOP
TOILET
NEWS
PAPER

MAD SCIENTIST TURNS INTO FROG

Doctor Greenblood's mother was quoted as saying "I told him never to lick the spoon after mixing a new potion!"

page 111 •
Look Again!

1. It Was The Dog!
2. How did the teen...
3. Why did the t.p. ...
4. Juicy Jobs?
5. Clean the Fridge!
6. Giraffe
7. Why was the pig farmer...
8. Rhinowhat?
9. Chop Chop

PART 2: Gross Jokes

Chapter 10

Creepy Critters

What did the slug say as it slipped down the sidewalk?

How slime flies.

What's the difference between an earthworm and a cookie?

An earthworm doesn't fall apart when you dunk it in milk.

Why is the letter T so important to a stick bug?

Without it, it would be a sick bug.

What do you get when you have 288 roaches crawling in your bed?

Too gross.

What is the last thing to go through a fly's mind as he crashes into a window?

His rear end.

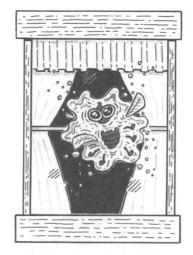

What am I?

I can disguise myself without you ever knowing I'm there! I have no real defenses, so I have to be creative. If I'm in danger, I can pretend to be something else. When a predator comes near, I freeze and look just like a piece of wood. **What am I?**

A treehopper.

What did one maggot say to the other when they found themselves stuck in an apple?

Let's see you worm your way out of this.

What do you get if you cross a centipede with a parrot?

A walkie talkie.

What did the mother worm say to her son when he came home late?

Where in earth have you been?

Customer: *Waiter, there's a big roach in my salad!*

Waiter: *Well, stop announcing it before everyone else wants one too!*

Park Ranger: *Sir, you can't fish in this pond.*

Man: *I'm not fishing—I'm teaching my pet worm to swim.*

What did the slime say to the mold when they saw each other after a long while?

You gruesome since I saw you last.

Customer: *Waiter, waiter, what's this roach doing on my ice cream?*

Waiter: *I think it's skiing downhill.*

What did the banana say to the maggot?

You're boring me to death.

Teacher: *If I have eight flies on my desk and swat one, how many are left?*

Student: *Just one—the dead one.*

Knock Knock

Who's there?
Spider.
Spider who?
Spider everything, I still think you're pretty gross.

What am I?

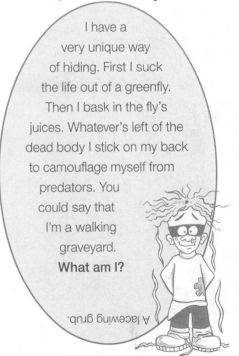

I have a very unique way of hiding. First I suck the life out of a greenfly. Then I bask in the fly's juices. Whatever's left of the dead body I stick on my back to camouflage myself from predators. You could say that I'm a walking graveyard. **What am I?**

A lacewing grub.

K	E	
P	L	A

Yummy!

A riddle and its answer were put into the large grid, and then cut into eight pieces. See if you can figure out where each piece goes, and write the letters in their proper places. When you have filled in the grid correctly, you will be able to read the puzzle from left to right, and top to bottom.

HINT: The black boxes stand for the spaces between words.

How do you make a moth bawl?

Hit it with a fly swatter.

How did the dog train his fleas?

He started from scratch.

Sally: *Do slugs taste good?*
Mother: *Why do you ask?*
Sally: *Well, you've got one on your fork.*

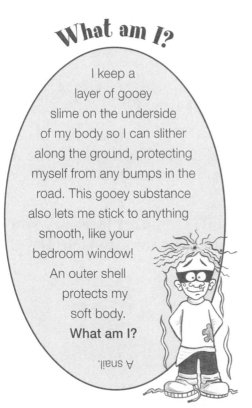

What am I?

I keep a layer of gooey slime on the underside of my body so I can slither along the ground, protecting myself from any bumps in the road. This gooey substance also lets me stick to anything smooth, like your bedroom window! An outer shell protects my soft body.
What am I?

A snail.

What's the best way to prevent getting sick from biting insects?

Stop biting them.

Why do maggots eat puke?

It's a dirty job but someone's got to do it.

What did the slug say after the other slug hit him on the head?

I'll get you next slime!

What's the difference between head lice and dandruff?

Lice crunches more when you eat it.

What's the definition of a caterpillar?
A worm in a fur coat.

What did the spider do when she couldn't carry the stick on her own?
She hired an assist-ant.

What did the cowboy maggot say when he walked into a saloon?
Give me a slug of whiskey.

What was the worm doing in the cornfield?
Going in one ear and out the other.

What am I?

I lurk in dark, filthy places and I only hunt in the pitch black of night. My sharp beak-shaped mouth drills a small hole into your flesh and I feast on your blood while you sleep. I don't travel alone but in swarms. If you wake and turn on the lights I will scurry back under the mattress to strike another day. **What am I?**

A bedbug.

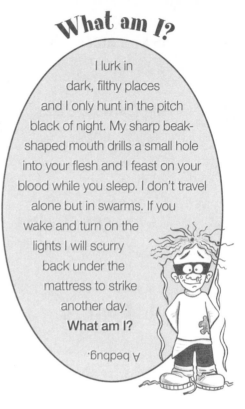

Foul Language

Coleopterist
This is a person who has the job of researching everything there is to know about beetles. A coleopterist handles beetles all day. This way, the rest of us can learn about beetles without actually having to touch the creepy, crawly critters.

Why did the blob always stay home?
He had no place to goo.

What did the mother leech say when someone went for a swim in the pond?
Lunchtime!

Totally Twisted

Make your own slime. Mash up bananas, mushrooms, leaves, and a drop of water. Store in a sealed plastic bag for a week in a warm place. You will then have the grossest slime you've ever seen. Share your new slime bag with your friends. They'll surely appreciate it.

Knock Knock

Who's there?
Throat.
Throat who?
Throat out, there are maggots crawling all over it.

How do you keep the flies out of the kitchen?

Keep a bucket of cow poop in the living room.

Knock Knock

Who's there?
Seymour.
Seymour who?
Seymour leeches in a lake.

Stink Pinks

A stink pink is a riddle with a special kind of two-word answer—both words are one syllable long and rhyme. Of course, one of the words is gross!

What's a large vehicle that hauls garbage?
Y U C K   T R U C K

Where can you buy plastic scars and fake blood?
_ _ _ _   _ _ _ _

What do you call a shovel used to pick up dog doo?
_ _ _ _   _ _ _ _

What do you call ghost throw up?
_ _ _ _   _ _ _ _

What do you call an intelligent gas?
_ _ _ _   _ _ _ _

What's a riddle about a dead frog?
_ _ _ _   _ _ _ _

Ed: *I once ate a slimy slug in my pajamas.*
Fred: *Really?*
Ed: *Yes, I still don't know how he got into them.*

Why did the beetle ground his children?

They were bugging him.

Knock Knock

Who's there?
Harry.
Harry who?
Harry, scary spider crawling on you.

What am I?

I build my nests by chewing wood into tiny bits. Then I spit the wood out and mush it on the wall of your house. I make a mansion for the eggs I produce. Each egg gets its own room. When my babies hatch, I feed them chewed-up caterpillar intestines. **What am I?**

A wasp.

Knock Knock

Who's there?
I-8.
I-8 who?
I-8 a slug for lunch, and now I don't feel so good.

How do you make a butterfly?

Flick it out of the butter dish.

How are roaches like raisins?

They both show up in your cereal.

Why didn't the fleas stick around on the dirty schoolboy?

The lice chased them away.

What did the cook do when he found a Daddy Long Legs in his meatloaf?

He turned it into a Daddy Short Legs.

What do you do with a scorpion the size of a horse?

Ride it to the hospital after it stings you.

How do you know if you have maggots in your fridge?

You'll see tunnels in the bean dip.

Why was the blob turned away from the restaurant?

No shirt, no shoes, no service.

What did one fly ask the other?

Is this stool taken?

Why do maggots like open wounds?

They don't have to fight over who gets the scab.

Why are mosquitoes so annoying at night?

They like a bite to eat before bedtime.

What am I?

I am a wiggly slimy glob that oozes. I can live in your yard, or hang out on your deck, or I can take over the whole neighborhood if you're not careful. I can be as small as a coin or as big as a table. If you try to break me apart, I just multiply and grow.

What am I?

Slime mold.

Knock Knock

Who's there?
Thistle.
Thistle who?
Thistle be the last chance for maggot pie.

What do you get if you cross a centipede with a homing pigeon?

A creepy crawler that just keeps coming back.

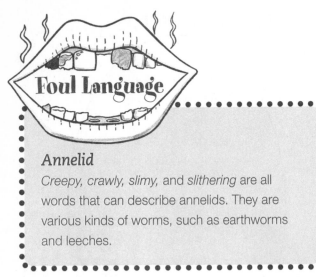

Foul Language

Annelid

Creepy, crawly, slimy, and *slithering* are all words that can describe annelids. They are various kinds of worms, such as earthworms and leeches.

What do you call tired bugs?

Sleepy creepies.

What do you call a bug that has worked its way to the top?

Head lice.

What's a blob's favorite drink?

Slime-ade.

What goes "Snap, crackle, pop"?

A dying firefly.

What do you get if you cross a scorpion with a rose?

I don't know, but I wouldn't try smelling it.

What kind of bugs live on the moon?

Lunar ticks.

How do fleas get around?

By itch hiking.

What lies on the ground 100 feet up in the air?

A dead centipede.

YAK YAK YAK

How do toilets keep in touch?

To find out, connect the numbered dots in order.
Then connect the lettered dots in order.

Customer: *There's a little worm in my salad!*

Waitress: *Shall I bring you a bigger one?*

Why was the mother flea so upset?

Because her children were going to the dogs.

What has fifty legs but can't walk?

Half a centipede.

Why did the mosquito get braces?

To improve his bite.

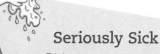

Seriously Sick

Did you ever notice that only some mosquitoes squirt blood when you squish them and others don't? This is because only females dine on your blood. A female needs your blood to feed her babies, and she lays anywhere from 100 to 500 eggs at a time.

What am I?

One of my favorite foods is rotten fruit. Give me a squishy banana left out in the sun too long, and I'll be the happiest creature you've ever seen! I've got a yellow and black jacket that makes me look pretty scary, but the truth is, I have no sting. **What am I?**

A hover fly.

Knock Knock

Who's there?
Wilfred.
Wilfred who?
Wilfred eat chocolate-covered ants?

Why are mosquitoes so annoying?

They have a way of getting under your skin.

Chapter 11

Barf-days and Other Celebrations

Boy Monster: *Did you get the heart I sent you for Valentine's Day?*

Girl Monster: *Why yes, thank you, it's still beating.*

What do you sing at a birthday party where everyone gets sick from the cake?

Happy Barf-day.

Seriously Sick

As soon as food gets to your stomach, hydrochloric acid attacks that chewed-up mush like there's no tomorrow. Acid rips apart and dissolves the food until it's ready to go through the rest of your digestive system. This acid is powerful enough to completely dissolve a stainless steel spoon, though this probably isn't your first choice for an afternoon snack!

What did the executioner say to his family?

Only fifteen chopping days till the holidays!

What's another word for bunny poop?

Easter eggs.

What happened to the snowman at the Fourth of July picnic?

They turned him into snow cones and ate him.

What do spider brides wear?

Webbing dresses.

Who did the gravediggers invite to their Halloween party?

Anyone they could dig up.

What do you get if an ax falls on your head?

Write as many answers as you can under the clues. Then, enter each letter into its numbered box in the answer grid. Work back and forth between the clues and the grid to get the answer to the riddle.

1D		2E	3B	4A	5A	6D	7C	8E	9E	10 D
a		s		L	I	T	H	i	n	g

11 C	12 B	13 B	14 A	15 C	16 B	17 E	18 C	
C			d	a		h	o	!

A. Top on a jar
$\underline{L}$ $\underline{i}$ $\underline{d}$
 4   5   14

B. Dracula's coat
$\underline{}$ $\underline{}$ $\underline{}$ $\underline{}$
 16   13   3   12

C. It makes you warm
$\underline{C}$ $\underline{o}$ $\underline{a}$ $\underline{t}$
 11   18   15   7

D. Kids' running game
$\underline{L}$ $\underline{a}$ $\underline{g}$
 6   1   10

E. Between knee and ankle
$\underline{}$ $\underline{}$ $\underline{}$ $\underline{}$
 2   17   8   9

153

What do you call an insect dance?
A moth ball.

What kind of ice cream makes you barf?
Van-ill-a.

Why did the birthday girl bring toilet paper to her party?
She was a party pooper.

Cannibal 1: What gorgeous eyes you have!
Cannibal 2: Thank you, they were a birthday present.

Did you hear about the pig who started hiding garbage on Halloween?
He wanted to do his Christmas slopping early.

What shoots stuffing across the room?
A turkey fart.

How did the man feel after eating the whole Christmas goose?
He felt pretty down.

Why did the monster get fired from his job at the candy store?
He kept biting the heads off the chocolate bunnies.

Totally Twisted
Here's a fun Halloween recipe to make your very own boogers on a stick. Just mix some Cheese Whiz with a few drops of green food coloring and dip pretzel sticks in it. Serve these treats to all your friends in costumes.

Use the banana decoder to break the code
and answer this riddle!

What's invisible and smells like bananas?

m F
o a
n r
k t
e s
y

A C E
F K M
N O R
S T Y

155

What did the mother turkey say to her misbehaving son?

If your father were here, he'd roll over in his gravy.

Why did Mr. and Mrs. Insect cancel their vacation?

The roach motel was full.

Always Listen to Your Mother

Mommy, Mommy, are you sure this is the right way to make gingerbread cookies?

Stop talking and get back in the oven.

Mommy, Mommy, can I play with Grandpa?

No, we already dug him up three times this week.

Mommy, Mommy, I hate my brother's guts.

Well then just leave them on your plate and we'll warm them up tomorrow.

Mommy, Mommy, Daddy puked.

Hurry up and get a fork before your brother gets all the big chunks.

Mommy, Mommy, Aunt Tina bruised herself.

Be quiet and eat around it.

Mommy, Mommy, the dog is going out.

Well, go throw some more gasoline on it.

Mommy, Mommy, what happened to all the cat food Tiger wouldn't eat?

Just eat your meatloaf.

Mommy, Mommy, do we have to visit Auntie?

Hush, and keep digging.

Mommy, Mommy, when are we going to have the neighbors for dinner?

You haven't even finished your cousins yet.

Mike: *What's your favorite party game?*
Eddie: *Pin the tail on the donkey.*
Mike: *Oh, that must make your behind really sore.*

Cannibal Mother: *Dear, go get some salt and pepper and some plates.*
Cannibal Son: *But why, Mom?*
Cannibal Mother: *Your sister has just fallen on the barbecue.*

What's cold and green and has a cherry on top?

A snot sundae.

Seriously Sick

Everyone knows it's fun to color eggs on Easter. But it's even more fun to make them gross, ugly colors! Instead of dying the eggshells yellow, purple, or green, mix all those colors together to make a yucky brown. Dye your eggs poop-brown or booger-green and then put them in an Easter basket on display.

GROSS-O-METER

In 2002, 38,000 people threw more than 120 tons of tomatoes at each other during the La Tomatilla Festival in Spain. By the end of the festival, streets were running over with tomato juices up to a foot high. Wading home in tomato juice gets a pretty solid seven on the Gross-o-meter scale.

Totally Twisted

Gross out your friends with a box of yuckiness! Get a bunch of grapes and cover them with olive oil. Then put them in a shoebox and cut a hole out of the box just big enough for only your hand. Label the box "Human Eyeballs." Then, with an adult's help, cook some spaghetti, drain it, and add oil. Put that in another box with a hole just big enough for your hand. Label it "Slimy Worms." Invite your friends over and dare them to feel what lurks inside each box.

What's a witch's favorite dessert?

Ice scream.

Customer: Waitress, what's that fly doing on my birthday cake?

Waitress: Laying eggs.

What game do elephants play with mice?

Squash.

How do slugs greet each other on January 1st?

Happy Goo Year!

To find the answer to this knock-knock, cross out all letters that follow these rules:

- Sounds like what you do in the toilet
- Third letter of a common word for "gas"
- First letter of an icky pimple name

When you are finished, read the remaining letters from left to right, and top to bottom.

Knock, knock. Who's there?

PZABPZBEPZRYZPR
APBPBPEYWPHPOP
RABPBERYSTPUZNG
MZEPONMYRBUTPT

Chapter 12

Cannibals, Vampires, and Other Freaky Folks

Did you hear about the cannibal who ate his uncle's wife?

He was an aunt-eater.

Why do cannibals leave space around a body at a funeral?

They need room to serve the appetizers.

What's worse than getting too close to a werewolf?

Getting too close to a werewolf with lice.

How do hairy scary monsters count to 100?

On their warts.

Cannibal 1: *I don't like my wife.*

Cannibal 2: *Perhaps a little pepper would help.*

What does a cannibal call a body on its way to a funeral home?

A moveable feast.

Totally Twisted
Make your own gaping wound with Vaseline, ketchup, cocoa powder, and a paper towel. Mix together a glob of Vaseline and some ketchup. Sprinkle in a bit of cocoa powder. Dip a piece of paper towel in plain Vaseline and stick it on your arm. Mold it so the ends stick up a bit. Then add your wound mixture.

What do you give a dragon with an upset stomach?

Lots of room.

Why did the vampire get fired from his job as zookeeper?

He kept biting the visitors.

How do you help a starving cannibal?

Give him a helping hand.

What does a man-eater call a bunch of bodies in a hearse?

Meals on wheels.

Why did the cannibal get expelled from school?

He kept buttering up the teacher.

What did the cannibal eat while he was on a diet?

Children.

What do vampires do to feel better?

Relax in a blood bath.

What do cannibals call a noontime funeral?

Lunch.

How do vampires travel the ocean?

By blood vessel.

What's a flesh-eater's favorite side dish?

Human beans.

How do you know who the waiter is at a cannibal wedding?

He's the one serving the guests.

GROSS-O-METER

About ten billion minuscule flakes of skin fall off your body every day. If you collected all that skin, by the end of your life you would have eighteen sugar bags full. That's just gross. Dead flaky skin all over the place gets an eight on the Gross-o-meter scale.

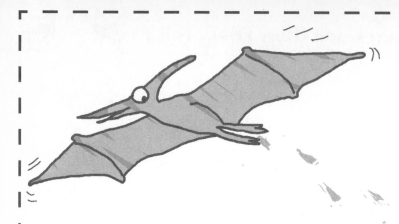

Divide the number of spaces between all of your toes by the number of nostrils in your nose.

What number do you get? Collect all the words from the word grid that have this number. Put them in the correct order to find the answer to this riddle:

Why couldn't the caveman hear the pterodactyl go to the bathroom?

4 silent	3 loudly	1 only
1 cavemen	1 poop!	2 Hear
3 too	3 The	4 pterodactyls
4 have	1 Because	3 was
3 wooly	4 "p"!	1 can
1 hear	3 burping	3 mammoth
4 a	2 what?	4 Because

Rain?

162

Why did Dracula's girlfriend dump him?
The relationship was very draining.

What did the alien say when he met the cat?
Take me to your litter.

What do you get if you cross a snowman and a vampire?
Frostbite.

What do you call a bunch of man-eaters that like sweaty feet?
Odor eaters.

Foul Language

Bromhidrosis
You know how sometimes at the end of a hot day you take off your shoes and socks only to be overwhelmed by an awful smell? It's sometimes enough to clear out a whole room! Well, this condition of stinky feet actually has a very scientific name: bromhidrosis. Some simple powder or foot deodorizer is an easy cure.

What does a cannibal call a man in a hammock?
Breakfast in bed.

Why did the cannibal eat the tightrope walker?
He wanted a balanced meal.

How did the monster stop her son from biting his nails?
She knocked his teeth out.

Why did the cannibal eat the brains of his victims?
It gave him food for thought.

Why couldn't the cannibal kids have their pets at the dinner table?
Pets are only served at breakfast.

What do witches use to style their hair?
Scare spray.

What do cannibals call a burial at sea?
Seafood.

Why did the vampire get taken away in a straitjacket?
He had gone batty.

Why do cannibals eat by candlelight?

So they can see who's being served.

How did the werewolf send his birthday cards?

By hair-mail.

What did the vampire eat after he had his teeth pulled?

The dentist.

What do sea monsters eat for dinner?

Fish and ships.

Did you hear about the young cannibal who hated his teacher?

His mother suggested he try her with ketchup.

What do you call a great big sea monster that hangs people?

The loch noose monster.

Why do people get so upset when a vampire bites them?

It's a drain in the neck.

What do you get if you cross a piranha with your nose?

Use a reverse alphabet code (A=Z, B=Y, C=X, etc.)
to figure out the answer to this riddle!

R wlm'g pmld,
yfg R dlfowm'g
dzmg gl krxp rg!

Seriously Sick

Ever wonder which muscle in the human body is the biggest? It's your gluteus maximus, or the muscle in your rear end. This muscle helps to hold you upright and also helps you swing your legs. Without the gluteus maximus, you couldn't sit *or* stand!

Why don't cannibals ever oversleep?

They don't want to be breakfast.

Why didn't the cannibal want to go to the crematorium for lunch?

They overcook everything.

What kind of mail does Dracula receive after doing a movie?

Fang mail.

What happens if you make a cannibal angry?

You end up in hot water.

What did the teacher give the cannibals?

Their first taste of education.

How do you tell when two monsters are getting along?

They see eye to eye to eye.

How did the cannibal like his guests?

Medium well.

What happened to the cannibal who ate the comedian?

He felt a little funny.

GROSS-O-METER

Pierre Beauchemin was the most flexible man in the world. He once dislocated both his legs to prove that he could fit in a box the size of a picnic basket. Doing strange things to your body to fit in unusually small places gets a nine on the Gross-o-meter scale.

How did the monster count to thirty-two?

On his fingers.

What kind of tiles did the witch have installed in her bathroom?

Reptiles.

How do you know if you have a monster in your bathtub?

The shower curtain won't close.

What is a cannibal's favorite dessert?

Ladyfingers.

What do body snatchers call it when they dig up a body and bring it home?

Take out.

Why do witches wear green eye shadow?

They like the way it matches their teeth.

What do vampires eat with their sandwiches?

Pickled organs.

Why did the single cannibal woman visit a matchmaker?

She was looking for an edible bachelor.

Why wouldn't the vampire eat his soup?

It clotted.

What did the cannibal say to his new neighbors?

I would love to have you for dinner sometime.

GROSS-O-METER

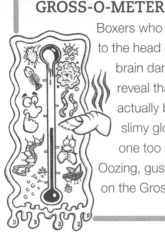

Boxers who suffer repeated blows to the head often have major brain damage. Autopsies reveal that a boxer's brain will actually become an oozing, slimy glob if the boxer has one too many matches. Oozing, gushing brains gets a ten on the Gross-o-meter scale.

What's a vampire's favorite drink?
A Bloody Mary.

Why do cannibals feel they are helping the environment?
They control overpopulation.

What do cannibals eat when they go to a restaurant?
The waiter.

What did they say to the cannibal who was late for dinner?
Everybody's already eaten!

Why wasn't there any food left at the monster café?
Because everybody there was a goblin'.

What does a vampire on a diet drink?
Blood light.

The silly reply to this statement is hidden in the letter grid. To find it, color in all the letters except P–U. When you're finished, read the dark letters from left to right and top to bottom.

"Your brother sure is spoiled!"

NPOPHPESPNOP
TUPHUPUEAPLW
AUPYPSPSPMEP
PLULUPPSPTPH
PUATPUWPAPYP

Totally Twisted

Make your own gross pie. Get a cooked pie shell, and combine a cup and a half of milk, one cup of flour, two eggs, and a little green food coloring in a bowl. With adult supervision, heat the mixture on low on the stove top. Pour the mixture into the pie crust. Add Gummy worms and let cool. Freeze pie before serving.

What's a cannibal's favorite wine?

One with lots of body.

Why did the vampire get sick after lunch?

He ate a stake sandwich.

Why did the monster eat his watch?

He was trying to kill time.

Did you hear about the vampire who keeps his teeth in the freezer?

He gives his victims frostbite.

Did you hear about the monster that threw up?

It was all over town.

What does a vampire say to his victims?

It's been nice gnawing you.

How do you know when there's a huge monster under the bed?

Your face touches the ceiling.

Why do mother monsters read to their children?

To engross them.

Foul Language

Sputum

This is basically another word for phlegm, or that mucus that seeps into your throat and makes you gag. If you're congested, your respiratory system makes a lot of sputum and you really have no choice but to spit it up or swallow it.

Why do vampires drink blood?
Grape juice makes them burp.

Why did the cannibal join the police department?
So he could grill his suspects.

Why don't cannibals like to eat internal organs?
They are hard to stomach.

What do you get when you cross a vampire with a nun?
A nasty habit.

What's worse than being a 300-pound witch?
Being her broom.

What do you call a vampire child's allowance for lunch?
Blood money.

What do cannibals call body parts that have been removed during surgery?
Leftovers.

What's it called when cannibals use embalming fluid on a body?
Seasoning.

Seriously Sick
Believe it or not, there are thousands of spores in the air just waiting to assault you. They're all over you, in every part of your room, and even on the food you eat. When they find a good landing place—usually some old leftover food or a dead animal—they implant themselves, causing gross, fuzzy mold.

Why don't cannibals eat clowns?
Because they taste funny.

What's yellow and smells of dead humans?
Cannibal puke.

Why did the vampire go to art school?
He needed to draw blood.

What happened when the gross green monster appeared on stage?

He got a lot of ooze and ahs.

What game do cannibals love to play?

Swallow the leader.

Why was the Cyclops such an attentive teacher?

He only had one pupil.

Why do cannibals like having their relatives for dinner?

It gives them a chance to serve loved ones.

Why don't vampires like steak?

It goes right through them.

Why don't man-eaters eat bratty, rich kids?

Because they're spoiled.

Chapter 13

Atrocious Animals

What did the leopard say after eating the tourist?

That hit the spot.

Why do gorillas have such big nostrils?

Because they have big fingers.

Fred: *My canary died of the flu.*
Ed: *How did that happen?*
Fred: *He flew into a car.*

What do you call it when one vulture throws a dead animal at another vulture?

A food fight.

What do you call a man who's been mauled by a tiger?

Gord.

Customer: *I'd like to buy a bird, please.*
Clerk: *I've got the perfect one. She sings and she's got red feathers.*
Customer: *Never mind that, how long does she take to cook?*

What did Jimmy say when his mother asked if he put the cat out?

Is the cat on fire again?

What am I?

I am such a slimy creature that I can turn a jar of water into a big slimy mess in a matter of seconds. Not only that, I eat my prey from the inside out, leaving nothing but a bag of skin and bones. **What am I?**

A hagfish.

What's wet, stinks, and goes thump de thump de thump?

A skunk in the dryer.

What's gray and furry on the inside and white on the outside?

A mouse sandwich.

What do you call a brontosaurus trapped in a glacier?

A fossicle.

Why did the mother hen roll her eggs around the henhouse?

She liked playing with children.

What do you do if you find a boa constrictor in your toilet?

Wait until he's finished.

How did the farmer feel when a bird pooped in his eye?

He was thankful that pigs can't fly.

Son: *The dog just ate the dinner mom made for us.*

Father: *Don't worry, son, we'll get you a new dog.*

How do you make your puppy disappear?

Use Spot remover.

Mother: *Why did you pull the dog's tail?*

Son: *I didn't pull it. I was standing on it and he pulled it.*

What am I?

I only have hair in one place on my body and it's not on my head. It's inside my mouth! When I'm born, my skin is so transparent you can see my insides. I live with others like me in deep, dark underground tunnels. I may be ugly, but I'm not alone.

What am I?

A naked mole rat.

Snot Milk?

This kid just heard a very funny joke. He laughed so hard that the chocolate milk he was drinking came out his nose! See if you can find the shadow that matches the drawing of this gross-out gaffaw.

What is small, furry, and smells like bacon?

A hamster.

Why aren't elephants allowed in public swimming pools?

They always drop their trunks.

What's the difference between a werewolf and a mean rabbit?

One is a hairy beast and the other is a beastly hare.

What do you call a frog with no back legs?

Unhoppy.

What did the rooster say when he stepped in cow poop?

Cock-a-doodle-poo.

What do you call your cat when he gets stuck in the dryer?

Fluffy.

What's black and white and red all over?

A zebra being eaten by a lion.

What happened to the cat that crashed into the screen door?

He strained himself.

What has twelve legs, six ears, a foul odor, and one eye?

Three blind mice and half a rotten fish.

What do you get when you cross a band with a chimpanzee?

A chimp-phony.

What am I?

If you try to catch me I will turn into a slippery glob of mucus and you'll never be able to hold me in your grip. I do this as a defense mechanism so no one can turn me into their dinner. I live underwater.
What am I?

An eel.

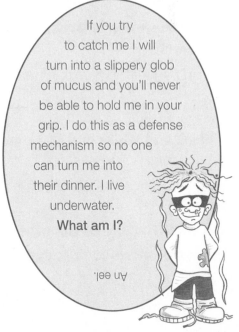

Why did the elephant paint himself brown?

So he could hide in a pile of manure.

Why was the kangaroo so upset after she'd been pick-pocketed?

Her whole family was missing.

Why are all the dogs raving about the newest dog food?

It tastes like the mailman.

What do you call a cat with a wooden leg?

Peg.

What's the difference between a rat and your spaghetti?

The rat won't slip off the fork when you go to eat it.

What's black and white and black and white?

A penguin rolling down a mountain.

What did one frog say to the other?

Time's sure fun when you're having flies.

Farmer: I had to shoot the cow.
Farmer's wife: Was she mad?
Farmer: She wasn't too happy about it.

Mother: Why did you put a toad in your brother's bed?
Sister: I couldn't find a python.

What do you call a dancing pig?

Shakin' bacon.

Delivery Man: Your dog bit my leg.
Lady: Did you put anything on it?
Delivery Man: No, he seemed to like it just the way it was.

When is a sheep like a dog?

When it has fleece.

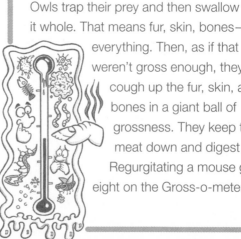

GROSS-O-METER

Owls trap their prey and then swallow it whole. That means fur, skin, bones—everything. Then, as if that weren't gross enough, they cough up the fur, skin, and bones in a giant ball of grossness. They keep the meat down and digest it. Regurgitating a mouse gets an eight on the Gross-o-meter scale.

What do you get if you cross a sheep with a black belt in karate?

Lamb chops.

What did the cat call the mouse?

Breakfast.

Why can't skunks keep secrets?

Someone is always catching wind of them.

Why do mother birds puke in their babies' mouths?

They want to send them out with a hot breakfast.

Sam: *Our new dog is like a member of the family.*

John: *I can see the resemblance.*

What am I?

Am I dead or alive? You'll never know. If you get too near, I may simply pretend to die. I may turn upside down, throw back my head, and even hold my mouth open. If I'm faking, you don't want to come too close. This is when I'll attack. **What am I?**

A hognose snake.

GROSS-O-METER

In 1945, Lloyd Olsen of Colorado cut the head off a chicken. The chicken, named Mike, lived for eighteen months without a head. The chicken became a celebrity and even went on tour. Headless chickens running around the yard rate a ten on the Gross-o-meter scale.

What was the pig's favorite karate move?

The pork chop.

Why did the vulture cross the road?

He had fowl reasons.

What happened to the boy who sat under the cow?

He got a pat on the head.

What did one toad say to the other?
Warts new?

What do you have left if a pig eats all your watermelon?
Pork rinds.

What do lions call antelopes?
Fast food.

Why did the lion feel sick after every meal?
It's hard to keep a good man down.

Foul Language

Scat
Have you ever been walking through a wooded area and all of a sudden you feel something mushy under your shoe? Chances are, you stepped in scat. Scat is the little poop pellets left behind by deer, rabbits, or other wildlife.

Why didn't the mother pig let her piglets play with toads?
She didn't want them to turn into wart hogs.

What happened to the hen that ate gun powder?
She laid hen grenades.

What did the pig play at the casino?
The slop machines.

Why was the mouse crying?
He found out his father was a rat.

What kind of shark would never eat a woman?
A man-eating shark.

What happens if you kiss an electric eel?
You have a shocking experience.

What's grosser than a three-headed spider with forty eyes?
Not much.

Why is a toothless dog like a tree?
It has more bark than bite.

Sick Change

You can change a normal word into a gross-out word by simply changing a letter!
Try it and pee—oops, that should be try it and <u>see</u>!

Change a small wagon
to smelly gas

_____ **to** _____

Change a flat piece of wood
to a crusty wound cover

_____ **to** _____

Change a tangle of string
to a booger

_____ **to** _____

Change the center of a
peach to a pimple

_____ **to** _____

Change a swollen spot
to a belch

_____ **to** _____

Change a large ring made
of metal to a pile of #2

_____ **to** _____

Why did Johnny put a dead mouse on the end of his fish hook?

He was fishing for catfish.

What do you call a woodpecker without a beak?

A head-banger.

Why did the bald man walk around with a rabbit on his head?

He really wanted some hare.

Seriously Sick

Did you know that bats eat about 100 bugs per second? Well, that's not even the gross part. In some parts of the world, bats are more than just bug-catchers. Broiled or boiled, fried or barbecued, these creatures make great meals. Dipping sauce, anyone?

How do you know owls are smarter than chickens?

You've never eaten fried owl, have you?

Why was the fish offended?

Because the sea weed.

Why are cats luckier than frogs?

Frogs croak all the time, and cats only croak nine times.

What do you get when you cross a young goat with a pig?

A dirty kid.

What's the worst thing that can happen to a bat while it's sleeping?

Diarrhea.

What's a frog's favorite flower?

The crocus.

What says "Gobble, gobble . . . catch me if you can"?

A suicidal turkey.

What do you get if you cross a slug with a cocker spaniel?

A dog that slithers on the ground after it rains.

What did the cat do after he ate the cheese?

Waited for the mouse with baited breath.

What do you get when you cross a dog with a solider?

A pooping trooper.

Fred: It's the dog days of summer.
Ed: How do you know?
Fred: I just stepped in a poodle.

What's worse than seeing a shark's fins in the water?

Seeing its teeth.

What am I?

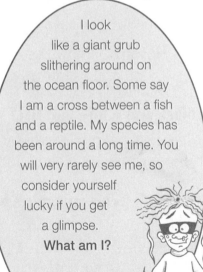

I look like a giant grub slithering around on the ocean floor. Some say I am a cross between a fish and a reptile. My species has been around a long time. You will very rarely see me, so consider yourself lucky if you get a glimpse.
What am I?

An axolotl.

Totally Twisted

Make some fake snot sculptures for your art collection. You'll need two tablespoons of glue, a quarter cup of water, a few drops of green food coloring, and yellow raisins. Stir it all together in a paper cup or plastic bowl and then let dry. Finally, fake a sneeze into the cup.

What has four legs and flies?

A dead cow.

How did the depressed frog die?

He kermitted suicide.

What did the angry pig say to his wife?

You take me for grunted.

What sound does a dog make when it's throwing up?

Barf, barf.

What am I?

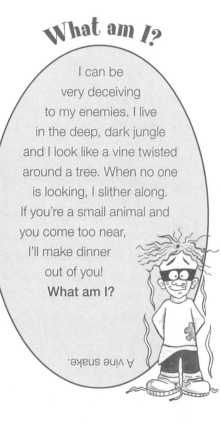

I can be very deceiving to my enemies. I live in the deep, dark jungle and I look like a vine twisted around a tree. When no one is looking, I slither along. If you're a small animal and you come too near, I'll make dinner out of you!

What am I?

A vine snake.

How do you get a whole set of teeth for free?

Make a lion angry.

On what day of the week do lions eat people?

Chewsday.

How do you turn a snake into a vegetable?

Slam it against a rock and you have squash.

Knock Knock

Who's there?

Howard.

Howard who?

Howard I know the dog would puke if I fed him cat poop?

What's black and white and flat?

A penguin that's been run over by a steam roller.

What's red and green and spins around really fast?

A frog in a blender.

What happened to the man who tried to cross a lion with a goat?

He had to get a new goat.

Did you hear about the dog that got first prize at the cat show?

He ate the first prize cat.

You know what they say about a bird in hand?

It poops on your wrist.

Why did the musical band eat the rabbit?

They wanted to play hip hop.

What animal always pukes after it eats?

The yak.

What's green and hangs from trees?

Monkey snot.

How do you know when you're eating rabbit pie?

It has hares in it.

Where do bats stay while they're on vacation?

The Caved Inn.

What do you get if you pour boiling water down a rabbit hole?

A hot, cross bunny.

Why did Jim put his German shepherd in the oven?

He wanted a hot dog.

What's worse than five dead cats in one garbage can?

One dead cat in five garbage cans.

Where do pigs go when they are sick?

The hog-spital.

Why did the frog ride a motorcycle with his mouth open?

He thought it would be easier to catch flies.

What did the pig do when he identified the butcher in a police lineup?

He squealed.

What do you get when you feed a cow too many worms?

Disgusting milk.

What kind of fish don't swim?

Dead ones.

What does a shark call a family he sees on the beach?

A five-course meal.

What do you get when you cross an ape with a bunch of earthworms?

Giant holes in the garden.

When is fishing bad for you?

When you're a worm.

What do you call a fairy that never showers?

To find out the answer to this riddle, figure out which letters are described by each fraction. Print the letters, in order, in the boxes from left to right.

1. First 2/5 of STALE
2. First 1/3 of INFECT
3. Last 1/2 of PUKE
4. Middle 1/3 of MORBID
5. Last 3/5 of SMELL

Ed: *We just sold our sheep for $100.00.*
Fred: *We just sold our new puppy.*
Ed: *What did you sell it for?*
Fred: *For pooping on the floor.*

What does a chicken that lays a square egg say?

Ouch.

What do you get if you cross an elephant with a cockroach?

I don't know, but if it crawls up your wall, you'd better get a new house.

What happened to the bear that ate a clock?

He got ticks.

What do you give a pig with pimples?

Oinkment.

Foul Language

Venom
Many creepy creatures, such as snakes and scorpions, have a very deadly way of defending themselves. Some of them can spew out enough venom, or poison, through their fangs, claws, or stingers to paralyze or even kill prey.

What do you get if you cross a skunk with a porcupine?

A stinky pin cushion.

What kind of bird do cats eat?

Swallows.

What did the man say when his dog got hit by a train?

Doggone.

What would we need if pigs really could fly?

Bigger umbrellas.

Little Mona: *I'd like to buy a kitty cat. How much do they cost?*

Shop Owner: *Fifty dollars apiece.*

Little Mona: *Oh no, how much is a whole one?*

What is green and prickly?

A sick porcupine.

Why do some animals eat their young?

They love them to death.

What do you call it when a chicken stumbles in the road?

A road trip.

What do you call a fish with no eyes?

Fsh.

Why are goldfish orange?

The water makes them rusty.

What happens when you put a baby goat in a blender?

You get a crazy mixed-up kid.

Why did the duck cross the road during rush hour?

To show the chicken he had guts.

Foul Language

Rabies

Rabies is one scary virus. Humans can only get this virus if an infected animal bites them. Rabid animals may foam at the mouth, act strangely, and tend to look sick. Rabies is common in raccoons, wolves, and other wild animals that might live near your home—so be careful!

What smells of fish parts and goes round and round?

A goldfish in a washing machine during spin cycle.

What do you get if you cross a goat with a baby cow?

Half and calf.

How do you know a sick frog when you see one?

He croaks out of both ends.

How does a cow get even when someone makes her mad?

She creams him.

Atrocious Animals

Where do you find a no-legged cat?
Right where you left him.

Why was the chicken kicked out of school?
He was being fowl.

What happened to the wolf that swallowed a sheep?
He felt baaaaaaaaad.

What do you call a deer with no eyes?
No eye deer.

What sound does a cat make before it eats a mouse?
The hiss of death.

What did the mother lion say to her cub who was chasing a man around a tree?
Stop playing with your food.

What did the piranha say when the students took a class trip to the beach?
Fresh meat just arrived!

Who goes into a tiger's den and comes out in one piece?
The tiger.

What did the freshly bathed dog say to the insect?
Long time no flea.

What's black and white and red all over?
A skunk with poison ivy.

What does a pig call his hot date?
Fine swine.

Did you hear about the limping dog?
He laid down to chew a bone and when he got up he only had three legs.

What do you get if you cross an eel and a sponge?
A shock absorber.

What do you get when you put a parrot in a blender?
Shredded tweet.

What's a vulture's favorite snack?
Road pie.

How do you raise a kitten?
By its neck.

What do you find under the feet of an elephant?

Squished mice.

Why did the turkey stop eating his dinner?

He was already stuffed.

How do you keep a rooster from waking you up in the morning?

Cook him the night before.

Why do giraffes have such long necks?

Because their feet stink.

What did the lady say when her parrot died?

Polygon.

Why did the girl laugh when the cow fell off the cliff?

There's no point in crying over spilled milk.

What words do skunks live by?

Eat, stink, and be merry.

Why did the dog laugh after chewing the bone?

It was a funny bone.

What did the snake say to his young son?

Stop your crying and viper your nose.

What's the definition of a slick chick?

Poultry that slid into a puddle of motor oil.

What does an aardvark take for indigestion?

Anta-seltzer.

What do you call a cow with no legs?

Ground beef.

What do frogs love to drink more than anything else?

Croaka-Cola.

What do you call a sheep in a rainstorm?

A wet blanket.

What do you get when you put a leopard in your dishwasher?

Spotty dishes.

What is black and white and red all over?

A sunburned penguin.

Chapter 14
Horrible Humans

Why did Mary hold up an ax to her sibling?

She always wanted a half sister.

What's the difference between Gross Grandma's cooking and a pile of slugs?

Gross Grandma's cooking comes on a plate.

Why are executioners so smart?

Because they always watch the noose.

Knock Knock

Who's there?
Huron.
Huron who?
Huron my toe! Ouch!

Bar of soap: "Sometimes I think I have the worst job in the world."

Toilet paper: "Think again."

Did you hear about the restaurant where you could eat dirt cheap?

Who wants to eat dirt?

What did one booger say to the other?

You think you're funny, but you're snot.

Why did Ned's mom say he ate like a bird?

He kept eating worms.

What happened to the mad scientist who fell into the bubbling acid?

He became absorbed in his work.

Knock Knock

Who's there?
One shoe.
One shoe who?
One shoe bathe once in a while?

What do you call a knight who picks his nose?

Sir Picks-a-lot.

Why did Jimmy tell his sister she reminded him of the sea?

Because he made her sick.

How do you make a handkerchief dance?

Put a little boogie in it.

Why did the leper go back into the shower?

He forgot his head and shoulders.

Why did the sword swallower switch to pins and needles?

He needed to lose weight.

What is it called when someone gets hit in the face with slime?

Goo-lash.

Seriously Sick

Did you ever hear the saying "Don't throw the baby out with the bath water"? Long ago only one bathtub full of water was used to bathe an entire family. The oldest went first, so by the time the baby was bathed, the water was so dirty you could hardly see him.

What do you call a man with no arms or legs holding up your car?

Jack.

Why did everyone tell the old hag she looked like a million bucks?

Because she was green and wrinkled.

Why do stabbing victims hate the ocean?

They don't like to pour salt in their wounds.

Foul Language

Plaque

This is a clear, sticky substance that builds up on your teeth. It is made up of leftover food and mucus. If you don't brush regularly, it will spread to your gums and tongue. It can cause cavities, gum disease, and really bad breath. Ew!

What do you call a man who sticks his right hand in an alligator's mouth?

Lefty.

What do babies with dirty diapers and security officers have in common?

They are both on duty.

What did the magician say to the fisherman?

Pick a cod, any cod.

Knock Knock

Who's there?
Urine.
Urine who?
Urine my way!

What happened when Jimmy's mother said she was going to take him to the zoo?

His father said not to bother—if the zoo wanted Jimmy, they could come and get him.

What did one toilet say to the other?

You look a little flushed.

Why did the drummer bring the chicken to band practice?

He needed new drumsticks.

Little Johnny: Mother, do you have holes in your underwear?

Mother: No, of course not.
Little Johnny: Well, then how do you get your feet through?

How do you get to the hospital in a hurry?

Stand in front of a bus.

Seriously Sick

Have you ever wondered what people did before indoor plumbing? If you lived in a crowded city, you peed and pooped in buckets kept in your bedroom. When the buckets were filled, you'd simply throw the nasty mix right out your windows and into the street! Now, there's a good use for an umbrella.

What did the audience do when the comedian bent over too far?

Cracked up.

When a knight dies in battle, what do they put on his gravestone?

Rust in peace.

What has a broom and flies?

A janitor covered in poop.

How come Johnny's mother used to say he was going to drive her to her grave?

Well, you don't expect her to walk, do you?

Seriously Sick

Earwax in your ear canal helps block out all the nasty stuff trying to get in there. You know, like dirt, dust, small insects, even germs. You've got over 2,000 glands in your ear working hard to make this wax.

How do you know if someone has a fake eye?

It usually comes out in conversation.

What happens to writers who don't make it to heaven?

They become ghost writers.

How did the man in the electric chair pay for his last meal?

He charged it.

Why do doctors study a lot before prescribing medicine for bad skin diseases?

They don't want to be rash.

Sluuuurp

These two sloppy slurpers are both eating bowls of soup. Can you find the 10 differences between the two?

Strange Soup

Some people make soup out of some pretty weird ingredients! Unscramble the letters at the bottom of this page to find the names of four different and unusual soups. Would you eat these?

IPCSORON UPOS

DIBR TENS UOSP

KHSAR INF POUS

XOLATI OSUP

GROSS-O-METER

A man in India named Radhakant Bajpai gets the award for the longest ear hair in the world, at over five inches long. Now, imagine that ear hair falling into your peanut butter sandwich. That gets a solid ten on the Gross-o-meter scale.

Pete: My doctor said to drink some tea after a hot bath.

Bob: Did you drink the tea?

Pete: Well, I haven't finished drinking the hot bath yet.

How did Sally Picker hurt her finger?

The school bully broke her nose.

Did you hear about the constipated musician?

He couldn't finish his last movement.

What are the two things that stopped Sheila from becoming a ballerina?

Her feet.

How do you make a baby drink?

Stick it in a blender.

Did you hear about the woman who thought she had the face of a sixteen year old?

Her husband told her to give it back.

What did the poor person do when he couldn't afford shoes?

He painted his feet and tied his toes together.

Why did the little boy bury his parents?

He wanted to grow a family tree.

What do you call the first person to ever discover fire?

Crispy.

What did Sven say when his brother Hans fell off the cliff?

Look Mom, no Hans.

What happened when the girl found out her future husband had a wooden leg?

She broke it off.

What usually runs in big families?

Noses.

Foul Language

Halitosis

This is a fancy word for stinky breath. If you eat lots of garlic or other strong-smelling foods and you start to notice people backing away from you, chances are you're suffering from a bad case of halitosis. Try brushing your teeth more often and carrying some breath mints in your pocket from now on.

Did you hear about the kid who missed his mother?

His father told him to take another shot.

What's worse than a plain old fart?

A fart with a lump in it.

What do you call a restaurant where everyone picks their nose?

Booger King.

GROSS-O-METER

 Long before doctors knew about germs, they would do surgery without washing their hands first. Hospitals were deadly places. Having a doctor stick his dirty fingers into a gaping wound while spreading thousands of germs rates a nine on the Gross-o-meter scale.

Knock Knock

Who's there?
Stella.
Stella who?
Stella 'fraid you'll poop in your pants?

What did one virus say to another?

Stay away, I think I've got penicillin.

What time is it when you sit on a sharp object?

Springtime.

Why was the cross-eyed teacher so upset?

He couldn't control his pupils.

What's the best way to talk to someone with bad breath?

From far away.

What do you do when your nose goes on strike?

Picket.

What do you call a person who makes two trips to Europe and doesn't bathe?

A dirty double-crosser.

What's the hardest part about sky diving?

The ground.

What did the caveman say when he saw bugs crawling on his dinner?

Mmmm . . . appetizers!

Where's the proper place to save rotten toenails?

In a nail file.

What's the difference between a window shop and a poke in the eyes in Italy?

One makes Venetian blinds and the other makes Venetians blind.

On what day of the week do lions eat people?

To find the answer to this gross riddle, fill in the words that answer each description below. Then read down the shaded column. We left you some S-C-R-A-P-S to get you started!

1. To chew with a crackling sound
2. To chew noisily
3. Flesh of an animal used as food
4. Take little bites again and again
5. To eat richly on a special occasion
6. One who is eating
7. What you do after you chew
8. Not neat; messy

What do you call a person with three ears, four eyes, and warts all over his face?

Ugly.

Did you hear about the patient who complained that he needed something for his liver?

The doctor told him to try adding onions.

What did Sally see when her friend Dawn bent over?

The crack of dawn.

What did the lady say to the man who came to the door with a funny face?

Thanks, but I've already got one.

Fred: Whenever I take my girlfriend out for dinner she eats her head off.

Ed: Stop complaining. She looks better that way.

Knock Knock
Who's there?
Blue.
Blue who?
Blue your nose on your sleeve again?

Why was the sword swallower arrested?

He coughed and killed two people.

How come the millionaire never showered?

He was filthy rich.

Why don't burn victims like to eat in the hospital?

The food makes their skin crawl.

Why did the toilet paper run down the mountain?

It wanted to get to the bottom.

What did one eye say to the other?

Between you and me, I think something smells.

What do you get when you mix tacos and a person who's not feeling so good?

I don't know, but you're standing in it.

What's it called when you pick your nose and hide it for later?

The pick and save.

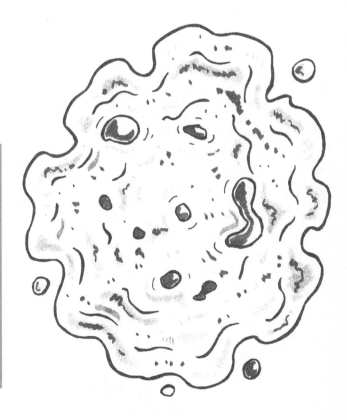

GROSS-O-METER

In the not-too-distant past, doctors would actually taste a patient's pee to see if it was sweet. If it was too sweet, that meant the patient might have a disease called diabetes. Pee-drinking ranks a solid ten on the Gross-o-meter scale. Would you like a cookie with that?

What do you call a person with no arms or legs floating in the water?

Bob.

What was the farmer able to prove when the chicken got run over by a steamroller?

That it had a lot of guts.

Did you ever see the movie "Constipation"?

It never came out.

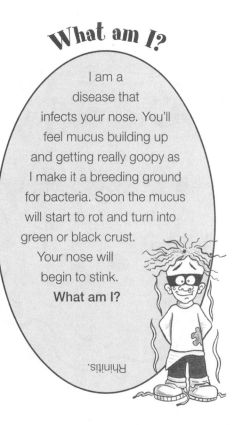

What am I?

I am a disease that infects your nose. You'll feel mucus building up and getting really goopy as I make it a breeding ground for bacteria. Soon the mucus will start to rot and turn into green or black crust. Your nose will begin to stink.

What am I?

Rhinitis.

Why did the kids call Johnny "flat-face"?

Because he kept his nose to the grindstone.

What's worse than two Siamese twins connected at the mouth?

Watching one of them throw up.

What do you get if you slime a telephone worker?

A smooth operator.

Why did the baby cross the road?

He was stapled to the chicken.

How do you stop a sleepwalker?

Cover the floor with tacks.

What's worse than a boy who picks his nose?

A boy who picks someone else's nose.

Do you know about Larry the Loafer?

He's so lazy that he sticks his nose out the window so the wind will blow it for him.

What happens when you cross a judge with poison ivy?

You get rash decisions.

How do you catch dandruff?

Shake your head over a paper bag.

What happened to the thief who stole from the blood bank?

He was caught red-handed.

Where do butchers go to dance?

The Meat Ball.

Knock Knock

Who's there?

Wendy.

Wendy who?

Wendy sneezes come,
snot goes everywhere.

Foul Language

Bile
This is yellow or greenish liquid that comes from your liver. Its job is to break down fats in your body. When it's done doing its job, it becomes part of your poop. As a matter of fact, that's what gives your poop its nice color.

Why was the fireman so upset?

He ran into an old flame.

Patient: *Doctor, I threw my back out, what should I do?*

Doctor: *Maybe you can catch the garbage truck before it leaves.*

What happened to the man who put his false teeth in backwards?

He ate himself.

How did the garbage man break up with his girlfriend?

He dumped her.

What kind of skin problem does a beekeeper have?

Hives.

What's the best cure for a headache?

Put your head through the window and the pane will go away.

What do people with weak bladders and people who wear old stockings have in common?

They both get runs down their legs.

Customer: *The water in this glass is cloudy.*
Waiter: *Don't worry—the water's fine.*
It's just the glass that's cloudy.

Why didn't the photographer develop his pictures of the boogeyman?

He was afraid to be alone in the dark with them.

Knock Knock

Who's there?
Emma.
Emma who?
Emma 'fraid you have an ugly face.

What do you call a vegetarian with diarrhea?

A salad shooter.

What did the first mate see in the toilet?

The captain's log.

What did the drooling butler say to the guests when he answered the door?

Greetings and salivations.

If vegetarians only eat vegetables, what do you call humans that eat other humans?

Sick.

What am I?

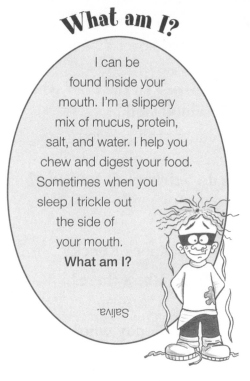

I can be found inside your mouth. I'm a slippery mix of mucus, protein, salt, and water. I help you chew and digest your food. Sometimes when you sleep I trickle out the side of your mouth.
What am I?

Saliva.

Did you hear what happened to the man who lost his left arm and leg in an accident?

He's all right now.

What kind of underwear is good for putting out fires?

Pantyhose.

What does a liar do when he's sleeping?

He lies still.

GROSS-O-METER

Think your toilet paper is doing a good job? Think again. The germs from human poop can go through over ten layers of toilet paper! That gets a solid ten (pun intended) on the Gross-o-meter scale. Don't forget to wash your hands!

Why did they lock up the man who thought he was a bird?

He was a raven lunatic.

What's the difference between a thermometer that goes in your bottom and one that goes in your mouth?

The taste.

Why was everyone amazed when they saw the Catskill Mountains?

Because cats usually only kill mice.

Mother: Why do you play the same song on the piano over and over?

Son: I find it haunting.
Mother: It should haunt you— you murdered it!

What happened to the thief who fell into the wet cement?

He went on to become a hardened criminal.

Patient: Is there anything else I can do for my pimples?

Doctor: No, that's zit.

Knock Knock

Who's there?

Goose.

Goose who?

Goose see a doctor, you look horrible.

What kind of training do you need to be a garbage collector?

None, you pick it up as you go along.

B-ughs!

Answer these questions about Bart's bug collection:

Are there more spiders or roaches?

If each fly has 6 legs, how many fly legs are there?

Which mosquito has just bitten someone? How can you tell?

SPIDER

ROACH

FLY

MOSQUITO

Why did the office aide chop off her fingers?

So she could write shorthand.

Why don't lepers like comedy shows?

It makes them laugh their heads off.

Did you hear about the constipated banker?

He couldn't budget.

Why was the teacher so upset when her eye fell out of her head?

She couldn't bear to lose another pupil.

Fred: *My brother does great farmyard impressions.*
Ted: *What animal does he sound like?*
Fred: *He doesn't, he just smells like a pig.*

GROSS-O-METER

In 1981, a twelve-year-old girl named Donna Griffiths began sneezing and didn't stop for 978 days. It was estimated that she sneezed a million times that first year until her sneezes slowed down to one every five minutes. A million snot rags ranks eight on the Gross-o-meter scale.

What do you call a person lying in front of your door?

Matt.

Fred: *This morning I gave my brother soap flakes for breakfast instead of corn flakes.*
Ed: *What happened?*
Fred: *He was so mad, he started foaming at the mouth.*

What do you call a leper who has good luck?

A leper-chaun.

What do you call it when a boy vomits up his steak?

Up-chuck.

How did the woman feel after she got run over by a car?

Tired.

How did the dunce burn his ear?

He got a telephone call while he was ironing.

There are three men in the bathroom. One is rushing toward the stall, one is on his way out, and the other is inside the stall. What nationalities are they?

Russian, Finnish, and European.

What's the medical term for a lady who throws up all the time?

Girl hurl.

How many people does it take to wallpaper a room?

Two, but only if they are thinly sliced.

Did you hear about the girl who had long blonde hair growing down her back?

Pity it didn't grow on her head.

How did the leper get into a car accident?

He left his foot on the gas pedal.

What am I?

I am a fungus that thrives in warm sweaty areas. My specialty is causing painful cracks and blisters between your toes. I lurk on all types of floors and in your shoes. If I want to be really nasty I'll make one of your toenails my home. **What am I?**

Athlete's foot.

What did Jane's mother say when Jane wanted to lick the bowl?

You must flush it like everybody else.

What happened to the man who flushed himself down the toilet?

He committed sewer-cide.

What's the meaning of bravery?

A person with diarrhea chancing a fart.

Patient: My kidneys have been giving me a hard time.

Doctor: Well, just take them back to the butcher.

What do a Slinky and a school bully have in common?

They're both fun to watch tumble down the stairs.

What happened to the man with amnesia when he farted?

It all came back to him.

How did Stinky Joe's mom stop him from biting his nails?

She made him wear shoes.

How do you make anti-freeze?

Hide her sweater.

The Proper Way to Pick

Deep Sea Picking

This is when you pick your nose so deep it's as if you were diving for buried treasure.

Fork Pick

This is when your fingers just aren't long enough to get what's up there, so you use a fork or other tool. This one is not recommended.

Lottery Pick

This is when you've been picking for days on end and finally hit the jackpot. Your excitement is so overwhelming, it's like you've just won a million bucks.

Sad Pickings

This is when you pick your nose just because you are unhappy and it gives you something to do besides think about what's making you sad.

Pick All Day

This is when you are absolutely obsessed with picking your nose. You use more than one finger and you just can't stop picking.

Secret Pick

This is when no one is around and you pick your nose with freedom and joy. You get way up in there, and you even fling what you find all over the room.

Picking with Pride

This is when you're in public, but you just can't resist the urge to pick. So you pick proudly (and hope that no one notices).

The Fake-Out Pick

This is when you pretend you have an itch, but what you're really doing is looking for boogers that may have strayed out of your nostrils.

Surprise Picks

This is when you sneeze and all of a sudden snot comes flying out of your nose and you have to clean it off your friend's shirt. You didn't even need to pick to loosen those boogers.

Flicking Your Pickings

This is when you use your boogers to taunt family members. You leave it on the tip of your finger and threaten to fling it if anyone comes too close.

Why was the boy's mother horrified when he came home with a broken nose?

He couldn't remember who it belonged to.

What did the doctor tell the patient with chronic diarrhea?

It runs in your family.

How do you say constipation in German?

Farfrompoopin.

What happened to the boy who ate a thermometer?

He was dying by degrees.

Why was the student so upset when she learned about the Dead Sea?

She didn't even know it was sick.

What do you call a coward in the electric chair?

Extra crispy chicken.

What's the best way to cure acid indigestion?

Stop drinking acid.

What do you do when someone rolls their eyes at you?

You pick them up and give them back.

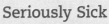

Seriously Sick

The average person can pee anywhere from 1.5 to 3.5 pints a day. But did you know that sweat and urine are virtually the same thing? They both contain something called urea, which causes them to smell bad. Pretty gross, huh?

What do you call a bearded woman who grants wishes?

A hairy godmother.

Lady: Am I too late for the garbage truck?
Garbage Truck Driver: Nope, jump right in.

How do you turn an ordinary scientist into a mad scientist?

Punch him in the nose.

What kind of illness do roofers get?

Shingles.

Why should you never pee in a public pool?

The public doesn't swim in your toilet so you shouldn't pee in their pool.

What magic word do you have to say if you want to get rid of your scabs?

Scabracadabra.

What happened to the hunter who was following tracks in the woods?

He got hit by a train.

What happened to the man who cut off his right butt cheek?

He was left behind.

Did you hear about the math teacher who was constipated?

He worked it out with a pencil.

What happened when the customer complained that his meal wasn't fit for a pig?

The waiter said he'd take it back and bring him a meal that *was* fit for a pig.

Why did Silly Sam get a pain in his nose every time he drank a cup of coffee?

He forgot to take the spoon out of the cup before sipping.

Seriously Sick

Did you ever stick your nose in the bud of a rafflesia flower? This flower smells disgusting, like rotting flesh or spoiled milk. The rafflesia is such a stinker it's even nicknamed the "corpse flower." It's better to give these flowers to your enemies instead of your loved ones.

What did the nice hangman say to his victim?

Is the noose too tight?

Why were the barber's hands so dirty?

No one had been in for a shampoo all day.

What did the waiter say when the customer asked if the chef had pig's feet?

I don't know, he's got his shoes on.

Should kids with the flu go to school?

It's snot for you to decide.

Knock Knock

Who's there?
Warren.
Warren who?
Warren earth did you get such
an ugly face?

How did the school teacher keep the boys on their toes?

He raised the urinals a couple of inches.

Did you hear about the Indian chief who drank twenty cups of tea and went to bed?

He drowned in his tea-pee.

Seriously Sick

Does it ever sound like a bulldozer is whipping through your stomach? Well, that sound comes from the digestive juices sloshing around in there. Your body makes about two gallons of that stuff a day, and it can stay there for up to four hours after you eat.

What do you call a man with mucus in his throat?

Fleming.

How do you keep from dying?

Just stay in the living room.

Knock Knock

Who's there?
Stan.
Stan who?
Stan back, I'm about to vomit.

Did you hear what happened to the plastic surgeon?

He sat in front of a fire and melted.

Why did everyone call Dirty Darrel a wonder child?

Because they all wondered when he was going to take a bath.

What's risky?

Eating raisin bran when your brother can't find his roach collection.

Why should you listen to your father when he tells you not to pick your nose?

Father nose best.

Chapter 15

Beyond the Grave: Ghosts, Ghouls, and Zombies

How does a mummy begin all his letters?

Tomb it may concern.

Why did the goblins show up at the cemetery before dark?

They didn't want to miss the early bird special.

Why didn't anyone want to go to the zombie hair salon?

Because the hairdressers all dyed on the job.

What do you call a dead chicken that haunts you at night?

A poultry-geist.

Did you hear about the ghoul who was sick to his stomach?

It must have been someone he ate.

What do ghouls eat for dinner?

A three-corpse meal.

Where do ghouls go on vacation?

Lake Eerie.

What did the zombie's friend say to him when he introduced his girlfriend?

Oh my, where did you dig her up?

Why do demons and ghouls go together so well?

Because demons are a ghoul's best friend.

GROSS-O-METER

In some ancient societies people honored their dead by eating them. Most of the body was cooked, except the brain. The brain was eaten raw. Eating the raw brain of your dear Uncle Harry gets a ten on the Gross-o-meter scale.

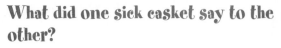
GROSS-O-METER

Until about sixty years ago, coffins were very rarely made to fit each person's body size. If you happened to be extra tall, you were out of luck. Undertakers would break a dead person's ankles and fold them over backward to fit. That ranks a nine on the Gross-o-meter scale.

What did one sick casket say to the other?

Is that you coffin?

How does a person who cremates bodies make his money?

He urns it.

Why was the mortuary makeup artist fired?

Everyone thought she was a stiff.

When is it not a good time to bury someone?

When he is still breathing.

Knock Knock

Who's there?
Turner.
Turner who?
Turner 'round—there's a giant ghoul right behind you!

Why did the zombie study Latin?

He wanted to learn a dead language.

What was the gravedigger's favorite song?

Oh What a Beautiful Mourning.

Seriously Sick

In the past, people were sometimes accidentally buried before they were actually dead! This became such a common occurrence that something had to be done. Mourners began tying strings attached to bells around the fingers of the dead before the burial. This way, if someone was really still alive, he simply had to ring the bell for help.

What About Jimmy?

There are three different letters missing from this riddle.
Once you fill in the blanks, you will find out
what happened to Jimmy!

Wh_t h_pp_n_d wh_n
Jimmy's m_th_r s_id
sh_ w_s g_ing t_ t_k_
Jimmy t_ th_ z__?

Jimmy's br_th_r s_id
"D_n't b_th_r. If th_
z__ w_nts Jimmy,
th_y c_n c_m_ _nd
g_t him!"

What did the man in the electric chair ask for?

To have the charges reversed.

Why did the gravedigger keep a pail on the sidewalk?

So someone would kick the bucket.

What's an ax murderer's favorite drink?

Slice.

How do morticians speak?

Gravely.

What's the hardest part about becoming a funeral director?

The stiff competition.

Why did the dead boy stay home from school?

He was feeling rotten.

GROSS-O-METER

In 1999, John Lamedica made the *Guinness Book of World Records* by getting into a coffin with 20,050 giant Madagascan hissing cockroaches. Getting into a coffin when you're not dead and then having 20,050 of anything, let alone giant hissing creatures, crawling all over you gets a ten on the Gross-o-meter scale.

Why couldn't the skeleton fart in a crowded place?

It had no guts.

What did the skeleton buy at the supermarket?

Spare ribs.

Fred: Did you hear about the coffin that just covers the head?

Ed: No, why's that?
Fred: It's for people like you who are dead from the neck up.

What are you supposed to do with an overweight ghost?

Exorcise him.

What do people do as they die?

They bite the dust.

What did the morbid mortician say when he walked into the crematorium?

What's cooking?

Why don't ghosts ever lie?

Because you can see right through them.

Goblin 1: Let's go get some dinner at the graveyard.

Goblin 2: Shall we order out some ribs?

Goblin 1: No, they're always cold by the time we get them home.

Why didn't the skeleton like his job?

His heart wasn't in it.

GROSS-O-METER

Killer seaweed known as caulerpa taxifolia covers thousands of acres of the ocean floor, destroying food for other sea creatures. It's known as a major underwater predator because its slimy clutches grab onto anything it can find. Deadly seaweed gets an eight on the Gross-o-meter scale.

How do you find a corpse at a zombie family reunion?

The corpse is the one with an expression on his face.

What lies at the bottom of the sea and twitches?

A nervous wreck.

Why don't skeletons play instruments in church?

They have no organs.

Why don't ghouls get up before sunrise?

It never dawned on them.

Why were there long lines at the cemetery?

People were dying to get in.

What did the mummy say when he entered the morgue?

Anybody home?

Why did the man get buried up to his waist?

Because he said he felt half dead.

What do you do if you meet a skeleton in a dark alley?

Jump out of your skin and say hello.

Why did the mortician prefer cremations?

It helped him urn more.

Why did the mortician cut up the corpse's nose?

To see what made it run.

Foul Language

Scavenger

Scavengers are animals such as vultures that prey on the already dead. For example, road kill is considerable cause for celebration among scavengers that don't like to work for their dinner.

Grime Time

PUZZLE 1: Find the one time in the letter grid that the word GRIME is spelled correctly. Words can run up, down, diagonally, backward, or forward.

PUZZLE 2: Can you figure out the one letter that is missing from these six words that mean GRIME?

CRD MD

GNK DST

MCK SMDGE

```
G I G G I G R E M I R E
I R M I R G E R G R I G
R G I M G R I G I G R I
I R G M R R I R E R I M
M I G R I M G M I G M E
E M E I M I E M I G I R
G G M G R I E M R M R I
R I E G I E E M I R G G
M M I R G R G E G E M M
E I G R G R I M M I R G
G R E M I M I R I G I E
```

Why do ghosts scream when someone dies?

The dead are hard of hearing.

Why did the mortician have such a big party?

The morgue the merrier.

Funeral Director: You're sure you want to buy these bodies?

Goblin: Yes, please.
Funeral Director: Shall I wrap them up?
Goblin: No thanks, I'll eat them here.

How do mummies make a phone call?

With a touch-tomb phone.

Seriously Sick

Did you ever wonder why dead people are often called stiffs? Well, it's because that's exactly what happens. Soon after someone dies, blood stops circulating and muscles become stiff. This condition is known as rigor mortis. It lasts for about two days until the body begins to relax again.

What do ghouls like on their potatoes?

Grave-y.

What do a corpse and an insect artist have in common?

They both draw flies.

Did you hear about the mummy that ate a light bulb?

He threw it up and now he's delighted.

Rude Rebus Riddles

To solve a rebus puzzle, you must identify each picture, adding or subtracting letters
as you read from left to right. The answer will sound correct, but may not be spelled correctly!
HINT: Some words are shown with only one picture—some take more.

What does a cannibal call a man in a hammock?

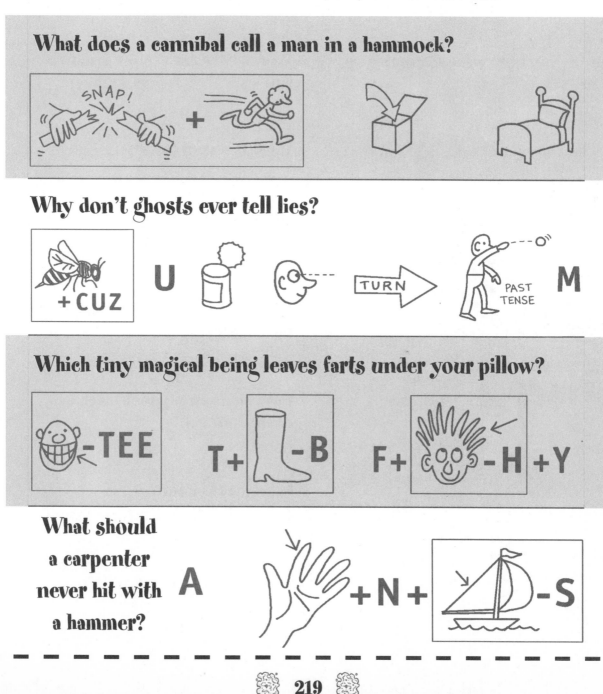

Why don't ghosts ever tell lies?

Which tiny magical being leaves farts under your pillow?

What should a carpenter never hit with a hammer?

What do you call a skeleton who goes around ringing bells?

A dead ringer.

How do you keep a ghoul from biting his nails?

Chop off his hands.

Why did the ghoul eat a light bulb?

He needed a light snack.

Seriously Sick

Did you ever hear of the Black Death? This was a plague that plowed through Europe during the 1300s. It wiped out entire villages, killing about one-third of the European population. Once you got hit with the plague, the only place you were headed was the grave.

How do you keep a dead body from smelling?

Cut off its nose.

Who writes scripts for demon movies?

Crypt writers.

What is a skeleton snake called?

A rattler.

What did the mummy son call his parents?

Mummy and Deady.

Why did the funeral director chop up the corpses?

He wanted them to rest in pieces.

How did the body look after cremation?

Ashen.

What's a skeleton?

Bones with the person scraped off.

Chapter 16

Stinky Stuff

Boyfriend: *What is that perfume you're wearing?*

Girlfriend: *High Heaven.*

Boyfriend: *I asked what perfume it is, not what it stinks to.*

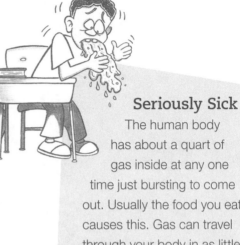

What's long, rotten, and smells of cheese?

Your toenails.

Seriously Sick

The human body has about a quart of gas inside at any one time just bursting to come out. Usually the food you eat causes this. Gas can travel through your body in as little as thirty minutes, but burps come up right away. You burp or fart about fifteen times a day!

Why do so many people hate their noses?

Because they smell.

What did the judge say to the skunk that was on trial?

Odor in the court.

Knock Knock

Who's there?
Consumption.
Consumption who?
Consumption be done about
the foul odor in here?

Gross A to Z

Write each of the seven-letter words into the boxes in alphabetical order, starting with the top row and working your way to the bottom. When you're finished, read down the shaded columns to get the answers to these two riddles:

1. **What science fiction movie features a toad?**

2. **What's a fat vampire called?**

RESENDS

BOWLFUL

BARRACK

ANTLERS

OUTWARD

MARINAS

CRACKLE

ABSURDS

AZALEAS

1
2
3
4
5
6
7
8
9

What prize do people get if they cure themselves of body odor?

The no-smell peace prize.

Knock Knock

Who's there?
Philip.
Philip who?
Philip the tub, you stink.

What do you call a man who smells like fish?

Poor sole.

What do diapers and garbage trucks have in common?

They both hold a smelly load.

Seriously Sick

Did you ever wonder why dogs sniff each other's rear ends? They have a scent gland right there that helps them recognize one another. Once they know if they're dealing with a dangerous Doberman or a precious poodle, then they can act accordingly.

Foul Language

Flatulence

This is just a fancy word for farts. When there's too much gas in your digestive tract, you've got flatulence. So if you want to impress someone the next time they fart, just tell them their flatulence is not appreciated. If you've got to talk about farts, why not do it in style?

Knock Knock

Who's there?
Dozen.
Dozen who?
Dozen anybody bathe anymore?
Pew!

What do body odor and peaches have in common?

They both grow around pits.

The Art of Fart

The Tire Fart

This fart is so powerful it sounds like a tire deflating in your pants.

Jail Fart

It's been inside you for some time and you want to let it out. However, you have to wait for the perfect opportunity for it to make its great escape.

Stuck-up Fart

This is when you think your farts don't stink—but they do!

Home Alone Fart

This is when you are home all by yourself so you just let them rip all over the place—loud and free.

Tie Your Shoe Fart

This is when you bend over to tie your shoe laces, and whoops! You let one loose, right in front of Grandma!

The Stainer

This is when you think it's just a fart but it turns out to be a bit more. Now you have to walk around like that all day and hope it dries up.

The Big Bad Fart

This fart makes its presence known in every way possible—with a puff of gas that could blow papers off a desk, a stench so horrible it could kill small animals, and a sound like thunder coming from your pants.

Firing the Missile

This one comes out fast and straight. You don't have much time to aim, but if you're good, you can use your little brother as a target.

The Unidentified Fart

This is when you know you farted, but nobody can prove it was you.

The Stubborn Fart

This fart just won't come out, no matter how badly you want it to. It could take minutes or even hours to release this gassy blast. But when it comes, you feel a lot better.

Knock Knock

Who's there?
Pea.
Pea who?
Pea U, stop farting!

What do you get when you cross a horse and a skunk?

Whinny the Pew.

What do you call a newborn skunk?

A little stinker.

Why did the fish smell so bad?

Long time no sea.

Knock Knock

Who's there?
Luke.
Luke who?
Luke out, here comes a big fart.

Mrs. Skunk:

Why did you buy so many boxes of tissues?

Mr. Skunk:

Because I have a stinking cold.

Totally Twisted

There's nothing like smelly feet to prove how gross you are. Follow this advice to really make a stink. Sweat a lot and don't wear any socks. Don't bathe for a week. After that, more than your feet will stink. Rub garlic all over the bottom of your feet to make them extra super-duper smelly. Then show them off to all your friends!

What did the blind skunk do?

He fell in love with a fart.

Foul Language

Pus

You know that slimy, oozing stuff that comes out of a cut when it's infected? That's pus. Sometimes it's yellow and sometimes it's green—and it doesn't smell very good. If you've got pus oozing out of any part of your body, it's probably time for a trip to the doctor's office.

What do you get if you cross a skunk and an owl?

A bird that smells but doesn't give a hoot.

Fred: *Did you hear about the man who ate 100 cloves of garlic and then passed out?*
Ed: *No, what happened to him?*
Fred: *The doctor said it was from inhaling his own breath.*

Knock Knock

Who's there?
Jurassic.
Jurassic who?
Jurassic person if you like
these gross jokes.

What goes "Ha, Ha, Ha, PLOP!"

To find out, start at the letter S marked with a dot.

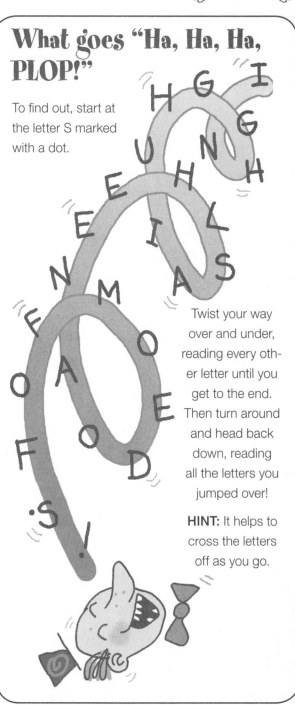

Twist your way over and under, reading every other letter until you get to the end. Then turn around and head back down, reading all the letters you jumped over!

HINT: It helps to cross the letters off as you go.

What do flies and stinky feet have in common?

You can shoe them but they never go away.

How do you keep a pig from smelling?

Plug his nose.

Knock Knock

Who's there?
Sara.

Totally Twisted

Make burping sounds using a balloon, baking soda, vinegar, and a funnel. Using the funnel, pour a quarter of a cup of vinegar in the balloon. Add a tablespoon of baking soda. Squeeze the balloon closed with your fingers. Slowly release your grip, but continue to hold on to the bottom of the balloon. You'll hear a nasty burp.

Gross Garret likes . . .

. . . to pick boogers, but not snot

. . . to sneeze, but not cough

. . . to hiccup, but not burp

. . . to poop, but not fart

. . . to get muddy, but not sticky

. . . to use the bathroom, but not the garage

Can you figure out why Gross Garret likes the things he does?

Sara who?
Sara bad smell in the room?

Do you want to hear some fart jokes?
No, they really stink.

What's invisible and smells like bananas?

Monkey farts.

Knock Knock

Who's there?

Inna

Inna who?

Inna minute there's going to be a bad smell in here.

Mother: *You have been burping all day!*
Daughter: *It's your fault, you gave me those belchin' waffles for breakfast.*

What kind of book does a skunk like to read?

A best smeller.

Why did the car smell so bad?

It was full of gas.

Totally Twisted
To become an expert farter, start eating fart-inducing foods. Cheese, broccoli, onions, milk, beans, and carbonated beverages are all fart fuel. Another fart tip: If you drink through a straw you'll swallow more air, and chances are you'll get some nice smelly toots.

What smells like a human but isn't a human?

A cannibal fart.

What do burps and kitchens have in common?

They both smell like dinner.

Chapter 17

The Gross-ery Store

Why did the crackers turn green?
They felt crumby.

What kind of meal has both pig parts and human parts?
Pork and beings.

Why did the ham go to the doctor?
It wanted to be cured.

What am I?

I am considered a delicacy by many people around the world. I am made up of cow cheeks or perhaps a pig's nose. Just wrap me up and throw me in a pot for a couple of hours, chill, and then serve on a great big sandwich.
What am I?

Headcheese.

Totally Twisted

Make a halitosis sandwich. Start with strong cheese like Gorgonzola. Put it on bread, add fresh garlic, and top with lots of onions. For an extra foul smell add tuna. Other stinky foods include hot pepper, Tabasco sauce, and scallions. Enjoy your lunch and then go breathe on someone you don't want to be friends with anymore.

Customer: *Waiter, why is my pie smushed?*
Waiter: *Because you said "A slice of cherry pie, and step on it!"*

What's sugary on the outside and green on the inside?
A snot-filled donut.

Why did the coffee smell like dirt?
It was just ground.

What do you get from a pampered cow?
Spoiled milk.

What do you eat on your crackers when you're stuck in traffic?

Traffic jam.

Why is food in a monastery so greasy?

It's cooked by friars.

What happens to babies that eat Rice Krispies?

They go snap, crackle, poop.

How did the beans affect Johnny's intestines?

They rectum.

What am I?

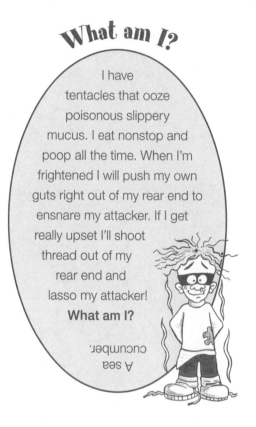

I have tentacles that ooze poisonous slippery mucus. I eat nonstop and poop all the time. When I'm frightened I will push my own guts right out of my rear end to ensnare my attacker. If I get really upset I'll shoot thread out of my rear end and lasso my attacker! **What am I?**

A sea cucumber.

What happened to the man who ate too much blue cheese?

He blew chunks.

What happened to the grocery store owner who sat on the meat slicer?

He got behind in his deliveries.

What do you get if you cross a skeleton with peanut butter?

Bones that stick to the roof of your mouth.

Who Foofed?

Someone in this room has accidentally passed some gas. Can you find the path that STARTs at the nose and ENDs at the smelly fellow who needs to say "Excuse me!"

START

END

END

END

The Gross-ery Store

Why are franks and beans good fuel?
Because they provide an endless supply of natural gas.

Is it okay to eat potato chips with your fingers?
No, it's a bad combination.

How do you make a casserole?
Put it on Roller blades.

Seriously Sick
The praying mantis has a pretty sickening diet. Once it chooses its prey, it stabs it with a sharp needle-like appendage. It eats lizards, small birds, and its own babies! Oh, and after the female praying mantis mates, she sometimes likes to eat her partner.

What's red and green and quivers?
Rotten Jell-O.

What's the most annoying thing about eating pigs-in-a-blanket?
The pigs squeal really loudly when you take a bite.

What's worse than eating fresh vomit pie?
Eating two-day-old vomit pie.

What do you get when you cross your dog with an omelet?
Pooched eggs.

Rita: *This gravy is awful.*
Leah: *I made it in my pajamas.*
Rita: *No wonder it's so bad.*

What am I?

You can hold me in your hand and I will slip and slide around. I am made up of water and protein, but I feel like slimy goo. When you think about me, you don't realize how gross I can be until you actually drop me on the floor. It's only when you can't clean me up because I'm so sticky and drippy that you realize how nasty I am. But the truth is, I could have been a baby!

What am I?

An egg yolk.

What's lumpy and green and comes in small containers?

Yogurt gone bad.

What do foot doctors eat for breakfast?

Corn flakes.

What happened to the grape when the ogre sat on it?

It let out a little wine.

How do you make a banana shake?

Sneak up on it and scream.

What do you get if you mix onions and beans?

Tear gas.

What happened to the toddler who ate too much?

He tossed his cookies.

Seriously Sick

Bacteria loves to live on sponges. It loves the grease from your dishes and the wet moistness that the sponge provides. Sponges are the perfect breeding ground for more bacteria. Think about that the next time you're washing dishes with an old sponge.

What's the difference between boogers and Brussels sprouts?

Kids don't eat Brussels sprouts.

What do you call someone who poisons your breakfast?

A cereal killer.

Doctor: *Why is your son crying?*

Mother: *He has baked beans stuck up his nose.*

Doctor: *Well, why is your daughter crying?*

Mother: *She wants her lunch back.*

Why do people who harvest vegetables have noses?

So they have something to pick during the cold season.

Mrs. Jones: *We're having Mother for dinner tomorrow night.*

Mr. Jones: *Can't we just have hamburgers?*

Knock Knock

Who's there?
Eyeball.
Eyeball who?
Eyeball every time I have to eat your food!

What do you call a millionaire with really bad body odor?

To find the answer to this riddle, color in the letters that appear more than two times. Read the remaining letters from left to right and top to bottom.

Customer: *I can't eat this food, it's horrible. Call the chef.*

Waiter: *It's a waste of time, he can't eat it either.*

What do you get if you eat prune pizza?
Pizzeria.

Waiter: *I have boiled liver, cow brains, and chicken feet.*

Customer: *I don't want to hear your medical problems, I just want some lunch.*

Customer: Waiter, waiter!
My dinner is talking to me.
Well, you asked for a tongue sandwich.

What did the pig name his supermarket?
Stop in slop.

Seriously Sick
Around the world insects of all kinds are considered tasty treats. In parts of China, people eat de-winged, fried grasshoppers. In parts of South America, biting the head off a live giant ant is the perfect snack. And in the West Indies, roasted grubs make an excellent lunch. Yum!

Why did the blueberry need a lawyer?
It was in a jam.

What's worse than finding a maggot in your cereal?
Finding half a maggot in your cereal.

What's green, brown, and slimy and comes out of your nose?
Chocolate milk after a good joke.

Totally Twisted
Quench your thirst with sludge water. You'll need melted chocolate ice cream and something carbonated such as seltzer or cola. Add bits of chocolate or raisins. Prepare this for your friends on a hot day. If they hesitate, offer to try it first.

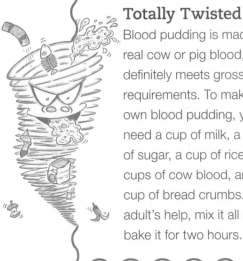

Totally Twisted

Blood pudding is made of real cow or pig blood, so it definitely meets gross factor requirements. To make your own blood pudding, you will need a cup of milk, a teaspoon of sugar, a cup of rice, four cups of cow blood, and a cup of bread crumbs. With an adult's help, mix it all up and bake it for two hours. Mmm.

How do you know when a dumpster is full of toadstools?

There isn't mushroom inside.

What do you call a guy who sells vegetables and throws up all day?

A green grocer.

How can you tell if there are rat pieces in your cookies?

Read the ingredients.

Knock Knock

Who's there?
Pudding.
Pudding who?
Pudding all that chili on your hotdog is going to make you puke.

If a nut on the wall is a walnut, what do you call a nut in the toilet bowl?

A pee can.

What's the difference between roast pork and pea soup?

Anyone can roast pork.

What's red and gooey and found in a shark's mouth?

Slow swimmers.

Knock Knock

Who's there?
Fajita.
Fajita who?
Fajita 'nother bite, I'll be sick.

Totally Twisted

Make edible acne with cherry tomatoes and cream cheese. Have an adult core out the center of the cherry tomatoes and then fill with cream cheese. Once the tomatoes (pimples) are filled, make sure to give them a good squeeze so the pus starts oozing out. Even if you don't have zits on your face, you can still pop these—and then eat them!

Foul Language

Curdle

Did you ever pour some milk in your cereal that had been sitting around a little too long? Not only is there a horrible smell, but the milk isn't even milk anymore, it's just clumps of goop. When something like milk or yogurt goes bad, it's considered curdled.

George: I just saw a man eating shark!

Ted: Where?

George: In a restaurant.

What do you get when you eat a lollipop that has a mosquito on it?

A bloodsucker.

What kind of sandwich do kids hate to take for lunch?

Peanut butter and jellyfish.

Why did the chef put exactly 239 beans in his pot of chili?

To find the answer to this riddle, drop the letters from each column into the squares directly below them. Careful—the letters won't always be in the same order! Black squares are the spaces between words.

	E̶	C	E									
	F	A	K	U̶	W̶	E				D̶		
M	M	R̶	A	T	Y	I	U	O	T	O		
B	O	A	R̶	E	S	O	T	L	N	E	O	
	E			U								
		R			W			D				
		R		!								

Chapter 18

Gooey Games and Sickening Sports

What position did the pig play in football?

Swinebacker.

What happens when a football player kicks a duck?

He foots the bill.

What is an insect's favorite game?

Cricket.

Why don't centipedes play football?

By the time they get their shoes on, the game is over.

Totally Twisted

To have a relay race with egg yolks, separate a group of friends into teams of three. Make sure each team member is standing a good distance away. The first person on each team gets a nice gooey egg yolk on a spoon. The goal is to pass the egg yolk to your teammates without breaking it. Whichever team gets to the finish line with the most yolk wins.

Why is it so hard to get a job as a sword fighter?

The competition is very cutthroat.

How do you know if a fly is a great American football player?

He's in the sugar bowl.

GROSS-O-METER

In 1998, thousands of black money spiders gathered on a ball field in England and created the largest spider web ever reported. It covered over eleven acres. Showing up to soccer practice and getting caught in a humongous sticky, nasty spider web ranks a solid eight on the Gross-o-meter scale.

What kind of competition do mosquitoes like?

Skin diving.

Why did the fans bring toilet paper to the baseball game?

The bases were loaded.

Where's Walmo?

Can you find Walmo by using this description?

- Food in teeth
- White shirt with dark stain
- Dark jeans with light stain
- 3 zits

Totally Twisted

To put together a gross scavenger hunt, make a list of the nasty things that lurk around your house and garden. For example, rotting fruit from the garbage, spider webs, slugs, worms, and dustballs. Gather your friends and start the hunt. The winner is the first to find all the items on the list.

What do vampires eat at a baseball game?

Fangfurters.

What do you call the head roach of a football team?

The roach coach.

What game do zombies play in the schoolyard?

Swallow the leader.

Do you remember when you lost your first tooth?

Yeah, I couldn't believe my brother could kick a football so well.

What was everybody's favorite game show at the leper colony?

Leperdy.

Totally Twisted

Drink a lot of carbonated beverages through a straw so you get real gassy. Your mission is to burp the entire alphabet—backwards. You'll have to practice a lot. Don't be discouraged if you only get up to S the first time around. Just try again, no matter how annoying people tell you you're being.

Name That Poop

Phantom Poop

This is when you think you have to poop, and you try really hard to poop, but no poop comes out.

The No Evidence Poop

This is when you poop a huge poop and you see it, but there's nothing on the toilet paper to prove it.

Sloppy Poop

This is when you wipe and wipe and the poop just won't go away. So, you have to either take a shower or just keep toilet paper in your pants till it dries up.

I'd Give My Kingdom for a Poop

This is when you have to go so badly that you throw your sister to the floor to stop her from going into the bathroom before you. But once you're seated, you just can't poop!

This is probably the worst kind of poop there is.

The Fake-Out Poop

This is when you think you're done pooping so you wipe and flush, but then you realize you still have more poop in you. Only now, your whole family is waiting by the door to get into the bathroom, so you have to hurry.

The Fart Poop

This is when you poop and fart at the same time, and it stinks so bad you can't even breathe. Everyone can hear you poop, too.

The Turtle Poop

This is when you're trying to poop and it comes out a little and then goes right back inside. It takes a couple of tries to finally get it out.

Name That Poop (Continued)

The Watermelon Poop

This poop doesn't smell like watermelon, but rather it feels like one! It feels like the biggest poop of your life and you wonder how in the world it's going to come out of your body. When it finally comes out, you're ready for a nap.

The Dump Truck Poop

This is when you've been holding it for so long that when it finally comes out, your whole rear end gets a giant splash from the force of the poop.

The Curly Poop

This poop is so long that it actually coils up inside the toilet bowl. If it weren't so gross, you'd want to show your friends just how long this poop really is.

Why do frogs join baseball teams?

They catch all the pop flies.

What kind of ball should you never play baseball with?

An eyeball.

What do you call a snowman with a suntan?

A puddle.

How did the ghosts win their football game?

They kicked a field ghoul.

How are shoes similar to a losing football team?

They hate to suffer defeat.

Totally Twisted
Play the putrid picnic game! Gather a group of friends and go around the circle naming gross things you might bring to a putrid picnic in alphabetical order. For example, if your letter is M, you can say, "I'm bringing moldy mushrooms." Keep going around the circle until you've completed the whole alphabet.

What's the best puzzle for someone with zits?

To find the answer to this riddle, think of a word that best fits each of the descriptions. Write the words on the numbered lines, and then transfer each letter into the numbered grid.

1A	2D	3B	4C	5B	6B	7B
		8D	9A	10A		
		11D	12C	13A	14A	

A. Place for pirate gold

‾ ‾ ‾ ‾ ‾
1 9 10 14 13

B. One penny

‾ ‾ ‾ ‾
6 5 3 7

C. Opposite of OFF

‾ ‾
12 4

D. Small round spot

‾ ‾ ‾
11 2 8

 **247**

Who's there?
Jamaica.
Jamaica who?
Jamaica mud pie today?

Totally Twisted

You can make your own edible barf. All you'll need is a cup of oatmeal, chocolate cocoa powder, and applesauce. Mix together in a pot until it bubbles, but don't let it burn. If you want vomit with chunks, throw in some dried pineapple. Then show your friends how you eat your own "vomit."

Hide the Gross Stuff

Can you underline the seven gross words hiding in these sentences?
The words you're looking for are in the list, but careful—there are a few extras!

1. "I hope Ellen likes spiders and worms!"

2. Fred's note was far too gross to read.

3. At the zoo, zebras were burping up lunch.

4. Said Mr. Plopp, "I'm pleased to poop!"

5. This lime color is a yucky label choice.

FART
SNORT
BELCH
SNOT
OOZE
GREASE
PEE
SLIME
WAX
PIMPLE
EEL

Chapter 19

Tales of the Gross and Famous

What am I?

I am famous for my strange parenting methods. I lay eggs, and after the father comes along to fertilize the eggs, I make sure to swallow every single one of them to keep them safe. When they hatch, I throw up the slimy babies.

What am I?

An Australian brooding frog.

What's green and smells?

The Incredible Hulk's fart.

What do you get when you cross a dinosaur and a pig?

Jurassic Pork.

How come Cinderella never made the football team?

She kept running away from the ball.

What's the most important thing Santa tells his reindeer?

Don't eat yellow snow.

What do you get if you cross a science fiction movie with a frog?

Star Warts.

Why does Tigger smell so bad?

Because he plays with Pooh.

What were Tarzan's last words?

Who greased this vine?

Dodging Dog Doo

A practical joker has covered this yard with dog doo—but only some of it is fake! Can you get from the top to the bottom of the yard without smooshing your shoe in the real doo? Put an X through each letter that appears more than three times. The piles that are left are perfectly plastic and safe to walk on.

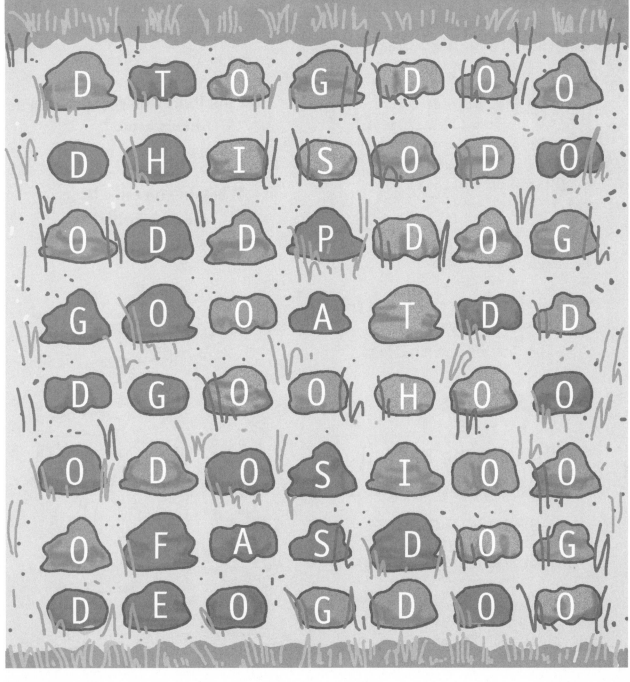

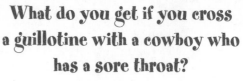
GROSS-O-METER

In 1998, Kevin Cole of New Mexico broke a world record by ejecting a 7.5 inch strand of spaghetti out of his nostrils. Then he nose-flossed by shooting one end of the spaghetti out of each nostril. Nose flossing gets a sticky nine on the Gross-o-meter scale. Spaghetti and snotballs, anyone?

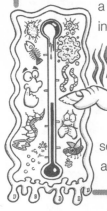

What do you get if you cross a guillotine with a cowboy who has a sore throat?

A headless hoarse man.

How did Pinocchio get splinters in his hands?

He was scratching his head.

What do you call a large, dancing gorilla?

King Conga.

Why did Frankenstein always get sick after a meal?

He kept bolting down his food.

What did the Big Bad Wolf say when he got a stomachache?

Maybe it was someone I ate.

How did Captain Hook meet his end?

He picked his nose with the wrong hand.

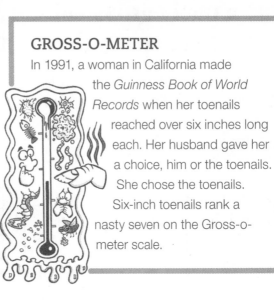

GROSS-O-METER

In 1991, a woman in California made the *Guinness Book of World Records* when her toenails reached over six inches long each. Her husband gave her a choice, him or the toenails. She chose the toenails. Six-inch toenails rank a nasty seven on the Gross-o-meter scale.

What do you call a pig that can climb the side of a building?

Spider ham.

What do you get if you cross a whale with a dead fish?

Moby Ick.

Why did Captain Kirk pee on the ceiling?

To go where no man had gone before.

How do you keep a really gross kid in suspense?

Break the letter code to find the answer to this riddle. **HINT:** Read the answer from top to bottom.

Z−1	G+2	V−2
L+3	Q−3	N+1
V−1	E−1	L+1
'	■	N−1
O−3	P−1	T−5
I+3	P+5	Q+1
■	U−1	M+2
A+5	■	Z−3

What am I?

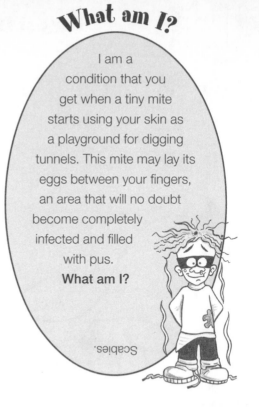

I am a condition that you get when a tiny mite starts using your skin as a playground for digging tunnels. This mite may lay its eggs between your fingers, an area that will no doubt become completely infected and filled with pus.
What am I?

Scabies.

What would George Washington do if he were alive today?

Scratch at the lid of his coffin.

What's brown and sits on a piano bench?

Beethoven's last movement.

Why did the Beatles break up?

They were bugging each other.

GROSS-O-METER

Kim Goodman takes the record for literally being able to pop her eyes out of her head. They don't come all the way out, but they do pop out to a little under half an inch from her eye sockets. Eyeballs that don't stay in your head rank a seven on the Gross-o-meter scale.

Why couldn't Batman go fishing?
Robin ate all the worms.

What do you call Batman after he's been run over by a truck?
Splatman.

GROSS-O-METER
The record for eating the most worms goes to a man in India nicknamed Snake Manu. He ate 200 earthworms in thirty seconds. Eating creepy crawly things gets a nine on the Gross-o-meter scale, but eating them really fast gets a ten.

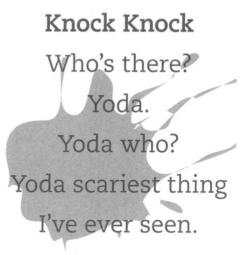

Knock Knock
Who's there?
Yoda.
Yoda who?
Yoda scariest thing
I've ever seen.

What do you call a booger that's been sneezed across the room?

To find the answer to this riddle, color in all the shapes with the letters S-N-E-E-Z-E.

Why did the Wicked Witch eat turkey?

Flying monkeys are too hard to catch on her broom.

What's the real reason Rudolph has a red nose?

Prancer beat him during a boxing match.

Why do cannibals love Wheel of Fortune?

They like to buy bowels.

Why did Dracula always have breath mints with him?

He suffered from bat breath.

What do you get if you cross Godzilla with a parrot?

A messy cage.

What do you get when you cross a serial killer with a pair of jeans?

Jack the zipper.

Who's green, has a lot of hair, and lives in a tower?

A barfing Rapunzel.

How do you know if the Hunchback of Notre Dame is upset with you?

He gets bent out of shape.

Which barbarian ate the Roman Empire?

Attila the Hungry.

What is Mozart doing now that he's dead?

Decomposing.

What do a spaceship and toilet paper have in common?

They both circle Uranus.

How did the Wicked Witch make yogurt?

She stared at a glass of milk until it curdled.

What do you get when you cross an ant and a rabbit?

Bugs Bunny.

What do you call termites that want to chew up the whole world?

Terminators.

More Books to Read

Branzei, Sylvia. *Grossology and You*. Price, Stern, Sloan. 2002.
This book is so much fun to read you won't realize how much you've actually learned. Great topics of interest such as farting, burping, toe cheese, and more are all part of this adventure into grossness.

Branzei, Sylvia. *Animal Grossology*. Planet Dexter Books. 1996.
If you want to know everything that's gross about animals, this is the book for you. All you'll ever need to know about ticks, leeches, tapeworms, slugs, flies, and even humans is right here.

Chatterton, Martin. *Yuck! The Grossest Joke Book Ever.* **Kingfisher. 2004.**
Over 100 foul and smelly jokes to make you sick and keep you giggling for hours.

Masoff, Joy. *Oh, Yuck! The Encyclopedia of Everything Nasty.* **Workman Publishing. 2000.**
Anything you would ever want to know about the world of the gross and nasty from acne to worms. Includes recipes, experiments, and lots of yucky photos. If you have a passion for the pukey, this will keep you engrossed for hours!

Pellowski, Michael. *Monster Jokes.* **Sterling. 2002.**
Frankenstein, Dracula, and all the werewolves come together in this book for a scary good time. A real chuckler!

Philips, Louis. *Invisible Oink: Pig Jokes.* **Viking Press. 1993.**
Get your fill of oinks and snorts with these hilarious pig jokes. After reading this book you'll surely want to have your very own pig sty.

Solheim, James. *It's Disgusting and We Ate It: True Facts from Around the World and Throughout History.* **Aladdin. 2001.**
Care for some squirrel pie? This book will take you on one of your grossest journeys yet. Travel through history and learn about the totally nasty things people used to eat. Roasted spiders, anyone?

Spoon, Ben. *Gross Jokes and Awesome Body Tricks.* **Element Books. 2000.**

This book will provide hours of fun! Between the jokes and the weird but cool tricks, you can keep your friends laughing for hours.

Stine, Jovial Bob. *101 Creepy Creature Jokes.* **Scholastic. 1997.**

If slimy, stinky creatures are your thing, this book is for you. Sure to leave you rolling with laughter, these jokes are some of the creepiest out there.

Strasser, Todd. *Kid's Book of Gross Facts and Feats.* **Troll Communications. 1998.**

Filled with really gross facts about the human body and amazing but gross things that people have accomplished, this book will satisfy anybody's curiosity about over-the-top grossness.

Szpirglas, Jeff. *Gross Universe: Your Guide to All Things Disgusting under the Sun.* **Maple Tree Press. 2004.**

This book will give you the lowdown on everything from farts to phlegm. You'll learn more about scabs, maggots, and mites than you ever imagined possible.

Color Me!

Web Sites

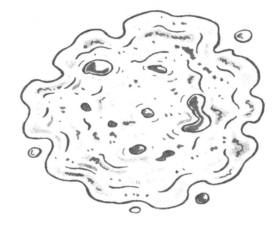

www.ahajokes.com

Amuse friends and family with the jokes on this Web site. Search by category for sick jokes, animal jokes, and much, much more.

www.grossology.org

This Web site discusses the science of everything gross. It focuses on your very stinky, crusty, and slimy body.

http://yucky.kids.discovery.com/noflash/body/index.html

This Web site will tell you all you ever wanted to know about how gross and disgusting your very own body really is. If you're dying to know why people vomit and how come your poop smells so bad, check out this site for all the answers.

http://kidhumor.glowport.com/animal_humor

You'll find tons of jokes about all sorts of animals, including creepy insects such as ants, spiders, fleas, and worms. This Web site will keep you laughing for hours.

www.kidsjokes.co.uk
Search this Web site for hours and you'll be laughing so hard you won't be able to stand up. This site offers all sorts of funnies, including some really gross ones about monsters and creepy crawlers.

http://www.jokesnjokes.net/funny.jokes.amusing.humor.laughs/kids.htm
This Web site will leave you in stitches with its great assortment of one-liners.

http://www.investigator.org.au/funStuff/grossOut.htm
This Web site offers some really cool and extremely gross facts about the human body. Check it out!

http://www.lsc.org/online_science/gross/gross_urinary.html
This official Web site from the Liberty Science Center answers all sorts of questions, such as why your pee smells so bad after you eat asparagus. It also provides a really yummy recipe for making some homemade snot.

http://library.thinkquest.org/03oct/00122/gross.htm
This Web site will totally gross you out with facts about antiquated medical practices. Did you know doctors used to cover sick people in slimy leeches in an effort to suck the disease out of their blood? Check the site to learn more!

http://www.squiglysplayhouse.com/JokesAndRiddles/index.html
This hysterical Web site contains jokes sent in by kids from around the world. It just goes to show you that humor is universal.

Puzzle Answers

page 142 • **Yummy!**

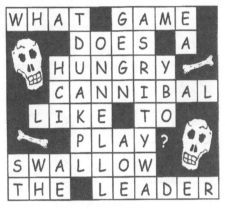

W H A T · G A M E
· D O E S · A ·
· H U N G R Y · ·
· C A N N I B A L
· L I K E · T O ·
· · P L A Y ? · ·
S W A L L O W · ·
T H E · L E A D E R

page 145 • **Stink Pinks**

What's a large vehicle
that hauls garbage?

Y U C K   T R U C K

Where can you buy plastic
scars and fake blood?

G O R E   S T O R E

What do you call a shovel
used to pick up dog doo?

P O O P   S C O O P

What do you call
ghost throw up?

S P O O K   P U K E

What do you call
an intelligent gas?

S M A R T   F A R T

What's a riddle
about a dead frog?

C R O A K   J O K E

page 149 • **How do toilets keep in touch?**

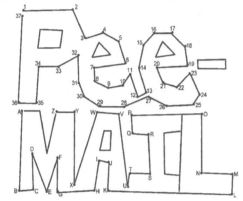

page 153 • **What do you get if an ax falls on your head?**

A. Top on a jar

$\underset{4}{L}\ \underset{5}{I}\ \underset{14}{D}$

B. Dracula's coat

$\underset{16}{C}\ \underset{13}{A}\ \underset{3}{P}\ \underset{12}{E}$

C. It makes you warm

$\underset{11}{H}\ \underset{18}{E}\ \underset{15}{A}\ \underset{7}{T}$

D. Kids' running game

$\underset{6}{T}\ \underset{1}{A}\ \underset{10}{G}$

E. Between knee and ankle

$\underset{2}{S}\ \underset{17}{H}\ \underset{8}{I}\ \underset{9}{N}$

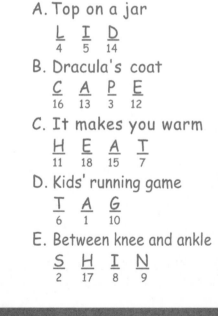

1D	2E	3B	4A	5A	6D	7C	8E	9E	10 D
A	S	P	L	I	T	T	I	N	G

11 C	12 B	13 B	14 A	15 C	16 B	17 E	18 C
H	E	A	D	A	C	H	E!

265

page 155 • **What's invisible and smells like bananas?**

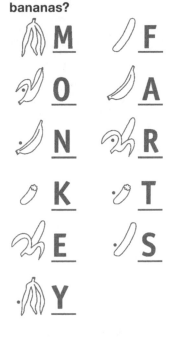

M O N K E Y
F A R T S

page 158 • **Knock, Knock**

RZABRZBERZYZPR
ARBYBREYWHHPOR
RABYBERYSTRUZNG
MZEPONMYRBUTPT

ABBEY. ABBEY WHO?
ABBEY (a bee) STUNG
ME ON MY BUTT!

page 162 • **Why couldn't the caveman hear the pterodactyl go to the bathroom?**

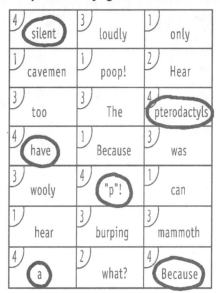

Because pterodactyls have a silent "p"!

page 164 • **What do you get if you cross a piranha with your nose?**

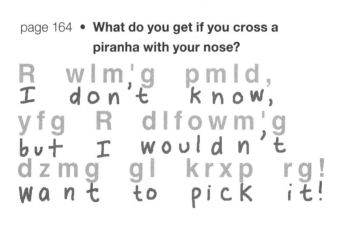

R wlm'g pmld,
I don't know,
yfg R dlfowm'g
but I wouldn't
dzmg gl krxp rg!
want to pick it!

Puzzle Answers

page 167 • **"Your brother sure is spoiled!"**

No he's not. He always smells that way!

page 174 • **Snot Milk?**

page 179 • **Sick Change**

Change a small wagon to smelly gas
CART to FART

Change a flat piece of wood to a crusty wound cover
SLAB to SCAB

Change a tangle of string to a booger
KNOT to SNOT

Change the center of a peach to a pimple
PIT to ZIT

Change a swollen spot to a belch
BUMP to BURP

Change a large ring made of metal to a pile of #2
HOOP to POOP

page 184 • **What do you call a fairy that never showers?**

S T I N K E R B E L L

page 194 • **Sluuuurp**

page 194 • **Strange Soup**

SCORPION SOUP

BIRD NEST SOUP

SHARK FIN SOUP

OXTAIL SOUP

page 198 • **On what day of the week do lions eat people?**

1. CRUNCH
2. CHOMP
3. MEAT
4. GNAW
5. FEAST
6. DINER
7. SWALLOW
8. SLOPPY

page 204 • **B-ughs!**

1. There are six roaches, but only five spiders. 2. There are six flies. If each fly has six legs, that makes 36 fly legs in all. 3. The mosquito that has just bitten someone is on the left-hand side of the page, near the bottom, between the two flies. You can tell it just had lunch because its belly is swollen with all the blood it just sucked up. Gross!

page 214 • **What About Jimmy?**

What happened when Jimmy's mother said she was going to take Jimmy to the zoo?

Jimmy's brother said "Don't bother. If the zoo wants Jimmy, they can come and get him!"

page 217 • **Grime Time**

```
G I G G I G R E M I R E
I R M I R G E R G R I G
R G I M G R I G I G R I
I R G M R R I R E R I M
M I G R I M G M I G M E
E M E I M I E M I G I R
G G M G R I E M R M R I
R I E G I E E M I R G G
M M I R G R G E G E M M
E I G R G R I M M I R G
G R E M I M I R I G I E
```

CRUD   MUD
GUNK   DUST
MUCK   SMUDGE

The missing letter is "U".

Puzzle Answers

page 219 • Rude Rebus Riddles

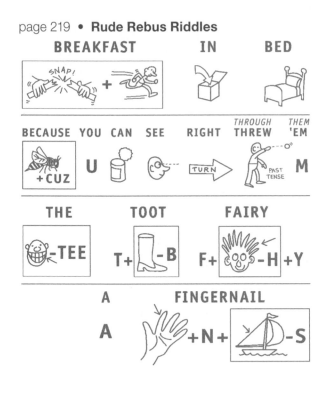

BREAKFAST   IN   BED

BECAUSE YOU CAN SEE RIGHT THROUGH THREW THEM 'EM

THE   TOOT   FAIRY

A   FINGERNAIL

page 223 • Gross A to Z

A	B	S	U	R	D	S
A	N	T	L	E	R	S
A	Z	A	L	E	A	S
B	A	R	R	A	C	K
B	O	W	L	F	U	L
C	R	A	C	K	L	E
M	A	R	I	N	A	S
O	U	T	W	A	R	D
R	E	S	E	N	D	S

page 227 • What goes "HA, HA, HA, PLOP!"

SOMEONE LAUGHING HIS HEAD OFF!

page 228 • Gross Garret likes . . .

Gross Garret likes anything spelled with double letters!

page 234 • Who Foofed?

page 237 • What do you call a millionaire with really bad body odor?

BOBOFPUBOIBO
PULBOPUBOBO
BOBOBOTBOPU
HPBOBOPUBOY
PUROBOPBOBO
PUIPBOCBOBOH

Answer: FILTHY RICH!

page 240 • **Why did the chef put exactly 239 beans in his pot of chili?**

E	C	E							
	F	A	K	U	W E			D	
M	M	R	A	T	Y	I U	O	T	O
B	O	A	R	E	S	O T	L	N E	O
B	E	C	A	U	S E		O N E		
M	O	R E			W O U L D				
	M	A	K E			I T		T O O	
	F	A	R	T	Y	! (240- get it?)			

page 243 • **Where's Walmo?**

page 247 • **What's the best puzzle for someone with zits?**

A. Place for pirate gold
<u>C</u> <u>H</u> <u>E</u> <u>S</u> <u>T</u>
1   9   10   14   13

B. One penny
<u>C</u> <u>E</u> <u>N</u> <u>T</u>
6   5   3   7

C. Opposite of OFF
<u>O</u> <u>N</u>
12   4

D. Small round spot
<u>D</u> <u>O</u> <u>T</u>
11   2   8

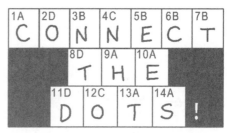

page 248 • **Hide the Gross Stuff**

1. "I hope Ellen likes spiders and worms!"
2. Fred's note was far too gross to read.
3. At the zoo, zebras were burping up lunch.
4. Said Mr. Plopp, "I'm pleased to poop!"
5. This lime color is a yucky label choice.

Puzzle Answers

page 251 • **Dodging Dog Doo**

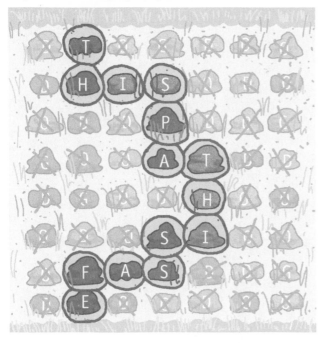

page 254 • **How do you keep a really gross kid in suspense?**

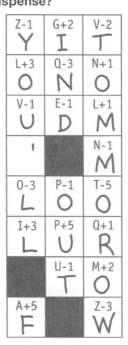

Z-1	G+2	V-2
Y	I	T
L+3	Q-3	N+1
O	N	O
V-1	E-1	L+1
U	D	M
I		N-1
		M
O-3	P-1	T-5
L	O	O
I+3	P+5	Q+1
L	U	R
	U-1	M+2
	T	O
A+5		Z-3
F		W

page 256 • **What do you call a booger that's been sneezed across the room?**

PART 3:
Gross Recipes

Appliance Monsters

Follow the dots to find out which kitchen tools these gross creatures have gobbled up.

Chapter 20

An Icky Introduction to Cookery

Here's an example of a recipe that you'll see in the next chapter:

Flies Floating in Bee Spit and Goatmeal

Rise and shine and suck down a bowl of mushy goatmeal (oatmeal) topped with flies (raisins) stuck in a glob of bee spit (honey) and swimming in cow juice (milk).

▶ **Difficulty: Medium**   ▶ **Serves 4**

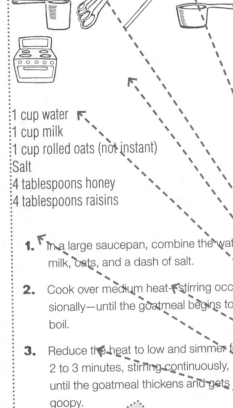

1 cup water
1 cup milk
1 cup rolled oats (not instant)
Salt
4 tablespoons honey
4 tablespoons raisins

1. In a large saucepan, combine the water, milk, oats, and a dash of salt.

2. Cook over medium heat—stirring occasionally—until the goatmeal begins to boil.

3. Reduce the heat to low and simmer for 2 to 3 minutes, stirring continuously, until the goatmeal thickens and gets goopy.

Are you ready to create deliciously gross grub? Good! Before you start cooking, though, there are some important terms, tools, and rules you need to know.

All of the recipes in this book are kid friendly, and you can do most of the stuff yourself. Of course, anytime you're preparing or cooking food, an adult should supervise and help you in the kitchen. This is especially important with recipes that involve using a sharp implement, such as a knife or grater, or an appliance, such as a blender, electric mixer, microwave, or stove.

In this chapter, you'll learn everything you need to know to get cooking in the kitchen. Read it and talk about it with your mom, dad, grandma, or whoever is your cooking assistant—and then let the slicing, dicing, simmering, and boiling begin!

Recipe Decoder

A recipe is a set of instructions for preparing a certain type of food—for example, macaroni and cheese. You should always read the recipe all the way through before you do anything else to make sure you know which ingredients, tools, and steps you'll need to create your culinary concoction. The recipes in this book include the following information:

- Number of servings (or quantity) the recipe makes
- How difficult the recipe is to make
- Tools needed to make the recipe
- Ingredients needed to make the recipe, with amount of each ingredient specified (if applicable)
- Cooking or baking temperature (such as 350 degrees), if applicable
- Step-by-step instructions for making the recipe
- Amount of time to bake or cook, if applicable

Tool Mess!

Welcome to Mr. Geezer's garage sale. He's going to be in deep doo-doo when Mrs. Geezer finds out he tossed her kitchen tools in a pile with his filthy-dirty garage tools. Find all the kitchen gadgets and color them in.

Gear and Gadgets

Each recipe in this section includes a set of small pictures that lets you know which appliances, utensils, and other widgets you'll need to make the recipe. The following picture key tells you the name and meaning of each of the cool tools you'll be using:

Baking pan—a square or rectangular pan made of glass or metal used for baking or roasting food in the oven

Blender—an electric appliance used for blending, chopping, or grinding foods

Cake pan (round)—a metal or glass pan used for baking a single layer of cake; may also be used for baking other foods

Can opener—an electric appliance or a manual tool (not pictured) used to open tin cans

Casserole dish—a glass, ceramic, or clay dish used to bake casseroles and other food in the oven; may be square, rectangular, round, or oval

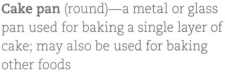

Colander—a metal or plastic bowl with holes in it used to drain water from food after you've washed it or liquid from food after you've cooked it (such as pasta and potatoes)

Cookie sheet—a flat metal sheet used to bake cookies, rolls, and other solid foods in the oven; sometimes called a "baking sheet"

Cutting board—a wooden, glass, or hard plastic board used to cut, chop, dice, and slice foods

Electric mixer—an electric appliance used for mixing, blending, and whipping ingredients together

Glass measuring cup—a glass cup with a spout and measurements marked on the side used to measure liquid ingredients

Grater—a kitchen tool with a handle and a single flat surface or four different flat surfaces (shaped like a box) upon which are sharp-edged grooves used to grate, shred, mince, or slice foods, such as cheese

Griddle—a flat, square pan used to grill pancakes, French toast, sandwiches, hamburgers, and other food

Ice-cream scoop—a deep rounded spoon with a stout handle that is most commonly used to scoop a ball (or chunk) of ice cream or sherbet out of a container

Knife—a utensil used to cut, chop, slice, and dice food; available in many shapes and sizes and with different edges, such as blunt (butter knife), serrated (ridges), and sharp

Ladle—a deep rounded spoon with a long handle used to scoop sauces, soups, and other liquids out of a pot, serving dish, or other container

Measuring cup—metal or plastic cups used to measure dry ingredients; usually come as a set of various sizes (¼ cup, ½ cup, ⅓ cup, ¾ cup, 1 cup, 2 cups) that are nested together

Measuring spoons—metal or plastic spoons used to measure liquid and dry ingredients; come as a set of various sizes (¼ tablespoon, ½ tablespoon, ⅓ cup, ¾ cup, 1 teaspoon, 1 tablespoon) that are nested together

Microwave oven—an electric appliance that uses electromagnetic (micro) waves to cook food, defrost food, and warm leftovers quickly

Mixing bowl—a large bowl used to mix together both dry and wet ingredients; available in several sizes

Muffin tin—a metal or glass pan with small round cups used for baking muffins and cupcakes

Oven mitt—specially designed mitts and pads made with flame-retardant material used to hold hot pots, pans, dishes, and plates

Pie pan—a round, shallow, metal or glass baking dish with slanted sides used for baking pies and tarts; sometimes called a "pie plate"

Pitcher—a large glass, plastic, or metal container with a handle and a spout, used for serving water or cold drinks

Plate—a flat dish used to serve food

Potato masher—a utensil with holes or thick wires on one end used to mash cooked potatoes, pumpkin, and other soft food to make it smooth

Rolling pin—a wooden, plastic, or metal roller with handles on each side used to flatten dough, such as for pie crust and sugar cookies

Saucepan—a pot with a long handle used for cooking on top of the stove; comes in several sizes such as 1 quart, 2 quarts, or 3 quarts

Skillet—a flat pan with sides and a long handle used for frying, stir-frying, and sautéing food in hot fat or oil

Spatula—a flat metal, plastic, or rubber utensil with a long handle used to flip, lift, turn, or spread food

Stove—a large gas or electric appliance used for cooking food; a stove that has burners for cooking on top and an oven for baking and broiling on the bottom is also called a "range," and sometimes the stove top and oven are two separate units that are built into the countertop and kitchen cabinets

Vegetable peeler—a sharp utensil shaped like a large keyhole used to peel the skin off of vegetables and fruits; also called a "potato peeler"

Toaster—an electric appliance with two or four slots used for toasting bread, English muffins, and bagels

Tongs—a metal utensil with rounded pinchers (for grabbing food with) at the end of a long handle

Whisk—a metal utensil with a bunch of wires on the end used for mixing or whipping wet ingredients together

Wooden spoon—a big spoon used for mixing and stirring all kinds of food before cooking and while cooking; some have slats or holes in them

Cooking Lingo

Every recipe uses certain words to specify how to prepare and cook food. Read the following descriptions of the most common cooking terms. Then ask your mom or dad or another adult to show you how to do each of these.

Bake—to cook food in the oven using heat from the bottom, usually putting the pan on the center or lower rack

Batter—a combination of wet and dry ingredients blended together to form a smooth or creamy mixture, such as the batter used to make cakes, brownies, cookies, and pancakes

Beat—to mix ingredients together by stirring very firmly and quickly, using a spoon, fork, whisk, or electric mixture

Blend—to mix foods together slowly and softly until the mixture is smooth

Boil—to heat liquid until it bubbles all over

Broil—to cook food in the oven using the heat source at the top, usually putting the pan on a top rack

Brown—to cook until a golden or brown crust forms on the food

Chill—to refrigerate food until it is cold

Chop—to cut food into small pieces with a knife, blender, or food processor

Cool—to let food sit at room temperature until it is cool enough to cut or eat

Cream—to mix ingredients together until they are smooth and creamy

Dice—to cut food into small squares of about the same size

Drain—to remove the liquid from food that has been cooked, defrosted, packaged, or stored

Common Cooking Methods

BAKE　　　　**BOIL**　　　　**SIMMER**　　　　**STIR-FRY**

Fold—to gently combine ingredients by lifting and turning ingredients from the top to the bottom until everything is mixed together

Fry—to cook or brown food in hot oil or fat in a skillet or deep-frying pan over high heat

Grate—to shred food into slivers with a grater, blender, or food processor

Grease—to coat a baking pan or baking dish with butter, margarine, oil, or shortening so food won't stick to the bottom while it is cooking (The coating can be applied by rubbing it on or spraying it from a can.)

Knead—to scrunch and turn dough until it's the right texture

Mix—to stir together two or more ingredients until they form one mixture (you can no longer see the different ingredients)

Preheat—to heat the oven or the pan on the stove to the temperature specified in the recipe before you start to cook the food in the oven or on the pan

Sauté—to cook food in a small amount of oil or liquid in a skillet on the stovetop over low to medium heat

Simmer—to cook over low heat until food almost boils

Slice—to cut food into long, thin pieces of about the same size

Steam—to cook food over boiling water so the steam cooks the food (The food doesn't touch the water or the bottom of the pan on the burner.)

Stir—to continuously turn and mix food with a spoon

Stir-fry—to cook food in a deep skillet and a small amount of oil over high heat while stirring constantly

Whip—to beat food very quickly with a fork, whisk, eggbeater, or electric mixer

How to Measure Ingredients

Sometimes it's okay to use a little less or a little more of an ingredient. For instance, who cares if you put extra cheese on your pizza or half a cup rather than a whole cup of walnuts in your brownies? For many recipes, though, it's important to use the exact amount of each ingredient listed. Otherwise, you can end up with something that tastes like pigeon poop or looks like cow caca. Not enough yeast can make bread too chewy, and too much salt can make soup too salty, for example.

By the way, the cups and spoons you use to serve and eat with don't provide accurate measurements. When you need to measure precisely, make sure to use the right measuring tools and use them correctly by following these guidelines:

Dry ingredients—Fill the appropriate size of nested measuring spoon or measuring cup with the dry ingredient, such as flour, sugar, salt, or ground cinnamon. Then run a blunt knife over the top of the ingredient to "level" it evenly with the rim of the cup or spoon—unless the recipe calls for a "rounded" measurement, in which case you don't need to level.

Solid ingredients—Use nested measuring spoons and cups for soft ingredients, such as brown sugar, butter, margarine, peanut butter, jam, shortening, and shredded cheese. Instead of rounding or leveling the ingredient, gently pat it down with a spatula to remove air pockets. Do not pack the ingredient (similar to packing sand to make a sand castle) unless the recipe calls for it. Brown sugar is one of the few ingredients that is normally packed.

Liquid ingredients—Use a clear (glass is best) 1-cup or 2-cup measuring cup with a pour spout to measure liquids, such as milk, water, syrup, or soy sauce. Place the cup on a flat surface, bend down so that your eyes are level with the measurement marks, and fill to the specified level. Don't lift the cup up to your eye level to see whether it's on the mark.

Packaged ingredients sometimes come in different measurements than the ones used in the recipe. For instance, a recipe may call for 1 cup of yogurt, but the yogurt comes in a ½ pint carton. If you knew that 1 cup is equivalent to ½ pint, you could just dump the carton of yogurt into the recipe without having to put it in a measuring cup.

Knowing measurement equivalents will also come in handy if you can't find the size of measuring spoon or measuring cup called for in the recipe.

CHEF'S SECRET:
Measuring Success

Always measure ingredients over a paper towel or sheet of aluminum foil—never over the mixing bowl, casserole dish, or pot. That way, if you accidentally overfill the measuring spoon or cup, the ingredient won't spill over into the mix, and you'll always use exactly the right measurement.

One of the neat things about recipes is that you can make more or less food than the recipe calls for by reducing or increasing the amounts of all of the ingredients. Then, if you know measurement equivalents, you can use bigger measuring spoons or measuring cups rather than more of the same size. For example, if you wanted to use a recipe for 1 dozen cookies to make 2 dozen cookies, you would double (multiply by two) the amount of each ingredient. Let's say the original recipe calls for 2 tablespoons of vanilla. Double that amount is 4 tablespoons, which is equivalent to ¼ cup. So instead of filling the tablespoon four times, you could just fill a ¼ cup measuring cup one time.

Weights and Measurements Equivalents

dash/pinch	=	less than ⅛ teaspoon
3 teaspoons	=	1 tablespoon
2 tablespoons	=	1 fluid ounce
4 tablespoons	=	¼ cup
⅓ cup	=	5 tablespoons + 1 teaspoon
1 cup	=	16 tablespoons
1 cup	=	½ pint or 8 fluid ounces
2 cups	=	1 pint or 16 fluid ounces
2 pints	=	1 quart or 32 fluid ounces
2 quarts	=	¼ gallon or 64 fluid ounces
4 quarts	=	1 gallon
4 ounces (dry)	=	¼ pound
8 ounces (dry)	=	½ pound
12 ounces (dry)	=	¾ pound
16 ounces (dry)	=	1 pound

CHEF'S SECRET:
Before You Begin Cooking

There are four simple things you can do to make your cooking experience easier:

Plan ahead. Make a shopping list of ingredients you'll need for the recipe you want to make.

Read the recipe. Make sure you understand every step and that you have all the ingredients and tools you'll need before you begin.

Set up your cooking area. Make sure you have a clean work area that you can reach. Set out all the ingredients and tools you'll need before you start.

Protect your clothing with an apron or old shirt. Make sure it fits snugly and won't drape on the food or stove.

Measurement Abbreviations

All of the measurement terms used in this book are spelled out, which makes it easier to follow the recipes. However, most packaging labels and many other cookbooks use measurement abbreviations. Here are the most common ones:

t. or tsp.	=	teaspoon
T. or Tbsp.	=	tablespoon
c.	=	cup
pt.	=	pint
qt.	=	quart
oz.	=	ounce
lb.	=	pound

Appendage-Saving Kitchen Safety

Did you know that most accidents are preventable? It's true. Follow these simple safety rules for preparing and cooking food to avoid accidents and injuries.

Ask for help. Your mom or dad or another adult should always supervise your kitchen activities. If something is difficult or scary for you—such as cutting something with a sharp knife or removing a hot dish from the oven—ask your adult kitchen helper to show you how to do it or do it for you.

Keep clothing and hair out of the way. Wear short sleeves or roll up long sleeves. Don't wear loose clothes that might brush against a hot burner, oven, or toaster or get caught in a blender or other equipment. Fasten back long hair.

FREAKY FOOD FACT:
Attack of the Gut Bugs

Most of the organisms that cause food poisoning need moisture, warmth, and a little time to multiply and destroy food. Some food-borne bacteria double in number every twenty minutes. Bacteria can make food go bad in two hours at temperatures above 40 degrees and in only one hour at temperatures above 90 degrees.

Make sure you can reach the cooking surface. If you need a boost, stand on a sturdy platform, such as a stepping stool; it's not safe to stand on a chair or sit on the counter.

Use knives and other sharp utensils carefully. Ask an adult for instructions or to cut, chop, slice, or grate the food for you. Always hold knives by the handle and always carry them with the sharp end pointed downward. Whenever possible, use a serrated dinner knife or plastic knife.

Be careful using electrical appliances. Keep them away from water. Make sure the cords are out of the way, so you won't trip or get tangled up in them. Never stick your hand or a utensil in a mixer, blender, toaster, or other appliance while it's running.

Don't overfill cooking containers. Some food expands when it cooks, and you don't want hot food to bubble or splatter out of the pot or pan and onto you or an open flame. Overfull containers also spill more easily when you are moving or lifting them.

Never add water to hot oil, butter, or fat. The water will make the oil pop and splatter, and it could burn you.

Turn pot handles toward the rear or center of the stove. This prevents someone from bumping into the handle and knocking over the pan—which makes a big mess and can cause burns.

Use oven mitts and potholders to handle hot pots and dishes, or ask an adult to move it for you. Never use dish towels, rags, or paper towels to lift or move a hot fork, spoon, lid, pan, bowl, cup, or dish. Never try to lift something that is too heavy for you to do easily.

Keep flammable items away from hot burners. Never put potholders, oven mitts, paper towels, or dishtowels on top of or close to the stove where they might catch on fire.

Turn off the stove or oven before removing cooked food. This reduces the risk of you getting burned. It's also a good idea to double-check the knobs to make sure they're all turned off when you're done cooking, before you leave the kitchen, which will prevent fires.

Use heat-retardant utensils. Metal handles can heat up and burn your hand, so always use wooden or plastic utensils or metal utensils with plastic handles to stir and turn food. Take the utensil out of the pan when you're done stirring or turning the food rather than leaving it in the pan while the food is cooking.

Don't touch electrical appliances or outlets when your hands are wet. To avoid shocking yourself, always dry your hands before plugging in or using an electrical kitchen gadget.

Never put out a fire with water or by yourself. If something catches fire, you should immediately ask an adult for help and step back so she can extinguish the fire and so you won't get burned! Small kitchen fires can usually be smothered with baking soda or a lid. If caught quickly, other kitchen fires can usually be put out with a fire extinguisher (a must-have for every kitchen).

When you're cooking, never leave the kitchen to go do something else. Leaving cooking food unattended is the leading cause of house fires.

Clean up spills quickly. If you accidentally spill something liquid or slippery (such as flour) on the floor, clean it up immediately so that no one slips and falls.

Never use your fingers to lift up a can lid. If the lid doesn't pop up after you open it, use a dull-edged knife or a spoon to pry the lid open.

Focus on one thing at a time. Take your time and follow the recipe step by step. The more you cook, the more your skill and confidence will build, and before you know it you'll be whipping out a whole meal. For now, take your time, concentrate, relax, and have fun.

Battling Bacteria

When food isn't handled properly, it can become infested with harmful bacteria, which makes it toxic for people (and pets) to eat it. Eating spoiled food often causes flu-like symptoms—nausea, stomach cramps, vomiting, diarrhea, headache—which usually go away once your body has digested and pooped out the bacteria-infested gunk. But some food-borne bacteria can cause more serious problems and can even be life threatening. So it's really important to always follow these food safety rules:

Use a clean kitchen and equipment. Everything you touch and use while preparing and cooking food—including the countertop, bowls, measuring cup, spoons, pots, and appliances—should be clean. If there are dirty dishes near where you'll be working, wash them with warm soapy water or put them in the dishwasher or sink, away from where you'll be working. Clean surfaces often while cooking. Keep pets, toys, backpacks, and other stuff off the counter and table.

Wash your hands. Use warm water and soap to clean your hands before touching any food or cooking equipment and after touching any raw meat, poultry, fish, seafood, or eggs.

Defrost frozen foods properly. The safest way to defrost food is to place a dish under it and put it in the refrigerator overnight (for about 12 hours). Using the defrost setting on a microwave is okay too. Frozen food that is sealed in a plastic package or other leak-proof container can also be safely defrosted in a bowl of cold water. Never defrost food in warm water or on the counter.

Use only fresh ingredients. Check the expiration label on packaged foods. Before using fresh produce or leftovers, inspect it and smell it (but don't put your nose on it). If it smells stinky or looks putrid, don't use it. If in doubt, throw it out. Never taste raw meat, raw eggs, or any uncooked food or leftovers that are stinky, discolored, or moldy.

Follow the safe food handling label. All packaged foods have a label that tells you how to handle the food safely.

Wash fresh fruits and vegetables. Before eating or cooking raw produce, wash it thoroughly with cool water.

Cook food completely. Cook raw meat and poultry until it's no longer pink in the middle and no blood drains out when you poke it with a fork, or use a meat thermometer to cook it to the right temperature. Follow the recipe instructions for all other foods.

Never reuse a kitchen tool without first washing it. Don't use the same knife, cutting board, spoon, plate, or pan for cooked food that you did for raw food.

Keep cold foods cool. Refrigerated and frozen foods cannot be left out at room temperature for more than two hours. For picnics and barbeques, the limit is one hour, and it's best to keep cold foods in coolers until you're ready to eat them. Put unused refrigerated ingredients back in the refrigerator when you're done using them.

Keep raw eggs and meats separate from other foods. Keep uncooked eggs, meat, poultry, fish, and seafood at least 12 inches away from fruits, veggies, flour, sugar, oil, and other ingredients you're using in a recipe.

Never sample uncooked or undercooked food made with eggs or meat. This includes cookie dough, cake batter, brownie batter, and other recipes containing raw eggs. Raw eggs are a major source of salmonella bacteria, and raw meat is a major source of E. coli bacteria, which cause two of the worst types of food poisoning.

FREAKY FOOD FACT:
Good Gut Bacteria

Some of the bacteria in your body are supposed to be there. In fact, billions of these microscopic critters—enough to fill a 6-ounce mug—live in your colon (your large intestine) all the time, where they work hard to digest your food and turn the leftovers into poop. Every time you take a dump, you get rid of bacteria, both the good guys and the bad guys. Fortunately, your body usually produces new good bacteria as fast as you squeeze them out.

Keep your hands out of your nose and mouth. Don't pick your boogers, wipe your snot, bite your nails, or lick your fingers while cooking. This not only prevents bacteria from transferring from uncooked food to your body, it also prevents bacteria and viruses in your body from transferring to the food.

Store leftovers quickly and correctly. Seal all unused foods in an appropriate container or package. Put perishable food in the refrigerator or freezer as soon as possible. (Remember, no more than two hours at room temperature.)

Heat leftovers until they're hot. Stir while heating to make sure all of the food gets hot all the way through.

Eat, Drink, and Be Healthy!

Making and eating good food is fun. It's also good for you. Food gives your body the nutrients it needs to grow, move, and think. Yes, even that big ball of twisty gray matter known as your brain needs food to develop and work properly. You don't need to eat gobs of food to be healthy. In fact, overeating can lead to obesity, which is bad for your health. To stay fit and to feel good, though, you need to eat enough of the right foods and limit the amount of not-so-good foods in your diet.

Scientists and doctors have researched the effects of diet on health, and we could write a book just about that. Lucky for us, the United States Department of Agriculture (more commonly known as the USDA) has put together a nifty food pyramid that makes it easy to understand how much of which kinds of foods to eat and drink to be fit and healthy. You've probably already heard about the food pyramid from school, so you'll just read about the basics here.

Most kids your age need at least 1,800 calories a day and sometimes more if they're very physically active. How many calories you consume is not nearly as important as how many servings of each food group you eat each day. The foods that appear at the top of the pyramid are the ones you need the least of, and the ones at the bottom are the ones you need the most of.

For most kids, a healthy diet is one that:

- Consists mainly of fruits, vegetables, whole grains, and fat-free or low-fat dairy products
- Includes some (not a large quantity of) lean meats, poultry, fish, eggs, beans, nuts, and legumes
- Is low in saturated fat, trans fat, cholesterol, salt, and refined sugars—in other words, junk food

Grains: Six Servings

The major portion of your daily diet—at least six servings (equivalent to 6 ounces) should come from grains. At least half of your daily serving of grains (three per day) should come from whole grains.

For nutritional purposes, grains are divided into two groups: whole grains and refined (processed) grains. Whole grains contain the whole kernel of each grain. Refined grains have been milled, a manufacturing process that removes the bran and germ from the grain. Refining gives the grain a fine texture and extends its shelf life, but some of the grain's dietary fiber, iron, and vitamins are removed in the process. Check out this list of common whole-grain and refined grain foods:

Whole Grain	Refined Grain
brown rice	couscous
oatmeal	crackers
popcorn	flour tortillas
whole-grain cereal	pasta
whole-grain cornbread	pita bread
whole-wheat bread	pretzels
whole-wheat tortillas	white bread
wild rice	white rice

Vegetables and Fruits: Five Servings

Fruits and vegetables add flavor, color, and variety to your diet. They also give you a slew of minerals, vitamins, and antioxidants (which help prevent and fight disease).

The USDA recommends three servings of veggies and two servings of fruits every day, but you can eat three servings of fruit and two servings of vegetables some days and still be healthy. That amounts to about 4 cups of fruits and veggies each day.

You can eat most fruits and veggies either raw or cooked (but always wash them first), and either fresh or preserved (but with little or no added sugars). There are hundreds of different types of fruits and veggies to choose from. It's best to eat more green and orange veggies than white veggies (which are higher in natural sugars). It's also better to get most of your fruit servings from the actual fruit rather than from fruit juice.

Dairy: Two Servings

Dairy foods are a good source of calcium, vitamin D, and protein, which are all essential nutrients for your body. The dairy group includes milk and milk products such as cheese and yogurt, which usually come from cows and goats. People who are allergic to animal milk or who are vegetarians can use soy or another vegetable-based dairy substitute that is high in protein and calcium (which may be added).

The majority of the dairy products you consume should be low fat or fat free, and they should have little or no added sugar. Technically, ice cream

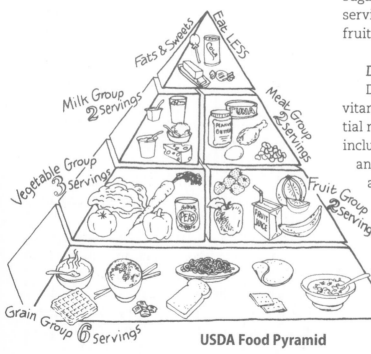

USDA Food Pyramid

in nutrients and high in fat, oil, sodium, and refined sugars—like candy, cheese puffs, cookies, donuts, French fries, potato chips, sugared cereals, and soft drinks. Though some of these foods are lip-smacking tasty, they don't help your body grow or stay healthy, and eating too much of this stuff for years and years can actually hurt your health.

There is no recommended daily serving for these foods because the USDA recommends eating very little of this type of junk food. The less saturated fat, trans fat, cholesterol, sugar, and salt (sodium) in your diet, the better it is for your health.

is a dairy product, but it is usually very high in fat and sugar, so you should limit the amount you eat and eat ice cream with as little fat and sugar as possible.

You need 3 cups (24 ounces) of milk per day. One cup of yogurt and 1½ ounces of cheese are each equivalent to one cup of milk.

Meat and Beans: Two Servings

You should eat about 5 ounces of protein-rich foods each day. The USDA recommends eating a balanced mix of lean meat, poultry (chicken and turkey), eggs, fish, shellfish, beans, peas, nuts, and seeds. One ounce of meat, poultry, fish, and shellfish is equivalent to one egg, ½ ounce of nuts or seeds, ¼ cup of dried beans, or a tablespoon of peanut butter.

Junk Food: Less Is Best

At the tip-top of the food pyramid is a food group labeled "fats and sweets." This group actually includes all foods that are low

Trouble at the Table

Cross out the letters that appear twice vertically and horizontally. Then write the remaining letters in order (left to right, top row to bottom row) in the blank spaces below to reveal what troubles Tina.

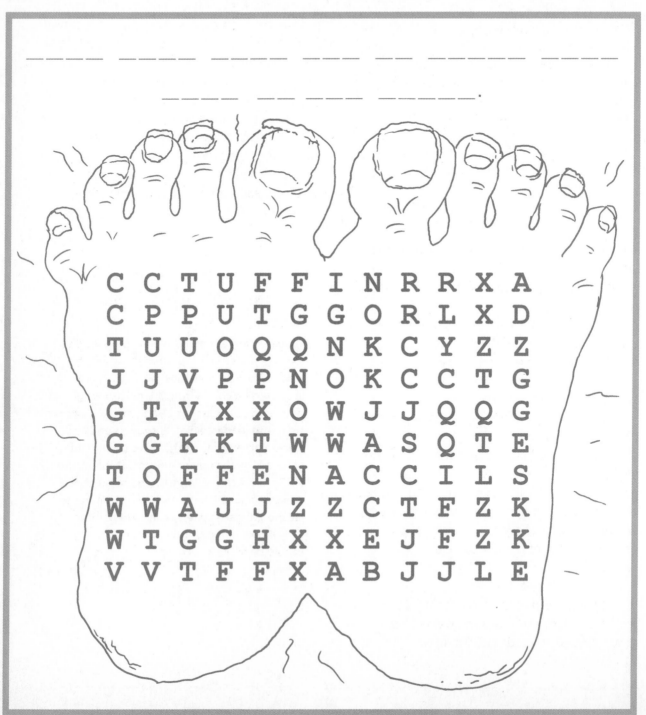

_____ ____ ____ ___ __ _____ ____

____ __ ___ _____ .

C	C	T	U	F	F	I	N	R	R	X	A
C	P	P	U	T	G	G	O	R	L	X	D
T	U	U	O	Q	Q	N	K	C	Y	Z	Z
J	J	V	P	P	N	O	K	C	C	T	G
G	T	V	X	X	O	W	J	J	Q	Q	G
G	G	K	K	T	W	W	A	S	Q	T	E
T	O	F	F	E	N	A	C	C	I	L	S
W	W	A	J	J	Z	C	T	F	Z	K	
W	T	G	G	H	X	X	E	J	F	Z	K
V	V	T	F	F	X	A	B	J	J	L	E

Chapter 21

Bizarre Breakfast

Squashed Gremlin Heads

These green pancake-heads are sticky, icky, and yummy!

▸ **Difficulty: Difficult** ▸ *Makes 12 pancakes*

2 cups white or whole-wheat flour
⅓ cup sugar
1 teaspoon baking powder
½ teaspoon baking soda
½ teaspoon salt
2 large eggs, slightly beaten
2¼ cups buttermilk (or whole milk)
1 tablespoon vegetable oil (for the batter)
Green food coloring

Vegetable oil (for the pan)
Whipped butter
Blueberries (2 berries per pancake)
Sliced strawberries (one slice per pancake)
Bananas, cut in half and then sliced in half lengthwise (one slice per pancake)
Raspberry syrup (about 1 ounce per pancake)

1. In a large bowl, combine the flour, sugar, baking powder, baking soda, and salt. Dump the eggs, milk, and oil into the flour mixture. Stir until the ingredients are all mixed together but still a little lumpy. Add a drop or two of food coloring and stir gently just until the batter turns green.
2. Pour ½ tablespoon of oil onto the griddle. Heat the griddle over medium heat until a drop of water sizzles when you flick it on the pan. Using a large spoon (or a cup), drop about 2 tablespoons of pancake batter onto the hot skillet. Cook until the edges turn brown and the batter bubbles up.
3. Flip over the pancakes and cook until the other side is browned. Repeat steps 4 and 5 until you've used up all the batter, adding more oil to the pan as needed.
4. Put one pancake on each plate and use the butter and fruit to make a gremlin face on each pancake.

CHEF'S SECRET:
Is It Holey Yet?
You can tell a pancake is ready to turn over when the bubbles in the batter start to pop and the edges are firm. Carefully slide the spatula all the way under the pancake, lift the spatula straight up about 6 inches, and then quickly flip the spatula upside down and let the pancake fall onto the griddle (cooked side up).

Serve with warmed blood (raspberry syrup warmed for 20 seconds in the microwave). If you don't have or don't like red blood, you can pass around some warmed brown bile (maple syrup).

Flies Floating in Bee Spit and Goatmeal

Rise and shine and suck down a bowl of mushy goatmeal (oatmeal) topped with flies (raisins) stuck in a glob of bee spit (honey) and swimming in cow juice (milk).

▶ *Difficulty: Medium*   ▶ *Serves 4*

1 cup water
1 cup milk
1 cup rolled oats (not instant)
Salt
4 tablespoons honey
4 tablespoons raisins
Milk (optional)

1. In a large saucepan, combine the water, milk, oats, and a dash of salt.
2. Cook over medium heat, stirring occasionally until the oatmeal begins to boil.
3. Reduce the heat to low and simmer for 2 to 3 minutes, stirring continuously until the oatmeal thickens and gets goopy.
4. Turn off the stove and remove the pan from the burner.
5. Pour the oatmeal into four cereal bowls.
6. Put 1 rounded tablespoon of honey in the middle of each bowl of oatmeal.
7. Sprinkle 1 rounded tablespoon of raisins on each glob of honey.

If you like creamier oatmeal, pour a little milk (¼ to ½ cup) into the bowl and stir it up before adding the honey and raisins.

FREAKY FOOD FACT:
Pass the Bee Spit, Pilgrim
Early European settlers brought honey bees to America more than 300 years ago. Not only did the pilgrims use honey (a.k.a. bee spit) in their food and drinks, they also used it as medicine and to make cement, furniture polish, and varnish.

WORDS to KNOW

breakfast to "break" means to end, and a "fast" is when you go for a while without eating or drinking anything—such as all night while you're sleeping—so put these two words together and you get "what you eat to put an end to the nightly fast"

CHEF'S SECRET:
Breakfast of Champions or Knuckleheads?
The best thing to eat for breakfast is:

A. Nothing
B. Donuts and soda pop
C. Cereal and chocolate milk
D. Ostrich-egg with boogies (green peppers), fungus (mushrooms), and mold (cheese); a slice of whole-grain toast; and a glass of orange juice

D. Duh! Your body needs a help-ing of every food group at every meal, including breakfast. Only knuckleheads skip breakfast (answer A) or load up on nothing but sugars (answer B). Cereal is good for you, but only if it's made with whole grains and is not too sugary.

Chunky Crud Cakes

These chunky apple-cinnamon muffins might look like baked bird doo-doo, but they sure are delicious!

▸ *Difficulty: Medium* ▸ *Makes 12 muffins*

1½ cups flour
1 teaspoon cinnamon
1 teaspoon baking power
½ teaspoon baking soda
½ teaspoon salt
2 eggs

⅔ cup brown sugar
1½ cups chunky applesauce
6 tablespoons butter, melted
½ cup chopped walnuts or pecans, or unsalted sunflower seeds, shelled (optional)

1. Preheat oven to 375 degrees. Spray the muffin tin with cook-ing oil (or use paper liners).
2. In a large bowl, combine the flour, cinnamon, baking pow-der, baking soda, and salt.
3. In another bowl, whisk together the eggs and brown sugar. Stir in the applesauce and melted butter (cooled slightly).
4. Dump the wet mixture into the dry mixture. Use a wooden spoon to gently stir (don't beat) until creamy. Slowly stir in the nuts and/or seeds (if you like them and aren't allergic to them). Use an ice-cream scoop to drop the batter into the muffin tin.
5. Bake for 20 minutes. Remove from the oven and let cool.

🐛◎ *Eat warm or cooled, with or without butter on top. Wash down the crud cakes with a glass of milk.*

Crusty Rusty Toast

This French toast, with its crusty (egg-dipped) and rust-colored (cinnamon) coating, looks like it came straight out of the junk yard. Add some oil (orange-maple syrup) and you're good to go gross.

▸ **Difficulty: Medium** ▸ **Makes 8 slices**

2 large eggs (or 3 medium eggs)
⅓ cup milk
1 teaspoon cinnamon
2 tablespoons butter (or cooking spray)

8 slices bread
¼ cup orange juice
½ cup maple syrup

1. Whisk the eggs, milk, and cinnamon together in a bowl.
2. Melt 1 tablespoon of butter on the griddle over medium heat, or lightly coat the griddle with cooking spray and heat to a medium temperature.
3. Dip the bread into the egg mixture to coat one side, turn it over to coat the other side, and place the bread on the heated griddle. Do one slice of bread at a time (you should be able to fit 3 to 4 slices on the griddle).
4. Cook until golden brown on the bottom (about 2 minutes). Flip over and cook until golden brown on the other side. Remove from the griddle and place on a warmed plate.
5. Repeat steps 3 and 4 until all the bread slices are cooked. (You may need to add the other 1 tablespoon of butter or more cooking spray to the griddle.)
6. To prepare the orange-maple syrup: mix the orange juice with the maple syrup and warm in the microwave on low for 30 seconds.

CHEF'S SECRET:
Do You Vant to Suck Some Varm Tree Blood?
To warm syrup for French toast, pancakes, or waffles, pour however much you think you'll need into a small pitcher (or measuring cup) and heat it in the microwave on low for 30 seconds. (Make sure the container is microwaveable.)

Chow down with a side of orange slices and a glass of milk. Napkins are optional—you can always just lick the syrup off your face.

Upchuckola

This concoction of dried upchuck (homemade granola) swimming in bile (smashed banana and brown-sugared milk) looks so close to the real thing it'll probably make your family gag. Nasty, yet tasty.

▸ **Difficulty:** *Medium*   ▸ *Serves 8*

½ cup honey
1 cup vegetable oil
3 cups rolled oats (not instant)
2 cups untoasted wheat germ
1 cup shredded coconut
1 cup dried milk
½ cup raisins
½ cup dried cranberries, blueberries, or cherries

¼ cup chopped walnuts
¼ cup slivered almonds
¼ cup shelled, unsalted sunflower seeds
Bananas, smashed
Brown sugar
Milk

1. Preheat oven to 350 degrees.
2. Spread the honey and oil in the bottom of a rectangular baking pan. Spread the oats and wheat germ over the wet mixture in the baking pan.
3. Bake 30 to 40 minutes, stirring every 5 minutes, until well toasted. Remove from oven and cool slightly (so you won't burn yourself).
4. Add the coconut, dried milk, raisins, dried fruit, nuts, and sunflower seeds to the pan and stir to mix everything all together.
5. Spoon the granola into serving bowls. Put about ½ cup of smashed banana on top of each bowl of granola.
6. In a creamer (small pitcher), stir the brown sugar into the milk until it is dissolved and the milk turns brownish. You'll need about 1 tablespoon of sugar and ½ cup of milk per bowl.

🐛🌀 *Pour the bile (brown-sugared milk) over the upchuck (granola). Store the unused granola in a sealed plastic container or bag.*

Poop in a Scoop

Bananas and peanut butter for breakfast!

▶ **Difficulty: Easy**   ▶ **Serves 1**

1 whole-wheat hot dog bun	1 tablespoon peanut butter
1 banana	¼ cup (handful) raisins

1. Toast the hot dog bun.
2. Peel the banana and place it in the hot dog bun.
3. Use a butter knife to spread peanut butter over the banana until it's completely covered.
4. Sprinkle the poop pellets (raisins) over the top.

Waffles Smothered in Pus and Scabs

Enjoy these nasty waffles smothered in pus (yogurt) and scabs (dried cranberries).

▶ **Difficulty: Easy**   ▶ **Makes 4 waffles**

4 frozen toaster waffles
1 (6-ounce) carton vanilla or custard yogurt
½ cup dried cranberries or cherries

1. Toast the waffles (in a toaster or toaster oven)
2. Drop a tablespoon of yogurt onto each waffle.
3. Sprinkle a handful of dried cranberries on top of the yogurt.

For added grossness, squeeze some Hershey squirts (chocolate syrup) over your creation.

A boy was frantically searching for a project he had made and wanted to take to school for show-and-tell. He suddenly remembered that he'd put it in a safe place the night before and dashed to the kitchen to retrieve it. He saw his sister sitting at the table eating a bowl of corn flakes. "Hey!" he said. "You found my scab collection!"

Bet you didn't know scabs were so chewy and yummy, did you? These pus-and-scab waffles are great with a glass of pee (apple juice).

Brain Scramble

These scrambled eggs are gray, gooey (melted cheese), and smothered with blood (ketchup).

▶ *Difficulty: Medium* ▶ *Serves 2*

4 eggs
¼ cup milk
¼ cup shredded jack cheese (or white cheddar)
1 drop blue food coloring
1 drop green food coloring
1 teaspoon salt
½ teaspoon pepper
2 tablespoons butter

1. In a large bowl, whisk together the eggs, milk, cheese, food coloring, salt, and pepper.
2. Melt the butter in a skillet over medium-low heat.
3. Pour the eggs into the heated skillet and cook until the eggs start to firm up. Then use a spatula to break up the eggs and turn them over. When the eggs are cooked all the way through (not runny), remove them from the pan and onto serving plates.

Enjoy this brain scramble with blood (ketchup or Tabasco sauce) squirted on top.

What do you get when you cross a pig with a centipede?

Bacon and legs!

Rolled Boogers and Snot

Now you can have nose crud in a breakfast pudding made of toasted oats (dried mucus), white raisins (boogers), and custard (snot).

▶ *Difficulty: Easy* ▶ *Serves 4*

1 cup plain yogurt (or vanilla or custard)
¾ cup prepared vanilla pudding (bought already made or made by your mom)
¼ cup white raisins
¾ cup rolled oats
2 tablespoons honey
3 bananas, peeled and smashed

PLAY IT SAFE:

Always use a long-handled cooking utensil to stir, turn over, or remove food in a pot or pan. Never cook with the small, short-handled forks and spoons you use to eat with. Cooking utensils have long handles for a reason—to prevent hot food and hot pots from burning you.

1. In a large bowl, stir together the yogurt, vanilla pudding, and raisins. Set aside.
2. Heat a dry skillet over medium heat. Spread the oats across the bottom of the skillet and toast for about 1 minute.
3. Drizzle honey over the oats and stir as you continue cooking the mixture over medium heat until the oats are crispy on the edges. Remove the pan from the burner.
4. Spoon about half the oats into the bottom of 4 small bowls (or ice-cream sundae dishes). Keep some of the oats for topping.
5. Spread half of the smashed banana over the oats in the bowls. Pour a layer of pudding mixture over the banana layer in each bowl, using about half the pudding.
6. Put another layer of oats, then another layer of bananas, and then another layer of pudding into each bowl. Sprinkle the tops with the rest of the toasted oats.

This breakfast pudding really does look like boogers and snot.

Moldy Mushroom Caps

The mold (blackberry jam and cream cheese) all over these mushroom caps (English muffins) make them messy to eat and disgusting to look at. They taste so good you'll be drooling the whole time you're making them.

▸ *Difficulty: Easy*   ▸ *Serves 2*

2 English muffins
Blackberry (or black raspberry) jam
Cream cheese
Sesame seeds

1. Toast both halves of each of the English muffins. Put one muffin (two halves) on each plate.
2. Spread a thin layer of jam on top of each muffin half and then over the sides. Drop a glob of cream cheese in the middle of each muffin half. Use a butter knife to shape the cream cheese into a mound that is higher in the center than at the edges.
3. Dab little blobs of jam on top of the cream cheese mounds.
4. Sprinkle some sesame seeds on top of each muffin half.

🌀 *This recipe is also grossly great using bagels instead of English muffins and apricot jam rather than blackberry jam.*

PLAY IT SAFE:

Never eat mushrooms you find outside, because some of them are poisonous. Only eat mushrooms you buy from the grocery store or the farmer's market.

Why do seagulls fly over the sea?

Because if they flew over the bay, they'd be bagels!

Barfo Breakfast Tacos

When you scramble up this concoction, your family will think you've barfed this stuff up. The joke's on them, because this mess of eggs, ground sausage, and cheddar cheese stuffed into a soft taco is excelente (excellent).

▶ *Difficulty: Medium*   ▶ *Makes 4 tacos*

¼ pound ground chorizo (Mexican sausage)
4 eggs
¼ cup milk
½ teaspoon salt
Pepper (pinch)

1 tablespoon butter
¼ cup shredded cheddar cheese
4 soft tacos (corn)
Salsa to taste (optional)
Sour cream to taste (optional)

1. Brown the sausage in a skillet on medium heat, making sure it is cooked all the way through. Put the cooked sausage on a plate covered with a paper towel, cover, and set aside.
2. In a bowl, whisk together the eggs, milk, salt, and pepper.
3. Melt the butter in a skillet over medium-low heat. Dump the egg mixture into the pan. Cook until the edges firm up and then use the spatula to break up the eggs and turn them over; you'll probably have to do this a few times. As soon as the eggs are cooked through and there is no more runny stuff, remove them from the pan.
4. Mix the scrambled eggs, the cooked sausage, and the cheese together in a large bowl.
5. Warm the tacos in a microwave for 30 to 60 seconds.
6. Spoon the egg-sausage-and-cheese mixture into each taco. Add a dollop each of blood (salsa) and guts (sour cream).

If you don't like chorizo or can't find it in the grocery store, you can use any kind of sausage you like—or you can use thin strips of ham. And remember, you can put anything in an egg scramble: diced green pepper, sliced mushrooms, chopped jalapeño (spicy pepper), bat's wings, frog's legs—you name it!

Can You Say Flatulence?

There must be fifty ways to say pppfffft! See if you can figure out these sixteen terms for the stinky puffs of air that lift you off your seat after you eat a huge plate of beans.

Across

1. Morning _____ (after lightning comes _____).
5. An ornery kid who smells bad.
7. Drop the _____ (another word for missile).
9. To tap a golf ball onto the green.
12. Break _____ (air that moves).
14. Two words that rhyme with one another and the naughty word for butt.
16. Trouser _____ (a type of horn in a brass band).

Down

1. The sound a horn makes.
2. When you pull the covers over your head and then let one rip.
3. Float an _____ (sky) _____ (a bread roll that's good with gravy).
4. Brown tracks left in your underwear.
6. Three words (3 letters, 3 letters, and 6 letters) that mean the same as "slice the cheddar."
8. _____ bongos (the cheeks you sit on).
10. Sphincter _____ (what the seven dwarfs did when they worked).
11. Rump _____ (rhymes with zipper).
13. Rhymes with heart.
15. _____ but deadly.

Chapter 22

What's for Lunch?

Grilled Sneeze Sandwich

To totally gross out your parents, take the lid off this melted white cheese sandwich topped with sautéed green bell pepper and onion, then pretend to sneeze on it, put the lid back on, and take a big bite.

▸ *Difficulty: Medium*   ▸ *Makes 2 sandwiches*

2 teaspoons olive (or canola) oil
¼ cup green bell pepper, diced
¼ cup onion, diced

4 slices bread
Butter (or margarine)
4 slices jack cheese

1. Heat the oil in a sauté pan (or small, shallow skillet) over medium heat for about 1 minute. Sauté the green pepper and onion in the pan, stirring constantly, until the onion is translucent (you can see through it). Remove the cooked veggies from the pan and set aside.
2. Butter two slices of bread on one side. Put each slice, butter side down, on the griddle.
3. Lay a slice of cheese on top of each slice of bread.
4. Spread about 1 tablespoon of the sautéed peppers and onions over each slice of cheese.
5. Butter one side of two slices of bread. Put each slice, butter side up, on top of the sandwich.
6. Cook the sandwiches over medium heat until the bottom sides are golden brown. Flip over each sandwich and cook the other sides until golden brown. Turn off the skillet and remove the sandwiches from the griddle immediately.

CHEF'S SECRET:
No More Onion Tears
To keep your eyes from watering when you cut an onion, first peel the onion under cold water, chew gum while slicing the orb, and don't cut near the root. The cold water will reduce the amount of fumes rising from the onion, which are strongest near the root. Chewing gum will reduce the amount of tears produced by your tear ducts.

🌀 For extra grossness, you can mix in some blood (ketchup) with your boogers and snot (sautéed peppers and onions) and spread the mixture over the cheese before adding the top slice of bread and grilling the sandwich. You can also substitute white cheddar or Swiss cheese for jack cheese.

Pickled Hambones

When cut into thick slices, these ham, cheese, and pickle rollups look like ham bones with gangrened marrow in the center—and they taste great.

▸ *Difficulty: Easy* ▸ *Serves 4*

2 (10-inch) flour tortillas
Honey mustard
4 ounces cream cheese, softened
6 ounces thinly sliced ham
6 ounces American cheese, sliced
Pickles, dill or sweet (small)
Ketchup (optional)

1. Spread a thin layer of honey mustard on one side of each tortilla.
2. Spread a layer of cream cheese on each tortilla.
3. Place a layer of ham slices on each tortilla.
4. Place a layer of American cheese slices on each tortilla.
5. Place a row of pickles on one edge of each tortilla.
6. Roll the tortilla into a log and secure with toothpicks.
7. Using a blunt knife, cut the rollup into 1-inch slices.

🌀 *These pickled hambones are extra gross (and yummy) dipped in blood (ketchup)! If you don't like pickles in your rollup, try celery sticks or asparagus spears instead—or just stick with ham and cheese. After all, you're the chef.*

CHEF'S SECRET:
Which of these foods should be kept in a sealed, insulated container to prevent sickening bacteria from forming on it?
A. Boiled egg
B. Chicken noodle soup
C. Ham sandwich
D. Macaroni and cheese

All of them! Boiled eggs and ham sandwiches should be kept cool. Chicken noodle soup and macaroni and cheese should be kept either hot (in a thermos) or chilled (in a sealed container until it's time to reheat them).

What is red and green and goes 300 miles an hour?

A frog in a blender!

Chopped Fingers

Want to enjoy a real fright fest? Serve these severed fingers (rolled turkey sandwiches) dipped in blood (ketchup) to your grandparents!

▸ *Difficulty: Easy*   ▸ *Makes 5 sandwiches*

5 slices thin-sliced bread
Butter (or margarine), soft or whipped
6 ounces sliced turkey (lunchmeat)

Cream cheese, softened
1 small red bell pepper
Ketchup

1. With a rolling pin, gently flatten the bread slices. (Thin slices of lightweight white bread work best for this recipe.)
2. Carefully spread a very thin layer of soft butter or margarine on each slice of bread.
3. Place a slice of turkey on each slice of bread.
4. Roll up the sandwiches. If the seam won't stay together, spread a small amount of butter or soft cream cheese on the seam to make it stick together. Turn over each sandwich so that the seam is on the bottom.
5. Ask your adult helper to cut the red pepper into five pieces shaped like long finger nails, rounded on the top and squared on the bottom.
6. Spread a dab of cream cheese on the back of each red pepper fingernail (the side that's not shiny). Gently press the fingernail onto one end of each sandwich.
7. Place the sandwiches on a plate in the shape of a hand, with the fingers spread apart at the tips (fingernail sides) and touching at the other end. Squeeze (or pour) a pool of blood (ketchup) on the plate where the severed fingers meet (for dipping) and on the bottom edges of the fingers.

CHEF'S SECRET:
Deli Math Quiz
If you wanted to make ten chopped finger sandwiches, how much lunchmeat in pounds would you need?
A. ½ pound
B. ¾ pound
C. 1 pound

B. ¾ pound (12 ounces)

🐛 You can make these severed sandwiches using any kind of lunchmeat, or you can use peanut butter instead of lunchmeat and strawberry or raspberry jam instead of ketchup. However you stuff them, these severed fingers are ghoulishly delicious.

Race to the Latrine

All the kids have a great time at Camp Wannagohomenow, except for when Chef Tootinscoot makes his infamous "leftover surprise meatloaf sandwich" for lunch. Then, as soon as the last chewy bite goes down, even the skunk has to hold his nose as the not-so-happy-campers make a mad dash to the poo-poo palace. Try to get from the mess hall to the outhouse before the rest of the campers do.

Toe Jam Griddle

Imagine scraping the gunk out from between your toes, making a sandwich out of it, and then dipping the toe jam sandwich in eggs and frying it on a griddle. It would look a lot like this peanut butter and jelly French toast. Of course, it wouldn't taste quite the same—thank goodness!

▶ **Difficulty: Medium** ▶ **Makes 8 slices**

4 tablespoons peanut butter
8 slices bread
4 tablespoons apricot jam (or jelly)
2 large eggs (or 3 medium eggs)
⅓ cup milk

2 tablespoons butter (or cooking spray)
4 teaspoons confectioners' sugar
Maple syrup (optional)

1. Spread peanut butter on four slices of bread. Spread jam on the other four slices of bread. Put each peanut butter slice on top of a jam slice to make four PB&J sandwiches.
2. Whisk the eggs and milk together in a large bowl.
3. Melt 1 tablespoon of butter on the griddle over medium heat, or lightly coat the griddle with cooking spray and heat to a medium temperature. Dip one sandwich into the egg mixture to coat one side, turn it over to coat the other side, and place the sandwich on the heated griddle.
4. Cook until golden brown on the bottom (about 2 minutes). Flip over and cook until golden brown on the other side. Remove from the griddle and place on a warmed plate.
5. Repeat steps 6 and 7 until all the sandwiches are cooked. (You may need to add the other 1 tablespoon of butter or more cooking spray to the griddle.) Sprinkle confectioners' sugar on top of each slice of French toast (about ½ teaspoon per slice).

FREAKY FOOD FACT:

A peanut is a:
A. Seed
B. Legume
C. Bean
D. Nut

D. Believe it or not, peanuts are not nuts. They're seeds from a leguminous shrub (not a tree), and the seeds from the peanut shrub are called legumes, which is another word for beans. Maybe that's why eating a bunch of peanuts can turn you into a fart factory!

Serve immediately, while the toast is still warm, with or without maple syrup.

Boiled Octopus

These juicy hot dogs have eight legs, just like slimy octopuses. They're delicious served open-faced on a bed of seaweed (pickle relish), creamy fish caca (mustard), and shark's blood (ketchup).

▶ *Difficulty: Medium* ▶ *Serves 4*

4 hot dogs
4 hot dog buns
4 teaspoons sweet relish (optional)

Ketchup (optional)
Mustard (optional)

1. Starting at about 1 inch from the end of a hot dog, cut a slit down the length of the hot dog. Turn the hot dog and make another slit about ½ inch to the left or right of the first slit. Keep making slits until the hot dog has eight "legs." Do the same thing for all four hot dogs. (Remember to leave a 1-inch "head" on one end of each hot dog.)
2. Spread open the hot dog buns and place them on plates.
3. Spread each bun with your favorite condiments: pickled seaweed (pickle relish), shark blood (ketchup), or creamy fish caca (mustard).
4. Fill a saucepan about three-quarters of the way with cool water. Bring to a boil over medium-high heat.
5. Reduce the heat to simmer. Use the tongs to carefully place the hot dogs in the boiling water. Cover and cook 3 to 5 minutes. (While the hot dogs are cooking, wash the tongs or grab clean ones.)
6. Remove each hot dog from the pot, gently grabbing it by the 1-inch "head" with the tongs, and place the hot dogs on a plate to cool for a minute or two. Arrange each octopus dog so that the "legs" spread out over the bun like an octopus, with the head sticking up in the center.

PLAY IT SAFE:

Always turn off the burner before removing food from a pot or pan, and always turn off the oven before removing a pan or dish from the oven.

You'll need a fork and a blunt knife to eat your hot dogs open-faced (with the bun opened up), and it's more gross and fun that way. If you want though, you can just stuff the legs into the bun, close the bun, and gobble it up.

Zit-Face Pizza

Every kid loves pizza! It's even better when you serve your friends these mini pizzas that look like pimply faces with oozing pus and greenheads just waiting to be popped!

▶ **Difficulty: Easy**   ▶ **Serves 4**

4 English muffins, split
1 (8-ounce) jar (or can) pizza or spaghetti sauce
1 cup shredded mozzarella cheese
Black olives, sliced
1 (8-ounce) can pineapple chunks
1 red bell pepper, cut in strips
¼ cup frozen peas

1. Lightly toast the muffins in a toaster (or oven toaster).
2. Preheat oven to 400 degrees.
3. Spread 1 rounded tablespoon of pizza sauce on each muffin half. Sprinkle each muffin with mozzarella cheese.
4. To make the eyes on the pizza face, place 2 olive slices near the top of each muffin half. To make the nose, place a pineapple chunk in the center of each muffin half. To make the mouth, place a slice of red bell pepper at the bottom of each muffin half. (You can slice the pepper with a blunt knife yourself or ask your adult helper to do it for you with a sharp knife.)
5. Place a few green peas on the cheeks of each muffin face.
6. Place the muffins on a cookie sheet and bake 5 to 6 minutes, until the cheese melts. Remove muffins from cookie sheet immediately.

What do you get when you eat a prune pizza?

Pizzarrhea!

FREAKY FOOD FACT:
Pizza My Heartland
Americans eat 100 acres of pizza a day!

If you like meat on your pizza, you can substitute pepperoni, folded in half and then folded in half again to form a triangle, for the pineapple chunk.

Cheesy Moose Veins

Tickle your funny bone with this macaroni and cheese made with moose veins (elbow macaroni dyed blue).

▸ **Difficulty:** *Hard* ▸ *Serves 4*

3 cups cheddar cheese, grated
2 drops blue food coloring
8 ounces elbow macaroni
2 tablespoons vegetable oil
2 tablespoons flour

3 cups milk
1 teaspoon salt
¼ teaspoon black pepper
Cooking oil spray
½ cup unseasoned bread crumbs

1. Grate the cheese. Divide the grated cheese into two portions—2 cups and 1 cup—and set aside.
2. Preheat oven to 350 degrees.
3. Fill a 2-quart saucepan three-quarters of the way with cool water (about 6 cups). Add the blue food coloring. Bring to a boil over medium-high heat.
4. Reduce the heat to medium and cook the macaroni in the boiling blue water until tender, about 10 minutes, stirring occasionally. Remove from heat, drain, and set aside to cool.
5. In a saucepan over moderate heat, whisk together the oil and flour. Cook for 5 minutes, stirring constantly. Gradually whisk in the milk. Reduce the heat to low. Add salt and pepper. Cook 1 to 2 minutes, stirring constantly. Fold in 2 cups of the cheese. Remove the pot from the heat
7. Lightly coat a 2-quart baking dish with cooking spray (or butter). Pour the cooked macaroni and the cheese sauce into the baking dish, and mix together with a wooden spoon.
8. Spread the remaining 1 cup of grated cheese and the bread crumbs over the macaroni. Bake about 30 minutes, until the casserole is bubbly and a golden crust forms on top.

CHEF'S SECRET:
No More Boil Overs
To help prevent pasta, rice, or potatoes from boiling over:
1. Butter or oil the rim of the pot before adding water.
2. Fill the pot no more than three-quarters of the way full.
3. Bring it to a boil slowly (never with the burner on full blast) and watch your pot.

For an added dose of gross and flavor, squirt some blood (ketchup) on top of your heaping helping of cheesy, chopped moose veins.

Fish-Eye Tacos

Here's an idea: Put two of these easy-to-make tuna eye-balls in a taco shell, hand the taco to somebody you love to gross out, and say, "Here's lookin' at you, tuna breath!"

▶ *Difficulty: Easy* ▶ *Makes 8 tacos*

2 (6-ounce) cans tuna
1 large mild green chili pepper or bell pepper, chopped (optional)
2 tablespoons onion, chopped
½ cup mayonnaise
2 cups lettuce, shredded
2 medium tomatoes, diced

2 cups jack or cheddar cheese, grated
8 hard taco shells
¼ cup sour cream
1 (2¼-ounce) can black olives, pitted and sliced

1. Open the cans of tuna, drain the water or oil completely, and spoon the chunks or flakes of tuna into a large bowl.
2. Chop the chili pepper and the onion (or ask your adult helper to do it) and put them in the bowl with the tuna.
3. Add the mayonnaise and use a wooden spoon to blend it in with the tuna and chopped onion and chili pepper.
4. Shred the lettuce. Chop the tomatoes. Grate the cheese. (Or ask your adult helper to do these things for you.) Use two wooden spoons to mix the lettuce, tomatoes, and cheese together in a bowl.
5. Use an ice-cream scoop to place two tuna balls in each taco shell. Place the tacos on a plate.
6. Put a dollop (about 1 teaspoon) of sour cream on each tuna ball, and then put an olive slice on the sour cream to complete each eyeball.

CHEF'S SECRET:
Got Milk?
The best way to neutralize capsaicin, the stuff in chili peppers that makes your mouth burn, is with casein, a protein found in milk. So, if a spicy pepper sets your tongue on fire, drink a cool glass of cow juice.

If you don't like chili peppers, substitute 1½ tablespoons of pickle relish (sweet) or 1½ tablespoons of chopped celery (salty). Ole!

Bloody Maggot Soup

Ah, there's nothing like a warm bowl of blood swimming with maggots (tomato-rice soup) on a cold winter's day. Schlurp!

▶ Difficulty: Hard ▶ Serves 6

1¼ cups cooked white rice
⅓ cup onion, diced
1 clove garlic, minced
1½ tablespoons butter
3 tablespoons flour
1 (28-ounce) can tomatoes, diced, in juice

2 cups chicken or vegetable stock (broth)
½ cup orange juice
¼ teaspoon salt
⅛ teaspoon sugar
⅛ teaspoon ground paprika or cayenne pepper

1. Prepare the white rice according to the directions on the package. Set aside.
2. Dice the onion and mince the garlic (or ask your adult helper to do it). In a large (3-quart) saucepan or soup pot, melt the butter in a skillet over medium heat. Add onions and garlic, and cook until tender but not browned.
3. Stir the flour into the pot and cook for 2 minutes.
4. Stir in the tomatoes, broth, and orange juice. Bring to a boil, and then reduce the heat to low and simmer for 15 minutes, stirring every 4 to 6 minutes.
5. Remove from heat and stir in the salt, sugar, paprika, and ½ cup rice.
6. Puree the soup in a blender or food processor.
7. Pour the soup back into the pot. Stir in the remaining rice and cook over medium-low heat for 5 to 10 minutes.

WORDS to KNOW

puree to mix and mash food until it is the consistency of baby food

The frog motioned the waiter to his table in the restaurant and asked, "Why isn't there a fly in my soup?"

🐌 For an extra crunch of gross, toss a handful of dried bones (croutons) on top of each steaming bowl of this bloody maggot soup.

Pick 'Em and Dip 'Em

Here's a chance to mix and match your favorite finger foods and then pair them up with your favorite dip: slimy snot (honey mustard), chunky monkey spit (sweet and sour sauce), horsey squirts (barbecue sauce), bloody nose blow (salsa), or pigeon poop (ranch dressing).

▶ *Difficulty: Easy*   ▶ *Serves 1*

1 cup fresh vegetables (sliced or bite-sized chunks of two or three veggies of your choice: carrots, celery, broccoli, jicama, sugar peas, bell peppers, cherry tomatoes, cucumber, pickles, olives, garbanzo beans, or soybeans)
1 or 2 slices of lunchmeat (turkey, ham, bologna, roast beef, chicken)
1 or 2 slices of cheese (American, Swiss, cheddar, jack)
3 or 4 crackers, pretzels, or other crunchy snack
4 tablespoons dipping sauce (any kind)

1. Wash and dry the veggies. Cut them into strips or chunks, if you want. Put them on a plate.
2. Put the lunchmeat and cheese slices on the plate. If you want to eat the lunchmeat and cheese on crackers, cut each slice into four pieces.
3. Put the crackers, pretzels, chips, or bread slices on the plate.
4. Put the dip in a small bowl or on the side of the plate.

PLAY IT SAFE:

Always wash fresh produce (fruits, vegetables, beans, and legumes) thoroughly with cool water before eating them raw or cooking them.

FREAKY FOOD FACT:

Which of these vegetables is actually a fruit?
A. Avocado
B. Eggplant
C. Olive
D. Tomato

They're all fruits!

When your friends come over for a sleepover or birthday party, you can make a whole platter full of a whole bunch of different finger foods and all five of these dips!

Flat Worm and Seaweed Soup

This chicken noodle soup will help stifle your sniffles when you've got a cold. Of course, you can enjoy the flat worms (egg noodles) slithering down your gullet anytime.

▸ **Difficulty: Hard** ▸ **Serves 4 to 6**

1 cup fresh baby spinach
2 tablespoons olive oil
1 clove garlic, minced
2 cups carrots, chopped
2 cups celery, chopped
½ cup green onions, chopped
1 teaspoon dried tarragon

1 teaspoon salt
1 teaspoon pepper
2 pounds chicken drumsticks or thighs
6 cups low-sodium chicken broth
8 ounces wide egg noodles (half of a 1-pound package)

> **CHEF'S SECRET:**
> To Sop Up Soup Grease
> Place a leaf of lettuce on top of soup while it's cooking. The lettuce will absorb grease that rises to the top. Remove the grease-soaked lettuce and discard it.

1. Wash the spinach well. Remove the stems. Set aside.
2. In a large soup pot, heat the olive oil over medium-low heat. Add the minced garlic and then the carrots, celery, and onion. Cook until the vegetables are soft.
3. Stir in the tarragon, salt, and pepper. Add the chicken and broth. Increase the heat to medium high and bring to a boil.
4. Reduce heat to low, cover, and simmer for 30 minutes. Turn off the burner.
5. Remove the chicken from the pot and cool on a platter for 10 minutes. Pull the chicken from the bone and skin with a fork. Cut the chicken into pieces of about the same size (1-inch thick). Throw away the bones and skin.
6. Return the soup to a boil. Add the egg noodles, reduce the heat to medium, and cook for 6 minutes. Add the chicken pieces to the soup and cook for 2 minutes. Add the spinach and cook until the spinach wilts, 2 to 3 minutes.

Ladle into bowls while your worms are still hot. Sprinkle with shredded Parmesan cheese. If you like a thinner soup, add more (1 or 2 cups) canned broth or water in step 3.

Spit-Wad Sandwiches

These peanut butter and spit-wad (mini marshmallow) sandwiches are easy to make and to pack in your school lunch.

▶ **Difficult: Easy**   ▶ **Makes 1 sandwich**

2 slices bread (any kind)
2 tablespoons peanut butter
1 handful mini marshmallows

1. Spread each slice of bread with peanut butter.
2. Rip the marshmallows in two and stick them all over the peanut butter on one slice of bread.
3. Put the two slices of bread together, with the peanut butter sides facing one another.

Your friends will love these too. And they'll give you and your pals plenty of energy to have a real spit-wad fight!

What do spiders like to order at a fast-food restaurant?

Burgers and flies!

PLAY IT SAFE:

Never pound or tap on a glass jar with a knife or other object to try to loosen a stubborn lid, and don't bang the jar on the counter or anything else. If you're having trouble opening the lid on a glass jar or bottle, try running it under cold water, then dry it off completely and try again. If that doesn't work, ask an adult to open it for you.

Fart Fuel

Gas up with these lip-smacking, finger-licking beans and weenies! You'll have energy—and air—to spare.

▶ *Difficulty: Easy* ▶ *Serves 4 to 6*

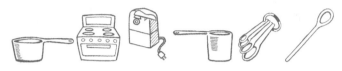

6 ounces mini bratwursts
2 (16-ounce) cans plain baked beans
1 tablespoon Worcestershire sauce
¼ cup brown sugar
2 tablespoons barbeque sauce (or prepared chili sauce)
1 tablespoon teriyaki sauce

1. Put the mini bratwursts in a separate saucepan and add water to completely cover the bratwursts. Cover and cook over medium heat for 8 to 10 minutes.
2. Remove the bratwursts from the heat. Drain the liquid from the meat and set aside.
3. Open the can of beans and empty into a saucepan.
4. Stir the Worcestershire sauce, brown sugar, barbecue sauce, and teriyaki sauce in with the beans. Cook over low heat for 5 minutes, stirring occasionally.
5. Add the cooked bratwursts to the beans. Cook another 5 minutes or until the mixture is completely heated through, stirring occasionally.

A bowl or two of these go down nice and easy. Then, just sit back and let the butt bongos begin!

CHEF'S SECRET:
Defuse a Stink Bomb
To remove gas-producing sugars from dried beans:
1. Soak beans overnight in cool water.
2. Rinse beans several times before cooking.
3. Never cook beans in the same water you soaked them in.

What can you make from baked beans and onions?

Tear gas!

Barf-A-Rhyme

Sometimes when you eat something totally gross—like rotten eggs or pickled Brussels sprouts—your stomach says, "No way, Jose!" and spews it right back out.

Write the rhyming words that mean the same thing as "toss your cookies."

scarf   _ _ _ _ _

comet   _ _ _ _ _ _

twirl   _ _ _ _ _

snow   _ _ _ _ _

woodchuck   _ _ _ _ _ _ _ _ _

sleeve   _ _ _ _ _ _

duke   _ _ _ _

shelf   _ _ _ _ _

use hunch (2 words)   _ _ _ _ _   _ _ _ _ _

fetch   _ _ _ _ _ _

chin up (2 words)   _ _ _ _ _ _   _ _

hesitate   _ _ _ _ _ _ _ _ _ _

Chapter 23

Wacky Snacks

Bugs on a Weed

When you bite into a stalk of crunchy celery stuffed with creamy peanut butter and chewy raisins, just close your eyes and think of shriveled beetles crawling up a sticky milkweed. Creepy crawly yummy!

▸ **Difficulty: Easy**   ▸ **Serves** 2

4 stalks celery
4 teaspoons creamy peanut butter
4 teaspoons raisins

1. Cut the leafy part and the root part off of the celery. Wash the celery and dry it with a paper towel. Cut each celery stalk in half. Put 4 pieces on each plate.
2. Fill the indented ridge on each piece of celery with peanut butter.
3. Stick the raisins in the peanut butter.

For some variety, you can substitute cream cheese or another soft cheese for the peanut butter and chocolate chips or dried cranberries for the raisins.

Oozing Pimples

The puss (cream cheese) will ooze into your mouth when you bite into these yummy pimples (cherry tomatoes).

▸ **Difficulty: Easy** ▸ **Serves 1**

6 to 8 cherry tomatoes (or 2 small round tomatoes)
1 tablespoon soft cream cheese (plain or flavored)

1. Choose the biggest cherry tomatoes you can find. Rinse the tomatoes and pat them dry with a paper towel.
2. Use the end of a vegetable peeler (or a small paring knife) to core each tomato.
3. Stuff each tomato with the cream cheese. Put all the stuffed tomatoes on a plate.

Lizard Eyes

Now you won't have to go to New Zealand to enjoy gecko eyes (crackers topped with cream cheese and kiwi), mate!

▸ **Difficulty: Easy** ▸ **Serves 2**

4 tablespoons cream cheese
8 round butter crackers (such as Ritz)
2 fresh kiwis

1. Spread a thin layer of cream cheese on each cracker.
2. Peel the kiwi and cut it into ½-inch slices.
3. Cover each cracker with a kiwi slice.

Before taking a bite, give the pimple a gentle squeeze to "pop" it!

WORDS to KNOW

core the center of a vegetable or fruit (such as an apple); to remove some of the inside of a fruit or vegetable, leaving the outer skin and enough flesh for the fruit to maintain its shape

Who likes gross things better: the daughter of a mortician or the son of a supermarket owner?

The son—he's a little grocer!

When your friends see you making these snacks, they'll be licking their chops just like a lizard!

Frozen Walrus Tusks

These frozen, chocolate-covered bananas might look like walrus tusks, but they're absolutely dee-lish!

▶ **Difficulty:** *Medium*   ▶ **Serves 4**

4 ripe bananas
8 Popsicle or candy apple sticks
Waxed paper
3 ounces chocolate chips

1. Peel the bananas and cut each in half.
2. Shove a Popsicle stick or something that will work like a handle into the cut end of each banana half.
3. Cover a freezerproof plate with waxed paper.
4. Put 3 ounces (half a 6-ounce bag) of chocolate chips in a small, deep bowl. Melt the chocolate in the microwave, following the directions for your microwave.
5. Dip each banana into the melted chocolate, leaving it in and twirling it around enough to completely coat the fruit. Place the bananas on the plate.
6. Put the plate in the freezer for an hour or two. Remove from the freezer when you're ready for your snack.

Frozen walrus tusks are a great snack for a summertime sleepover with your friends. For variety, you can roll these chocolate-covered bananas in something crunchy, like chopped nuts, Grape-Nuts cereal, crumbled Butterfinger candy bars, or toasted rice, before freezing them.

What did the right eye say to the left eye?

Between us, something smells!

PLAY IT SAFE:

Always use glass and other microwave-safe containers in microwave ovens. Never use plastic containers, which can melt, or metal containers, which can get too hot and cause sparks. If you're using a piece of pottery, such as a clay bowl, make sure that the bottom is stamped "made for microwave use." Some pottery and pottery glazes contain trace amounts of metals, which can be hazardous when heated in a microwave oven.

Putrefied Eyeballs

You'll say "Yuk!" before and "Yum!" after you bite into a squishy eyeball (peeled grape with a blueberry pupil) floating in slime (Jell-O) and topped with flotsam (whipped cream).

▶ *Difficulty: Easy* ▶ *Serves 4*

2 cups water
1 (3-ounce) package Jell-O, any flavor (suggest Berry Blue or Strawberry-Kiwi)
20 large grapes
20 blueberries
4 tablespoons whipped cream (optional)

1. Boil 1 cup of water. While the water is boiling, dump the Jello-O powder into a plastic or heat-resistant glass bowl.
2. Pour the boiling water over the Jello-O powder. Stir until the granules are dissolved. Slowly stir in 1 cup of cold water. Put the bowl of Jell-O in the refrigerator to cool for 10 minutes.
3. While the Jell-O is cooling, wash the grapes and blueberries.
4. Peel the grapes. You should be able to do this with your fingers. With the end of a vegetable peeler, cut a small divot (about ¼ inch wide and deep) in one of the grapes. (Instead of using a vegetable peeler, you can use the tip of a paring knife to cut a small × in the grape.) Stick a blueberry into the slit. Repeat until all the eyeballs (grapes) have pupils (blueberries).
5. When the Jell-O is semi-firm (it jiggles a lot but doesn't splash when you shake it), remove it from the refrigerator. Plop the eyeballs into the gelatin. Return the bowl to the refrigerator until the Jell-O sets completely, about 2 to 3 hours.

FREAKY FOOD FACT:
Hoof in Mouth?
One of the ingredients in gelatin is ground-up horse cartilage, which helps make the gelatin "gel." Cartilage is flexible bone tissue, like the stuff in your ears and nose. Horse hooves aren't made of cartilage. They're made of keratin, which is the same stuff your fingernails and toenails are made of.

🐚🌀 *These slimy eyeballs look the most putrid floating in blue, pink, or green gelatin—and taste best when topped with a poof of whipped cream. To pucker you up, try Jell-O Ex-Treme Green Apple flavor.*

For a tangy, tasty treat, dip your giant grubs in chilled phlegm (ranch dressing) rather than warmed blood (marinara).

Chicken-Fried Giant Grubs

Chewy guts will ooze over your teeth when you munch these baked grubs (breaded cheese sticks) dipped in warm blood (marinara).

▶ *Difficulty: Medium*   ▶ *Serves 4*

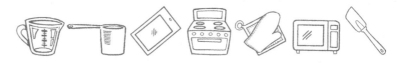

Cooking oil spray
1 egg
¼ cup milk
1 cup Italian-style breadcrumbs
8 sticks string cheese (or 1-ounce strips of mozzarella)
1 cup prepared spaghetti or pizza sauce, warmed in microwave

1. Spread a sheet of aluminum foil on a cookie sheet. Spray the foil lightly with vegetable oil (such as canola).
2. Break the egg into a large bowl and whisk for 30 seconds. Add the milk and whisk until the egg is broken up (but not frothy). Dip a cheese stick into the egg mixture and then into the breadcrumbs, coating completely. (You might need to dip it twice to thoroughly cover the cheese stick in egg and breadcrumbs.) Place the breaded cheese stick onto the cookie sheet. Repeat until all the cheese sticks are coated with crumbs and arranged on the sheet so they don't touch one another.
4. Let the cheese sticks set for 10 to 20 minutes. While the cheese sticks are setting, preheat oven to 400 degrees.
5. Bake in the oven 8 to 10 minutes, until the crumb coating is crunchy and the cheese is soft (the sticks will squish down with a spatula).
6. Remove the cheese sticks from the oven. Use a spatula to remove the cheese sticks from the cookie sheet and place them on a plate. Serve hot with warm marinara (pizza or spaghetti) sauce.

Eewwww! Who Eats This Stuff?

Here's stomach-churning proof that one person's dream is another person's nightmare. Check out these freaky foods from around the world. On the line next to the food item, write the name of the place where you guess it is a disgustingly favorite munchie.

Baked rooster combs _____

Beef blood pudding _____

Bird's nest soup _____

Blubber (raw whale fat) _____

Boiled fish eyes_____

Broiled beetle grubs _____

Deep-fried monkey toes _____

Fried squirrel brain_____

Raw turtle eggs _____

Roasted bat _____

Salted, sun-dried grasshoppers _____

Sautéed camel's feet _____

Spoiled yak milk _____

Warm cow urine _____

White ant pie _____

United States (Southern)

Tibet

The Philippines

The Arctic

Tanzania

Samoa

Norway

Nicaragua

Mexico

Kenya

Japan

Italy

Indonesia

France

China

Hot Fresh Hippo Turd

This peanut-butter bread slathered with squished bananas smears all over your lips like globs of guts oozing over a chunk of hippo dung. Deliciously grotesque!

▶ **Difficulty: Hard**   ▶ **Makes 1 loaf**

Cooking oil spray	½ cup peanut butter
2 cups flour	⅓ cup sugar (or honey)
4 teaspoons baking powder	1½ cup milk (or soymilk)
1 teaspoon salt	Fresh bananas

1. Preheat oven to 375 degrees.
2. Grease an 8×4×3-inch loaf pan with the cooking oil spray.
3. In a large bowl, combine the flour, baking powder, and salt.
4. In a separate bowl, mix together the peanut butter, sugar, and milk. Stir until mixed thoroughly and creamy. Add the peanut-butter mix to the flour mix. Stir well, until the wet and dry ingredients are all blended together and icky-sticky-gooey. Dump the batter into the pan, scraping the sides of the bowl to get all the goop. Spread the batter evenly in the pan.
6. Bake in the oven for 45 to 50 minutes, until the top of the bread is a crusty golden brown. Cool for about 10 minutes.
7. While the bread is cooling, peel a banana. In a small bowl smash the peeled banana with a fork or potato masher.
8. When the bread is cool enough to touch, slide the bread out of the pan and onto a cutting board. (Now it really looks like a big old hippo turd!)
9. Use a sharp, serrated knife to carefully slice off a chunk of bread (or ask an adult to do it for you). Spread the squished banana on the slab of hippo turd.

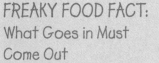

FREAKY FOOD FACT:
What Goes in Must Come Out

The average person eats three pounds of food a day. By the time you reach age seventy, that amounts to thirty-three tons of food—which comes out the other end to make a pile of poop the size of a car.

🐌🐌 *Eat warm or at room temperature. To mix it up, slather with butter, margarine, or cream cheese and your favorite jam instead of bananas. Cover the leftover bread loaf snugly with plastic wrap to keep it fresh.*

Funky Crunchy Skunk Bones

Toss some stinky (garlic and onion) croutons with grease (butter) and dried blood (paprika), toast them in the oven, and voila! Tasty bits of bones to die for!

▸ *Difficulty: Medium*   ▸ *Serves 4*

4 to 6 ounces garlic-and-onion croutons
½ cup (1 stick) butter
2 tablespoons sesame seeds
2 teaspoons celery salt
1 teaspoon paprika

1. Preheat oven to 275 degrees.
2. Pour the croutons into a large bowl.
3. In a smaller bowl, melt the butter in the microwave.
4. Combine the sesame seeds, salt, and paprika with the butter.
5. Pour the butter mixture over the croutons. Toss lightly with two wooden spoons until all the croutons are coated.
6. Spread the croutons out on a cookie sheet. Toast in the oven for 10 minutes, turn over the croutons and toast another 10 minutes. Cool before serving and eating.

If you want to really gross out your family, breathe on them after eating a handful of these garlicky bits of skunk bones!

FREAKY FOOD FACT:
Puke Parlors
Rumor has it that the royal palaces of ancient Romans had vomitoria, where people who had pigged out at a feast would go to vomit to make room for more food. After retching in the puke parlor, they'd return to the table and continue stuffing their faces. How revolting is that?

Ghoul Fingers

It doesn't get much grosser or yummier than this: snacking on fermented fingernails (pepperoni) and cheesy corpse fingers (breadsticks)!

▶ *Difficulty: Medium*   ▶ *Makes 8 breadsticks*

1 (11-ounce) package refrigerated breadstick dough
8 slices pepperoni
Olive oil spray
Garlic salt, to taste
Grated Parmesan cheese, to taste
Marinara (prepared pizza or spaghetti sauce) or ranch dressing

1. Preheat oven to 350 degrees.
2. Separate the breadsticks and place on an ungreased cookie sheet.
3. Cut each slice of pepperoni into the shape of a fingernail.
4. Press a pepperoni fingernail onto the end of each breadstick. About ½ inch from the pepperoni fingernail, use a blunt knife to make 2 small knuckle creases. About 1 inch from the first knuckle creases, cut 2 more knuckle creases.
5. Spray the breadsticks lightly with olive oil.
6. Sprinkle the breadsticks with garlic salt.
7. Sprinkle the breadsticks with grated Parmesan cheese.
8. Bake according to the directions on the breadstick package (14 to 18 minutes).
9. Immediately remove the breadsticks from the cookie sheet and place on a plate.

Drizzle these ghoulish breadsticks with warm blood (marinara) or dip them in chilled bat saliva (ranch dressing).

Pigeon Poop

This sticky, icky cereal snack looks just like chunks of poop from a great big fat pigeon.

▶ *Difficulty: Medium* ▶ *Makes 20 servings*

2 cups small pretzel sticks
5 cups Peanut Butter Crunch cereal (or any crunchy corn puff cereal)
3 cups Rice Krispies cereal (or any crisped rice cereal)
2 cups mini marshmallows
1 (12-ounce) bag white chocolate chips

1. Break the pretzels in half.
2. Mix the pretzel sticks, cereal, and marshmallows in a large bowl.
3. Dump the chocolate chips in a microwavable bowl and melt (about 1 minute).
4. Pour the melted chocolate over the cereal mix and toss lightly with a wooden spoon to make sure all the dry ingredients get wet.
5. Cover a large cookie sheet with wax paper. Spread the gooey mixture out on the wax paper to cool.
6. Once the gooey goop is set (cool and stuck together), break into chunks the size of a big splat of pigeon poop.

🐛🔍 *For a fun variation, substitute Cocoa Puffs cereal for the Peanut Butter Crunch.*

Why did the teacher say that Megan eats like a bird?

Because she snacks on worms!

FREAKY FOOD FACT:
True or False?
Sugar comes from grass.

True! Sugar comes from sugar cane, which is a type of giant grass.

Funky Fridge

No wonder the cat barfed when Uncle Festus opened his funky old fridge! Find the one continuous line that runs from the top of the refrigerator (Start) to the bottom (End). Then color all of the sickening stuff that Uncle Festus should get out of his fridge!

Chapter 24

Digging Up Dinner

Festering Burgers

Bet you can't wait to sink your teeth into this all-American favorite: burgers oozing with guts (cheese), crawling with worms (bean sprouts), and lathered in pus (mayo), blood (ketchup), and baby poop (mustard).

▸ **Difficulty: Medium**   ▸ **Makes 4 to 6 burgers**

1½ cups mung bean sprouts
1 cup cheddar cheese, shredded
1 pound ground beef (or ground turkey)
1 egg
Salt and pepper, to taste

4 to 6 hamburger buns (depending on the size of the burgers)
Mayonnaise (optional)
Ketchup (optional)
Mustard (optional)

1. Wash the sprouts with warm water and drain.
2. Shred the cheese (or just buy it already shredded).
3. Using your hands, mix 1 cup of the sprouts, the cheese, the ground beef, and the raw egg together in a large bowl.
4. Using your hands, form the burger meat into separate patties, all about the same size. (You'll be able to make 4 to 6 burgers, depending on how big you want each patty.) Place each patty on a cold griddle (or skillet).
5. Sprinkle salt and pepper on each burger.
6. Cook the burgers on the stovetop on medium heat until they are completely browned underneath. Carefully turn over the patties and cook on the other side until they are completely browned. When you press down on the burgers lightly with a spatula, no red juice should escape.
7. Place the burgers on open hamburger buns.
8. Sprinkle the rest of the bean sprouts (worms) on the hamburgers as a garnish. Serve with your favorite condiments: pus (mayonnaise), blood (ketchup), and baby poop (mustard).

Instead of mung worms (bean sprouts), you can use stinky worms (onion cut in long strips). Serve on a plate with pickle slices and lettuce leaves that you've poked holes in so it looks like the worms have been munching on them.

Crunchy Pterodactyl Talons

These are ideal for dipping and crunching!

▶ *Difficulty: Medium* ▶ *Makes 4 servings*

Cooking oil spray
4 skinless, boneless chicken breasts
1 cup corn flakes
¼ cup warm water
¼ cup honey

8 to 10 large black olives, pitted
Your favorite dipping sauce
  (barbecue sauce, ketchup, honey,
  ranch dressing)

1. Preheat oven to 425 degrees. Spray the cookie sheet with oil.
2. Rinse the chicken in cold water and pat dry with a paper towel. Cut (or ask your adult kitchen helper to cut) the chicken into strips about ¾ inch wide.
3. Put the corn flakes in a clean paper lunch bag and roll the top of the bag twice to close it. (Instead, you can use a plastic food storage bag and seal it most of the way, leaving an opening for air to escape.) Roll the rolling pin over the bag until the corn flakes are crumbled. Put the crushed corn flakes on a plate.
4. Mix the warm water and honey together. If they don't mix, warm the honey water in the microwave on low for 15 seconds. One by one, dip the chicken strips in the honey water, and then coat with crumbled corn flakes. Place on a baking sheet, making sure there is an inch between each strip.
5. Bake in oven for 5 to 6 minutes, turn over the chicken strips, and bake for another 5 to 6 minutes, until the chicken strips are golden brown and cooked in the center. Remove immediately from the baking sheet and place on a serving platter.
6. Slice the olives in half lengthwise. You'll need 1 olive for every 2 chicken strips, so if you have 16 chicken strips, you'll need 8 olives. Place an olive half at one end of each chicken strip.

CHEF'S SECRET:
Eggshells Be Gone!
Crack eggs into a cup or a small bowl rather than into the mixing bowl. That way you can remove any bits of shell that fall into the egg when you crack it—before you mix the egg in with the other ingredients. Then you won't be crunching on egg shells when you chow down on your creations!

Serve these crunchy claws with blood (barbecue sauce or ketchup), bee spit (honey), or pureed pigeon poop (ranch dressing).

Fishtails and Ear Wax Fondue

You'll have an easier time making these juicy fish tails (tenders) with hot ear wax (cheese sauce) than you will scooping out the goop in your ears. These are tastier, too!

▸ *Difficulty: Easy*   ▸ *Makes 4 to 6 servings*

8 to 12 frozen fish sticks, fillets, or tenders
1 cup American cheese, shredded
Fresh lettuce
1 or 2 lemons

1. Arrange the frozen fish sticks on an ungreased cookie sheet or shallow baking pan.
2. Bake the fish in the oven according to the directions on the package (usually, at 400 degrees for 15 to 20 minutes).
3. Shred the cheese (or buy it already shredded). Put the cheese in a microwavable bowl. Melt the cheese in the microwave.
4. Wash and drain the lettuce. Separate into individual leaves, break off the root end, and pat dry with a paper towel. Place a lettuce leaf on each plate (or arrange them all on a platter).
5. Slice the lemon into wedges (or ask your adult helper to slice it). Place 2 or 3 fish sticks and a slice of lemon on each lettuce leaf.

🐌 *To add to the fun, serve these crunchy fish tails with three different dips: warm ear wax (cheese sauce), blood and guts (cocktail sauce), and boogers and snot (tartar sauce). Dip, bite, chew, and enjoy!*

FREAKY FOOD FACT:
Eat with Feet

All humans have the ability to feed themselves with their feet. In fact, many people who have no hands or arms do just that. Of course, unlike butterflies—which eat and also taste through their feet—people ingest food through their mouths, and they taste food with their tongues and noses. (That's why you can't taste as well when your nose is stuffed up with boogers and snot.)

What do whales eat?

Fish and ships!

Skewered Road Kill

Whether broiled in the oven or grilled over hot coals, these grilled teriyaki meat and vegetable shish kabobs are to die for!

▸ *Difficulty: Hard*   ▸ *Makes 8 servings*

1 (16-ounce) can pineapple chunks
⅓ cup soy sauce
1 teaspoon ground ginger
1 teaspoon brown sugar
½ teaspoon garlic salt
2 pounds top round steak (or skinned, boneless chicken breasts)

1 green bell pepper
1 zucchini, small to medium sized
Pearl onions
Cherry tomatoes

What do cats call mice on skateboards?

Meals on wheels!

1. Open the pineapple and drain the syrup into a large bowl.
2. To make the teriyaki marinade: combine the pineapple syrup with the soy sauce, ginger, brown sugar, and garlic salt.
3. Cut the steak (or chicken) into 1-inch cubes. Add the meat to the teriyaki marinade. Cover the dish with plastic wrap and let the meat stand at room temperature for 30 minutes. Turn the meat over to marinate the other side, pull the plastic wrap back over the dish, and let stand for another 30 minutes.
4. Wash the vegetables, drain, and pat dry with paper towels. Scoop the seeds out of the green bell pepper. Cut into 1-inch pieces. Cut the zucchini into 1-inch cubes.
5. When the meat has finished marinating, drain and discard the marinade. Assemble the shish kabobs, alternating the meat and vegetables on long skewer sticks. Broil the kabobs in the oven or on an outdoor grill, turning frequently until the meat is brown and the veggies are tender.

Skewered teriyaki road kill is deliciously gross served with maggots (steamed or fried rice)!

Tapeworms and Hairballs

Your whole family will love sucking up these tapeworms (spaghetti) topped with hairballs (meatballs).

▶ *Difficulty: Hard*   ▶ *Makes 6 servings*

Olive oil spray	½ cup grated Parmesan cheese
1 egg	½ teaspoon salt
½ medium onion, finely chopped	½ teaspoon ground black pepper
1 pound ground beef, lean	1 (1-pound) package spaghetti
½ cup Italian breadcrumbs	3 to 4 cups prepared spaghetti sauce

1. Preheat oven to 350 degrees. Spray the bottom of a 9×13-inch glass baking dish with olive oil.
2. Break the egg into a bowl. Beat until the egg is yellow. Chop the onion into small pieces. Add to the bowl. Add the ground beef, breadcrumbs, Parmesan cheese, salt, and pepper to the bowl. Combine ingredients with your hands until well mixed.
4. Spray olive oil on the palms of your hands. Form the mixture into golf balls by rolling a fistful between the palms of your hands. Place the raw meatballs in the baking dish.
5. Bake the meatballs in the oven for 30 minutes.
6. Pour the spaghetti sauce into a large heavy saucepan. Use a big spoon to gently place the meatballs in the spaghetti sauce. Warm over medium-low heat, stirring occasionally.
7. Fill a large saucepan halfway with water. Add a dash of salt. Bring to a boil. Add the pasta to the boiling water, reduce the heat to medium high, and cook until tender, about 8 minutes.
8. Drain the pasta in a colander and rinse with cold water. Put the pasta on a serving platter or individual dinner plates. Use a ladle or large spoon to cover the tapeworms (pasta) with hairballs (meatballs) and blood (spaghetti sauce).

CHEF'S SECRET:
Milder Tomatoes
Tomatoes are an acidic food, but that doesn't mean your spaghetti sauce has to taste that way! Add a pinch of baking soda to your sauce to remedy this.

Top each serving of tapeworms and hairballs with a tablespoon or two of dried pinworms (Parmesan cheese). If you want to spice and gross it up a notch, sprinkle some dried scabs (crushed red pepper) on top too!

Butchered Snake Bits

These chewy, juicy snake bits (sausage) are swimming in blood (barbecue sauce) and guts (grilled onion and green pepper)!

▶ *Difficulty: Medium*   ▶ *Makes 4 servings*

½ cup green bell pepper, diced
½ cup onion, diced
1 tablespoon vegetable oil
1 pound cooked mild sausage
1½ cups prepared barbecue sauce

1. Wash the green pepper and pat it dry with a paper towel. Clean out the seeds. Using a clean knife and cutting board, cut about half of the green pepper into very small pieces until you have ½ cup.
2. Peel the onion and dice it into very small pieces.
3. Heat the oil in a large saucepan over medium heat. Sauté the diced green pepper and onions until the onion is translucent, about 5 minutes.
4. Cut the sausage into bite-sized chunks. Put the meat in the saucepan.
5. Pour the barbecue sauce over the sausage, peppers, and onions in the saucepan. Cook over medium-low heat for about 30 minutes, stirring every 5 minutes.

🍴 *Serve heaped on a snake's nest (shredded lettuce or wilted spinach), open-faced over Texas toast, or in a sandwich roll.*

PLAY IT SAFE:
Never use the same knife and cutting board to cut two different foods. To prevent the spread of potentially harmful bacteria, always use a different knife and cutting board or wash the knife and cutting board with warm, soapy water before reusing it.

Why do maggots eat garbage?

It's a dirty job, but somebody's got to do it!

Baked Hog's Head

The jelled blood (cranberry sauce) under the chinny-chin-chin of this severed pig's head (sliced ham with egg eyes, yam ears and nose, and pineapple smile) gives this gruesome entrée extra zing!

▶ *Difficulty: Medium*   ▶ *Makes 4 servings*

1 egg
1 sweet potato or yam
1 (1-inch thick) slice smoked ham (about 1 pound)
2 small black olives, pitted
1 (3-ounce) can pineapple rings
¼ cup jellied cranberry sauce

1. Boil an egg in a small saucepan filled halfway with water, about 8 minutes. Cool for about 10 minutes.
2. Preheat oven to 350 degrees.
3. Wash the sweet potato and pat dry with a paper towel. Cut three slices of sweet potato from the thickest part of the potato. Cut the tops off two of the slices so that one end of the slice is flat and the other end is rounded. These will be the pig's ears. Leave the third slice round (don't cut off the end) to use for the nose.
4. Place the ham slice in a shallow baking dish. Use a dish you can serve from. Position the two slices of sweet potato with the tops sliced off on the top rim of the ham slice, with the rounded side pointing downward, to make the hog's ears.

Baked Hog's Head (continued)

5. Peel the egg. Cut a small slice off each end of the egg (to make the ends flat). Slice the egg in half. Position the egg slices about one-third of the way from the top rim of the ham slice and close together to make the pig's eyes.

6. Open and drain the olives. Slice 1 black olive in half lengthwise. Place the olive flat side down in the center of each egg slice to make the pupils in the pig's eyes. Place the round sweet potato slice directly under the eyes to make the pig's nose. Slice another black olive in half lengthwise. Position the olive slices flat side down on the nose to make the pig's nostrils.

7. Open the pineapple. Drain the juice into a small bowl and save. Slice 1 pineapple ring in half and position it directly under the pig's nose to form the pig's mouth. Place the rest of the pineapple rings in the baking dish, on either side of the hog's face. Mix the brown sugar with the reserved pineapple juice. Pour over the hog's head.

8. Bake in the oven for 30 to 35 minutes, until the sweet potato slices are tender.

9. Remove from the oven. Spread some jelled blood (cranberry sauce) under the pig's chin. Serve in the baking dish.

🐌 Baked hog's head is superb served with a revolting side of Wormy Apples (page 82)!

What do garbage collectors eat?

Junk food!

FREAKY FOOD FACT:
Porking Out on Pork
Americans eat 300 million sandwiches a year, and their favorite is a ham sandwich, followed by a BLT (bacon, lettuce, and tomato). Oink!

Rotting Mummies

Bet you didn't know a rotting corpse (bean-and-cheese burrito) crawling with maggots (rice) could taste so good and be so disgustingly fun. Just watch your family's faces when they bite into the enshrouded head (tomato) and it pops and squirts into their mouths.

▶ *Difficulty: Medium* ▶ *Makes 4 burritos*

1 cup cooked brown rice
4 small Roma tomatoes
½ cup red bell pepper, diced
½ cup onion, diced
1½ tablespoons vegetable oil
1 (15-ounce) can black beans
1½ teaspoons chili powder
1½ teaspoons garlic powder (or 2 garlic gloves, minced)
1 cup cheddar cheese, shredded
4 (12-inch) flour tortillas
2 cups chopped lettuce
¼ cup prepared salsa

1. Cook the rice according to the directions on the package. Let stand to cool.
2. Wash the tomatoes and red bell pepper and pat them dry with a paper towel. Remove the seeds from the pepper. Cut about half the pepper into small pieces.
3. Peel the onion. Cut about half the onion into small pieces.

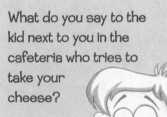

What do you say to the kid next to you in the cafeteria who tries to take your cheese?

It's nacho cheese!

Rotting Mummies (continued)

4. Heat the oil in a large skillet over medium heat. Cook the diced pepper and onion until you can see through the onion, about 3 minutes.

5. Pour the can of beans into a colander. Rinse and drain the beans. Add the beans to the skillet.

6. Stir in the chili powder and garlic powder. Cook the beans over medium heat for 3 minutes, stirring once about half-way through.

7. Add the rice and cheddar cheese to the skillet, and stir to mix together the ingredients. Cook over medium-low heat another 3 to 5 minutes, until the cheese melts, stirring once halfway through.

8. Warm the tortillas in the microwave for 5 seconds (or on a flat grill over low heat, about 15 seconds on each side). Spoon a strip of the rice-bean mixture onto the middle of each flour tortilla. The strip of filling should be about 3 inches wide and should go from the left edge of the tortilla to about 2 inches from the right edge of the tortilla. Place a tomato at one end of the rice-bean mixture to form the head of the mummy.

9. Wrap the burrito like this: (a) Fold the right flap of the tortilla over the filling; (b) Fold the bottom flap of the tortilla over the filling and tuck the edge under the filling; (c) Fold about 2 inches of the upper-right corner of the tortilla down sideways to make a small diagonal flap; (d) Fold the top flap of the tortilla over the filling.

🐛 *For older and grosser (and healthier) mummy shrouds, use whole-wheat tortillas.*

FREAKY FOOD FACT:
French Froggie
People in France (including kids) eat 200 million frogs each year.

Turkey Eye Pie

These turkey eye pies (turkey meatballs in cheese pastry shells) take a little time to prepare, but they're totally creepy and tasty to gobble, gobble, gobble.

▶ **Difficulty: Hard**   ▶ **Makes 12 tarts**

¼ cup (half a stick) butter, softened
1½ tablespoons cream cheese, softened
1½ tablespoons milk
¾ cup flour
Dash salt
Cooking oil spray
1 egg, slightly beaten
¾ cup onion, diced
1 pound ground turkey
1¼ cup unseasoned bread crumbs
1½ teaspoon garlic powder
1½ teaspoons salt
1 teaspoon black pepper
⅓ cup processed cheese spread
¼ cup cheddar cheese, shredded
2 tablespoons vegetable oil
12 slices mozzarella cheese
6 large ripe black olives

What did the cannibal order for take-out?

Pizza with everyone on it!

Step One: Make the Pastry Shell

1. In a large bowl, combine the butter and cream cheese until creamy.
2. Beat in the milk.

Turkey Eye Pie (continued)

3. Add the flour and salt. Mix well and shape into a ball.
4. Cover and chill at least 2 hours.
5. Preheat oven to 425 degrees. Spray the cups of a miniature muffin tin with cooking oil.
6. Form about 1 tablespoon of dough into a small ball. Press the dough into a muffin cup, lining the bottom and sides with dough. Repeat until all the dough is used. Bake in the oven 4 to 6 minutes until the pastry is light golden brown. Cool.

Step Two: Make the Meatballs

1. Preheat oven to 350 degrees.
2. In a large bowl, beat the egg slightly.
3. Peel the onion. Cut into very small pieces.
4. Add the onion, ground turkey, bread crumbs, garlic powder, salt, and pepper. Using your hands, mix all the ingredients together well and form into 12 balls of about 2 inches each. Put the meatballs in a 9×13-inch baking dish. Bake in the oven for 30 minutes. Remove from the oven and cool.

Step Three: Make the Turkey Eye Pies

1. Preheat oven to 350 degrees.
2. Remove the pastry shells from the muffin pan and put them on a platter.
3. In a small bowl, combine the cheese spread and cheddar cheese.
4. Put a small blob of the cheese spread in each of the pastry shells.
5. Put a meatball on top of the cheese in each pastry shell.
6. Put a slice of mozzarella cheese on top of each meatball.
7. Cut the olives in half lengthwise. Place an olive half upside down (so the rounded part faces up) on each slice of mozzarella cheese. Bake in the oven 5 to 8 minutes, until the mozzarella cheese melts.

For easier turkey eye pies, use prepared pastry shells and frozen meatballs from the grocery store. And if you want to make the eyes even grosser, place a few thin strips of pimento on each slice of mozzarella cheese.

Chopped Fooey

This concoction of chopped up critters and vittles (chicken and vegetables) takes a long time to stew. So make it on a rainy weekend when you have to play indoors anyway—or on a sunny day in an electric crock pot that doesn't need constant watching.

▸ Difficulty: *Medium*　▸ *Makes 4 servings*

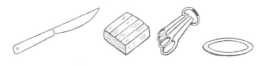

wok a wide and deep pan with a rounded bottom used to stir-fry food in a small amount of very hot oil

2 cups chicken broth
2 tablespoons soy sauce
1 tablespoon corn starch
1 teaspoon salt
1 teaspoon ginger (ground or minced crystallized)
2 whole chicken breasts (4 halves), skinned and boned
2 stalks celery, sliced
1 onion, sliced
1 (5-ounce) can water chestnuts, sliced
1 cup mushrooms, sliced
1 cup mung bean sprouts
¾ cup slivered almonds (optional)

Serve soupy fooey on a heap of steamed maggots (white or brown rice) with broken bird bones (slivered almonds) sprinkled on top.

1. In a crock pot (or a heavy soup pot), combine the broth, soy sauce, corn starch, salt, and ginger.
2. Cut the chicken into strips, about 2 inches long and ½ inch thick. Add to the pot. Wash the celery and pat dry with paper towels. Slice and add to the pot. Peel the onion. Slice and add to the pot.
3. Add the water chestnuts to the pot. Cover and cook on low for 5 to 6 hours. Then turn the heat to high.
4. Wash the mushrooms and pat dry. Slice the mushrooms and add to the pot. Add the bean sprouts to the pot. Cover and cook on high for 15 minutes.

Slurp-ghetti

Calvin loves to go to the buffet on Tuesday nights! To find out why, color in the sections of his platter of pasta that have fleas (dots) on them.

Blubber Roll-Ups

These are foul-looking (but good-tasting) fish roll-ups!

▸ **Difficulty: Medium**   ▸ **Makes 4 servings**

¾ cup cooked white rice
⅓ cup onion, minced
1 tablespoon vegetable oil
1½ cups fresh spinach, chopped
¾ cup mozzarella cheese, shredded
¼ cup Parmesan cheese, grated
1 egg white

1 teaspoon garlic powder
¼ teaspoon salt
⅛ teaspoon pepper
4 thin, flat fillets of white fish (sole
   or tilapia)
1 tablespoon lemon juice
Toothpicks

1. Cook rice according to directions on the package. Set aside.
2. Peel the onion. Chop the onion into very small pieces. Heat 1 tablespoon of oil in a small skillet. Sauté the onion for about 5 minutes, until tender.
3. Wash and drain the spinach. Pat dry with paper towels. Remove the stems and tear the leaves into pieces.
4. Shred the mozzarella cheese. In a large bowl, combine the rice, onion, spinach, mozzarella cheese, Parmesan cheese, egg, garlic powder, salt, and pepper. Mix together well.
5. Cut each fish fillet lengthwise into two skinnier strips of about the same size, 2 to 4 inches wide (or have your adult kitchen helper do it for you).
6. Pour the lemon juice into a shallow glass 10-inch baking dish. Spread about ¼ cup of the rice mixture onto a fish fillet. Roll the fillet to enclose the filling. Skewer the roll-up with a toothpick to hold it together. Place the roll-up in the baking dish. Repeat for each of the fish fillets.
7. Microwave on high for 10 to 12 minutes, until the fish flakes easily with a fork. Let stand 5 minutes before serving.

What fish smells like feet?

Fillet of sole!

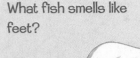

Serve with lemon slices and shark's blood (cocktail sauce) or squid guts (tartar sauce).

Dragon Bile

Tell your family that this stew (chicken and dumplings) came hurling out of the mouth of a fire-breathing lizard.

▶ *Difficulty: Medium*   ▶ *Makes 6 to 8 servings*

1 pound chicken thighs, skinned and boned
1½ pounds chicken breasts, skinned and boned
2 celery ribs, sliced
8 cups chicken broth
2 tablespoons butter

1½ tablespoons flour
½ cup milk
Bisquick
Milk (for Bisquick dumplings)
1 (16-ounce) package frozen mixed vegetables

1. Cut the chicken into cubes (1-inch thick by 2-inches square).
2. Wash and drain the celery. Cut off the ends and throw away. Cut into thick slices.
3. Pour the chicken broth into a large, heavy-bottomed pot (such as a Dutch oven). Bring the broth to a boil over medium-high heat. While waiting for the broth to boil, melt the butter in a bowl. Add the flour to the melted butter, stirring to make a paste. Slowly stir in the milk. Add the milk mixture to the boiling broth, stirring constantly.
5. Reduce the heat to medium low. Add the chicken and celery. Cover the pot and cook 20 minutes.
6. While the chicken is cooking, prepare the dough for the Bisquick dumplings, following the directions on the box.
7. Return the stew to a boil over medium-high heat. Stir in the frozen mixed vegetables. Drop spoonfuls of the dumpling dough into the bubbling stew. Reduce heat to medium and cook uncovered for 10 minutes. Reduce heat to medium low, cover, and cook another 10 minutes.

PLAY IT SAFE:
When removing a lid from a cooking pot, always use an oven mitt and stand tall—never bend forward or put your face over the pot! Steam escaping from the pot can burn your skin and eyes.

You'll know your dumplings are cooked to perfection when slimy on the outside (like they're covered in dragon saliva) and airy on the inside (like a biscuit).

Fish Eggs and Guts

There's nothing like a helping of fish gut (tuna noodle) casserole speckled with fish eggs (baby peas) and topped with a crunchy layer of crud (cheese-and-cracker topping) to make your family say, "It's so repulsive, it's delicious!"

▶ Difficulty: *Medium* ▶ *Makes 4 servings*

2 cups elbow macaroni, cooked (about 4 ounces uncooked)
½ cup milk
1 (10-ounce) can cream of mushroom soup
¼ teaspoon garlic powder (optional)
1 teaspoon salt
⅛ teaspoon pepper
1 (7-ounce) package cooked tuna chunks, drained
1 cup frozen peas
¾ cup buttery crackers, crushed (such as Ritz)
½ cup grated Parmesan cheese

1. Fill a large saucepan about half full with water. Add a dash of salt. Boil the water over medium-high heat.
2. Cook the macaroni in the boiling water for 8 to 10 minutes, until the noodles are tender. Drain and rinse in a colander.
3. Preheat oven to 375 degrees.
4. Pour the milk into a casserole dish (1½ to 2 quarts).
5. Open the can of soup. Add the soup, garlic powder, salt, and pepper to the milk Use a fork to mix together well.
6. Open the can of tuna and drain all the liquid. Add the tuna, peas, and noodles to the casserole. Stir with a spoon.
7. Use a rolling pin to crush the crackers. Sprinkle the crushed crackers over the casserole.
8. Sprinkle the Parmesan cheese over the crushed crackers.
9. Bake in the oven for 10 minutes, until the casserole is heated all the way through and the topping is crispy.

al dente an Italian word that means "to the tooth;" cooking pasta until it is tender but still firm and gives a slight resistance when you bite into it

🐌 *For the casserole topping, you can use dried scabs (corn flakes) instead of crackers and gassy cheese (Swiss cheese) instead of Parmesan cheese.*

Ralpharoni Alfredo

Now you can produce a pile of puke (macaroni Alfredo) that tastes disgustingly good!

▶ **Difficulty: Easy** ▶ *Serves 6*

2 cups mini macaroni, cooked (about ½ package of either ditali or tubetti pasta)
½ cup red bell pepper, diced
1½ tablespoons olive oil
1 cup fresh spinach, chopped (or frozen, thawed and drained)

1 cup small white beans (about half of a 15-ounce can)
½ teaspoon salt
⅛ teaspoon pepper
1 (26-ounce) jar prepared Alfredo sauce (2 to 2½ cups)
Romano cheese, grated (optional)

1. Fill a large saucepan half full with water. Add a dash of salt. Bring to a boil over medium-high heat.
2. Boil the macaroni in the water 8 to 10 minutes, until tender.
3. Drain the macaroni and rinse with cool water.
4. Wash the pepper and pat dry with paper towels. Remove the seeds and cut the pepper into small pieces.
5. Heat the olive oil in a skillet over medium-low heat. Sauté the pepper for 3 to 5 minutes, until tender.
6. Wash and drain the spinach. Remove the stems and throw away. Tear the spinach into smaller pieces.
7. Put the beans, macaroni, peppers, spinach, salt, and pepper in a glass (2- to 2½-quart) casserole dish and stir together. Pour the Alfredo sauce over the top and stir again, coating the pasta and beans. Microwave on high power for 4 minutes. Stir and microwave on high power for another 4 minutes or until heated all the way through.

🐚🐌 *Top with a handful of grated Romano cheese. Leftover Ralpharoni makes a great lunch, too. Just store in a sealed container in the refrigerator, and then zap in the microwave tomorrow or the next day.*

Find and Sing

Sing the "Diarrhea Song" on this page. If you don't know the melody, just make one up. Then, find the song's underlined words in the hidden-word puzzle and circle them. The hidden words go this way → and this way ↓.

The Diarrhea Song

When you wake up in the morning,
Put your <u>feet</u> on the floor,
Do the 50-yard dash to the <u>bathroom</u> door,
Diarrhea, diarrhea!

When you're <u>sliding</u> into first,
And you feel something <u>burst</u>,
Diarrhea, diarrhea!

When you're sliding into third,
And you lay a <u>juicy</u> <u>turd</u>,
Diarrhea, diarrhea!

When you're sliding into home,
And you feel something <u>foam</u>,
Diarrhea, <u>diarrhea</u>!

```
C  P  D  B  U  R  S  T
S  M  X  A  H  W  O  R
L  J  E  T  U  R  D  F
I  U  N  H  S  A  F  O
D  I  A  R  R  H  E  A
I  C  K  O  T  H  E  M
N  Y  B  O  J  E  T  O
G  R  E  M  L  D  V  G
```

EVERYBODY SING!

Chapter 25

Sick Salads and Sides

If broccoli makes you want to barf, you can use an 8-ounce package of frozen corn and ¼ cup of blood clots (pimento) instead of the Birds Eye Broccoli, Corn & Peppers.

Puke au Gratin

Oh yeah! Scalloped corn definitely looks like vomit. It even feels like a mouthful of barf. Good thing it tastes extra good.

▸ Difficulty: *Medium*   ▸ *Serves 6*

Cooking oil spray
1½ tablespoons butter (or margarine), melted
1 egg, slightly beaten
¾ cup milk
½ teaspoon salt
¼ teaspoon paprika
1 cup (half of a 1-pound bag) of frozen Birds Eye Broccoli, Corn & Peppers
1 (15-ounce) can creamed corn
⅓ cup cheddar cheese, grated
1 cup cracker crumbs (such as Ritz crackers)

1. Preheat oven to 350 degrees. Spray the inside of a large casserole dish with cooking oil.
2. Melt the butter in a microwaveable bowl or cup.
3. Beat the egg slightly, until it is partially blended.
4. Combine the butter, egg, milk, salt, and paprika in the casserole dish. Add the frozen mixed vegetables and creamed corn to the casserole and stir.
5. Sprinkle the grated cheddar cheese on top of the casserole.
6. Use a rolling pin to crush the crackers into fine crumbs. Spread over the casserole.
7. Bake in the oven for 45 to 50 minutes.

Lemony Lice

Just try not to think about squirming lice and chewy head scabs when you eat this lemony couscous with dried cranberries!

▸ **Difficulty:** *Medium*   ▸ *Serves 4*

1 teaspoon lemon zest
1 tablespoon lemon juice (from 1 lemon)
2 cups chicken broth
½ teaspoon salt
⅛ teaspoon curry
1 tablespoon butter or margarine (or olive oil)
1 cup instant couscous
⅓ cup dried cranberries

1. Before cutting the lemon, grate the zest (lemon peel). Grate only the yellow part. The pieces of zest need to be very small, so your adult kitchen helper might need to cut the grated pieces into smaller pieces with a knife.
2. Cut the lemon in half. Squeeze the juice into a small bowl or cup. Remove the seeds.
3. Combine the lemon zest, lemon juice, chicken broth, salt, curry, and butter in a medium saucepan (1½ to 2 quart). Bring to a boil over medium-high heat.
4. Turn off the heat. Remove the pot from the burner. Stir in the couscous.
5. Cover and let stand for 10 minutes, until broth is absorbed. (Don't lift the lid during the 10-minute wait.)
6. Add the cranberries. Fluff up the couscous with a fork.

CHEF'S SECRET:
Juicy Fruit
Heavier lemons produce more, and tastier, juice. To get the most juice from a lemon, keep it at room temperature (don't refrigerate) and before squeezing it, roll it on a hard surface while pressing down with the palm of your hand. Or microwave it on low for about 30 seconds.

Instead of scabs (cranberries), you can use ⅓ cup of boogers (cooked baby peas) or rabbit poop (raisins). By the way, couscous can be eaten warm or cold, so it makes a good side dish for dinner, school lunches, and picnics.

Sea Scum Drizzled in Eel Spit

Have you ever noticed the white scum left on the beach after a wave washes onto shore? Well, serve it as these smashed potatoes with a crater of eel spit (melted butter tinged a revolting brownish green)!

▶ *Difficulty: Medium*   ▶ *Makes 4 servings*

5 or 6 large potatoes (1½ to 2 pounds, Russet or baking potatoes)
⅓ cup milk
½ teaspoon salt
¼ teaspoon pepper
2½ tablespoons butter or margarine, melted
Red and green food coloring

1. Wash the potatoes. Peel off the skin with the vegetable peeler. Cut each potato into 1-inch cubes. Put the potato chunks in the colander and rinse with cold water.
2. Put the potato chunks in a large saucepan. Fill the pan with just enough water to cover the potatoes.
3. Cook the potatoes on high heat until the water boils. If it looks like the water might spill over the sides, reduce the heat. When the water starts to boil, reduce the heat to medium low. Cover the pot with a lid and cook 20 minutes, until the potatoes are tender when you poke them with a fork. Drain the potatoes and transfer them to a glass bowl.
4. Beat the potatoes with an electric mixer (or a potato masher) just until the potatoes are smooth. Stir in the milk, salt, and pepper while the potatoes are still hot.
5. Melt the butter in the microwave. Stir a drop of red food coloring and a drop of green food coloring into the melted butter. Use a big spoon to make a crater in the top of the smashed potatoes. Pour half of the melted butter into the crater and drizzle the other half over the top of the smashed potatoes.

FREAKY FOOD FACT:
Fastest Worm Eater in the East
The world record for fastest worm eater was set in 2003 by a man named "Snake" Manoh-oran from Madras, India, who ate 200 earthworms in 30 seconds. That broke the previous world record set by the fastest worm eater in the West, Mike Hoggs, of the United States.

For added grossness (and flavor), sprinkle a few shakes of red mites (paprika) on top of the soap scum. If you like garlic, add ½ teaspoon of garlic powder when you stir in the milk, salt, and pepper.

Gangrenous Intestines

This slimy green pasta (buttered spinach linguine) is tossed with curdled crud (Parmesan cheese) for a savory side dish that's great with broiled fish or baked chicken.

▶ *Difficulty: Easy* ▶ *Makes 4 servings*

½ teaspoon plus a dash salt
½ pound spinach linguine or spaghetti noodles
2 tablespoons butter or margarine
½ teaspoon garlic powder
⅛ teaspoon ground pepper (black or white)
⅛ teaspoon basil (dried or fresh)
2 tablespoons Parmesan cheese, grated

1. Fill a large saucepan about halfway with cool water. Add a dash of salt.
2. Bring the water to a boil over high heat.
3. Reduce the heat to medium. Stir in the spinach noodles. Cook for 8 to 10 minutes, until the spinach noodles are tender but not mushy.
4. Drain the noodles in a colander. Rinse with cool water.
5. Return the noodles to the pan. Stir in the butter, salt, garlic powder, pepper, and basil.
6. Turn the burner to low. Stir in the Parmesan cheese. Toss the pasta with a large fork until the cheese is evenly distributed and starts to melt, about 2 minutes.

For a healthier form of fat, substitute the butter with pigeon saliva (olive oil).

What pasta has lots of pimples?

Zit-i!

FREAKY FOOD FACT:
Sniff and Taste
An apple, a potato, and an onion all taste sweet if you eat them with your nose plugged. Give it a try and see for yourself!

Wormy Apples

These baked apples are rotten to the core (stuffed with apple butter) and squirming with worms (of the gummy variety).

▶ *Difficulty: Easy*   ▶ *Makes 4 servings*

Cooking oil spry
4 large apples
4 tablespoons apple butter
9 gummy worms

1. Preheat oven to 350 degrees. Spray the bottom of a baking pan with cooking oil (or grease with butter or margarine).
2. Core each apple from the stem end, leaving about ½ inch on the bottom. Do not push through the blossom end of the apple.
3. Spoon 1 tablespoon of apple butter into the hole of each apple.
4. Place the apples in the baking pan. Bake in the oven for 35 to 45 minutes, depending on the size of the apples, until the fruit is tender and the apple butter is bubbly.
5. Put each apple in a bowl. Spoon the syrup in the bottom of the baking pan on top of each apple. Slide 2 gummy worms into the hole of each apple so that half of the gummy worm is in the apple butter and half is sticking out of the apple.

For spicier apples, put a stick of cinnamon in the squishy rot (apple butter) before baking.

FREAKY FOOD FACT:
Mmm...Snails!
People in France eat 500 million snails a year, most of them in a dish called escargot.

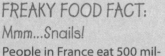

Say this tongue twister as fast as you can as many times as you can:

Frank fried fritters for fruit flies.
Frank fried fritters for fruit flies.
Frank fried fritters for fruit flies.

Monkey Vomit

This is what happens when a monkey stuffs his belly with tropical fruit and coconut milk and then swings upside down from the branches (look out below!). Lucky for you, primate puke never tasted so good!

▸ *Difficulty: Easy*   ▸ *Makes 4 servings*

1 (20-ounce) can pineapple chunks, drained
1 (11-ounce) can mandarin orange sections, drained
2 bananas, sliced
¼ cup shredded coconut
1 single-serving (6-ounce) container vanilla-flavored yogurt

1. Open and drain the pineapple and the oranges. Dump into the bowl.
2. Peel the bananas. Cut the bananas crosswise into slices. Put in the bowl with the other fruit.
3. Add the coconut and yogurt. Stir to mix together well.

It is best to eat monkey vomit (otherwise known as "ambrosia salad") immediately or store in the refrigerator for no more than a few hours before serving it. Otherwise, the pineapple will start to turn the yogurt into a watery mess, and the banana slices will start to turn brown.

CHEF'S SECRET:
Banana Toots
Don't store bananas in a bowl or basket with other fruit. Bananas give off a gas that makes other fruit ripen and rot more quickly. And you thought people farts were silent but deadly!

FREAKY FOOD FACT:
A group of bananas is called:
A. A hand
B. A bunch
C. A cluster

A. Each hand (group) of bananas has ten to twenty "fingers" (bananas).

Medusa's Dreadlocks

Dip these oven-fried dreadlocks (zucchini, carrot, and onion strips) into a bowl of snake spit.

▶ *Difficulty: Hard*   ▶ *Serves 4*

Cooking oil spray
1 medium zucchini
1 medium carrot
½ medium onion
4 tablespoons Italian bread crumbs
1½ tablespoons Parmesan cheese
¼ teaspoon salt
⅛ teaspoon garlic powder
⅛ teaspoon paprika
⅛ teaspoon ground black pepper
3 teaspoons vegetable oil
1 tablespoon water
¾ cup ranch dressing
Green food coloring
1 medium black olive
1 baby dill pickle
1 red bell pepper strip

1. Preheat oven to 475 degrees. Spray oil on a cookie sheet.
2. Rinse and drain the zucchini and carrot. Cut the zucchini in half lengthwise. Cut each of the 2 pieces in half lengthwise. Cut each of the 4 pieces in half crosswise. Cut the carrot in half crosswise. Cut each half into 4 carrot sticks.

What did the skeleton say before eating?

Bone appétit!

Medusa's Dreadlocks (continued)

3. Peel the onion and cut into thick slices. From the biggest slices, separate 8 to 12 of the outer rings. Cut 1 side of each ring so that it is no longer a ring and has 2 ends.

4. In a large zip-top plastic bag, combine the bread crumbs, Parmesan, salt, garlic powder, paprika, and pepper. Zip the bag to close it. Shake to mix together the ingredients.

5. Place the zucchini, carrot, and onion pieces in a different zip-top bag. Add the oil and water to the bag. Zip the bag to close it. Shake to wet the vegetables.

6. Place 2 or 3 of the wet vegetable pieces into the bread crumb bag. Close the bag and shake to coat the vegetables. Remove the veggies from the bag and place on a baking sheet. Repeat until you've breaded all the vegetables. Bake in the oven for 10 minutes, until golden brown and tender.

7. While the veggies are oven frying, pour the ranch dressing into a shallow bowl. Stir in a drop of green food coloring.

8. Slice the olive in half lengthwise. Carefully place each slice on top of the bowl of ranch dressing (Medusa's face), with the cut side down and the rounded side up, to form two eyes. Cut a slice of dill pickle on a diagonal. Use the tip of a sharp knife to make 2 small holes (nostrils) on the wider bottom of the pickle slice. (The easiest way to make a nostril is to stick the tip of the knife into the pickle and twirl the handle of the knife a few times.) Place the pickle slice on the ranch dressing to form Medusa's nose. Cut a thin strip of red bell pepper, about ½ inch wide by 3 inches long. Place on the ranch dressing to form Medusa's mouth.

9. Place the bowl on a platter. When the veggies are done baking, remove from baking sheet and arrange to form a semicircle of dreadlocks on the top edge of the bowl (Medusa's face).

In which country do people's tummies rumble most?

Hungary!

🐛📖 For creepier-looking Medusa locks, use this recipe to whip up a batch of oven-fried calamari (about ½ pound small squid, cut into thin strips), rather than veggies. Then dip it in squid guts (tartar sauce) rather than snake spit (ranch dressing).

Caterpillars and Chiggers

Chiggers are tiny red bugs that crawl all over your body and nibble on your skin, which then itches like the dickens. These giant shriveled chiggers (cranberries) combined with slimy green caterpillars (honey-coated green beans) will really make your skin crawl . . . and your mouth water.

▸ **Difficulty:** *Medium*   ▸ *Makes 4 servings*

2 cups fresh green beans
1 tablespoon orange juice
2 tablespoons honey
½ cup dried cranberries
¼ cup slivered almonds

1. Wash the green beans. Cut off the stems. Cut the green beans crosswise into bite-sized (2- to 3-inch) pieces.
2. Put the green beans in a large saucepan. Fill with water until it just covers the green beans.
3. Cook the green beans on the stovetop on medium-high heat for 8 to 10 minutes, until tender.
4. Drain the green beans using a colander. Return the green beans to the pot.
5. Stir in the orange juice, honey, cranberries, and almond slivers. Warm over medium heat, stirring constantly, for about 2 minutes.

PLAY IT SAFE:

Never throw grease or water on a fire. The best ways to put out a small food fire is to smother it with a metal lid from a pot or to toss a few handfuls of baking soda over the fire. If a fire breaks out while you're cooking, get out of the way and let your adult helper take care of it.

This recipe is easier to make using frozen cut green beans or canned green beans, but it tastes much better with fresh green beans, especially organic ones.

Bug-Eating Veggie Ogress

When this veggie ogress waddles through the garden, she sings a riddle: "I eat my dinner, and my dinner eats me." Get it? (The bugs eat her, and she eats the bugs.) Draw a line between the word and the object on the ogress.

Ant

Bee

Ladybug

Moth

Snail

Spider

Worm

Broccoli

Carrots

Corn

Eggplant

Peas

Pumpkin

Tomato

What animal pukes every time it eats?

A yak!

🐛 *For a healthy, tasty, disgusting-looking snack, spread cow cud on crackers or tortilla chips.*

PLAY IT SAFE:

When using a microwave, cover the dish with a lid or plastic wrap, but wrap it loosely so that steam can escape. The moist heat will help destroy potentially harmful bacteria, and the cover will keep the hot food from splattering all over the microwave and you.

🐛 *This chunky baby doo-doo is lip smackingly good cold, too.*

Cow Cud

This is a great side for any gross-loving kid's meal!

▶ **Difficulty: Easy**   ▶ *Makes 4 servings*

½ cup alfalfa sprouts
1 medium carrot, grated
4 whole leaves of green lettuce

2 ripe avocados (Hass are best)
2 tablespoons Italian salad dressing

1. Wash and drain the alfalfa sprouts, carrot, and lettuce.
2. Grate the carrot.
3. Scoop the avocado into a bowl. Use a fork to mash the avocado until it is fairly smooth. Add the sprouts, carrots, and Italian dressing to the mashed avocado. Stir to mix well.
4. Use an ice-cream scoop to plop a mound of avocado salad onto each salad leaf.

Diaper Dump

Get your baby doo-doo (chunky applesauce) while it's warm.

▶ **Difficulty: Easy**   ▶ *Makes 6 servings*

1 (24-ounce) jar prepared chunky
   applesauce (plain)
¼ cup raisins

1 teaspoon cinnamon
1 tablespoon brown sugar

1. In a large microwaveable bowl, combine the applesauce, raisins, cinnamon, and brown sugar. Stir together well.
2. Cover the bowl loosely with plastic wrap. Warm the applesauce in the microwave for 2 minutes. Stir and continue microwaving until warmed all the way through.

Rotten Eggs

The best part about these spongy eggs (baby potatoes) is the putrid green slime (broccoli-cheese) covering them. It's enough to send shivers right up your spine.

▸ *Difficulty: Medium*   ▸ *Serves 4 to 6*

1 dozen small red potatoes
1½ cups broccoli florets
Pinch salt
8 ounces American cheese

1. Wash potatoes and broccoli.
2. Put the potatoes in a large saucepan. Add a pinch of salt. Fill with just enough water to cover the potatoes.
3. Put the broccoli in a separate saucepan. Fill with just enough water to cover the broccoli.
4. Cook the potatoes over medium-high heat for about 15 minutes, or until tender.
5. Cook the broccoli over medium-high heat for 8 minutes, or until tender.
6. Drain the potatoes. Put the potatoes in a serving bowl and cover to keep warm.
7. Drain the broccoli. Put the broccoli in the blender pitcher (or food processor).
8. Put the cheese in a bowl and melt in the microwave, following the directions for the microwave.
9. Pour the cheese in with the broccoli. Blend until the cheese turns green. Pour the green cheese over the potatoes.

WORDS to KNOW

new potatoes very small potatoes that are harvested early, before they can grow large; sometimes called "young" or "baby" potatoes, they have a thinner skin and their flesh is sweeter and firmer than mature potatoes

What is the difference between boogers and broccoli?

Kids don't eat broccoli!

These foul-looking potatoes are great served with fowl (such as chicken, turkey, or Cornish hens).

Buzzard Innards

Repulse and delight your dinner guests with this steamy, creamy, blood-and-guts casserole made with spaghetti squash, chunky spaghetti sauce, and three different cheeses.

▸ **Difficulty: Hard**   ▸ *Serves 4 to 6*

1 large spaghetti squash
Cooking oil spray
2 cups mozzarella cheese, grated
1 cup Parmesan cheese, grated or
 shredded
1 cup cottage cheese

1 teaspoon salt
½ teaspoon ground black pepper
1 (26-ounce) jar prepared spaghetti
 sauce, chunky style with onion
 and bell pepper

1. Wash the squash. Cut it in half lengthwise. Clean out the seeds and pulp, leaving only the rind. *Note:* Spaghetti squash has a thick, tough rind, sort of like a pumpkin's, that is difficult to cut. So to be safe, your adult kitchen helper should cut the squash with a large, sharp knife or a cleaver.
2. Cook the squash in the microwave for 6 to 8 minutes. Let stand for at least 5 minutes.
3. Preheat oven to 350 degrees. Spray a large casserole dish with cooking oil.
4. Separate the strands of squash by running a fork lengthwise from stem to bottom and put them in the casserole dish.
5. Grate the mozzarella cheese (or buy it already grated).
6. In a bowl, mix together the mozzarella, Parmesan, and cottage cheeses and the salt and pepper.
7. Spoon half of the cheese mixture into the casserole dish. Mix it in with the squash. Stir in the spaghetti sauce.
8. Spread the other half of the cheese mixture on top of the casserole. Bake in the oven for 40 to 45 minutes.

CHEF'S SECRET:
Make Your Own
Oil Sprayer
Fill a clean spray bottle, which you can buy at most grocery and discount stores, with cooking oil from a bottle. When the oil runs out, just wash the bottle and refill it.

🐌 *Buzzard gut casserole goes great with a bowl of weeds (green salad) and garlic bread.*

Spewed Salad

This gelatinous mess of chilled chunky vomit (pineapple-mandarin cole slaw in lime gelatin) topped with a dollop of bile (whipped cream and mayo topping) is sure to make everyone at the table gag with pleasure.

▸ *Difficulty: Medium*   ▸ *Serves 8 to 10*

What do you call a vegetarian with diarrhea?

A salad shooter!

1 (6-ounce) box green gelatin (lime or green apple)

2 cups cole slaw mix (shredded cabbage and carrots)

1 (8-ounce) can crushed pineapple, drained

1 (11-ounce) can mandarin orange segments, drained

2 cups whipped cream (or whipped cream substitute, such as Cool Whip)

½ cup mayonnaise

¼ teaspoon curry

1. Prepare the gelatin according to the directions on the box. Refrigerate 2½ hours, until partially set.
2. Wash and drain the cole slaw vegetables.
3. Open the cans of pineapple and mandarin orange, and drain off all the juice.
4. Put the cole slaw mix, pineapple, and mandarin orange in a large bowl or casserole dish. Use a fork to mix and mash it all together so that it looks like it's been chewed and digested. Pour the gelatin in with the veggie and fruit mixture, and gently fold it in with a wooden spoon.
5. Cover the gelatin salad with plastic wrap. Put in the refrigerator for 2 to 4 hours, until it has the consistency of a giant glob of fresh, shiny puke.
6. In a separate bowl, mix together the whipped cream, mayonnaise, and curry. Cover and refrigerate until you're ready to serve the gelatin.

Top each serving of spewed salad with a glob of dry-heave foam (the whipped-cream and mayo topping).

Poo-ey!

All of these foods have one thing in common: They're odiferous! Use the letters from the word S T I N K Y to complete these foul-smelling food words.

STINKY

v _ _ _ e g a r

Bru _ _ _ el _ _ prou _ _ _

blu _ _ chee _ e

_ _ u _ a f _ _ _ h

mold _ _ bread

ro _ _ _ e _ egg _

_ _ po _ led mil _

ra _ _ c _ _ d mea _

Chapter 26

Disgusting Desserts

Troll's Toes

Dip these troll's toes (sugar cookies) in toe jam (apricot jam)!

▸ **Difficulty: Hard**   ▸ **Makes about 4 dozen cookies**

1 cup (2 sticks) butter or margarine, softened	2¾ cups flour
1 cup sugar	1 teaspoon baking powder
1 egg	1 teaspoon salt
1 teaspoon almond extract	Cooking oil spray
1 teaspoon vanilla extract	1 small tube green cake decorating gel
	¾ cup whole blanched almonds

1. In a large bowl, combine the butter, sugar, egg, and almond and vanilla extracts. Beat together until creamy.
2. In a separate bowl, combine the flour, baking powder, and salt.
3. Pour the dry mixture into the wet mixture. Beat until all of the dry ingredients are mixed in and the batter is smooth. Cover the dough and put it in the refrigerator for 30 minutes.
4. Preheat oven to 325 degrees. Spray cooking oil on a cookie sheet.
5. Divide the dough into 4 equal pieces. Leave one piece out and put the rest back in the refrigerator.
6. Place a heaping teaspoon of dough on a pastry board (or a sheet of waxed paper). With your hands, roll the dough and shape it into fat toes. Squeeze the edges together about one-third of the way down each toe to form a knuckle shape. Squeeze a small dab of decorating gel on the tip of each toe. Put an almond on the gel and press to secure the toenail. Use a blunt knife to make two knuckle lines across each toe.
7. Arrange the cookies on a cookie sheet. Bake for 20 to 25 minutes, until golden brown. Let cool 3 minutes. Remove from the cookie sheet and put on a wire rack to cool.
8. Repeat steps 6 through 9 until you've used up all the dough.

CHEF'S SECRET:
No-Spill Measuring
To measure small amounts of liquids—such as vanilla extract—use a medicine dropper with measurements marked on it. You can find these droppers in drugstores.

These troll's toes spread while baking, so form the dough a little smaller than you want the toes to be.

Barf Biscuits

It's a good thing these no-bake peanut butter and oat-meal cookies are mouth-wateringly scrumptious, because they look like splats of dried puke.

▶ **Difficulty:** *Medium*   ▶ *Makes about 3 dozen cookies*

Waxed paper
2 cups sugar
½ cup milk
¼ cup semi-sweet or unsweetened cocoa powder
½ cup (1 stick) butter or margarine
1 teaspoon vanilla
½ cup peanut butter
3 cups quick-cooking oatmeal

1. Line the bottom of a large glass baking pan or plastic storage container with waxed paper.
2. Combine the sugar, milk, cocoa, and butter in a large saucepan.
3. Stir constantly over medium-high heat to blend ingredients and bring to a boil. Let boil for exactly 1 minute. Remove pan from heat.
4. While still warm, stir in the vanilla, peanut butter, and oatmeal.
5. Let cool for 5 minutes. Drop by teaspoons onto the waxed paper. With the back of the spoon, press down on the batter to squash it into a thick disk shape.
6. Refrigerate until the cookies are chilled and chewy (firm).

To make these barf biscuits look even more revolting, add ½ cup of spewed nuts (chopped peanuts).

Grubs in Dirt

Chocolate pudding mixed with Oreo cookie crumbs and chopped up gummy worms looks and feels likes slimy, gritty mud crawling with repulsive bugs.

▶ **Difficulty: Easy**   ▶ *Serves 6*

1 small box chocolate pudding, instant or cooked
12 chocolate sandwich cookies (such as Oreos)
6 gummy worms (preferably yellow, white, or clear)
6 flat-bottomed ice-cream cones

1. Prepare the pudding according to the directions on the box. (Let cooked pudding cool to room temperature.) Spoon the pudding into a bowl.
2. Crush the Oreos into small crumbs.
3. Use a blunt knife to cut the gummy worms into 1-inch pieces.
4. Stir the gummy worm pieces and half the cookie crumbs into the pudding.
5. Spoon the pudding mixture into each of the ice-cream cones.
6. Sprinkle the rest of the cookie crumbs on top of the pudding in the cones.

Want to really disgust your parents? Take a bite of grubs in dirt, swish it around your mouth without swallowing, and then give your folks a big toothy smile.

FREAKY FOOD FACT:
Pass the Moss, Please
A type of seaweed called carrageen moss is often used as a thickener in pudding and ice cream.

CHEF'S SECRET:
To Make Cookie Crumbs
Seal the cookies in a plastic zip bag. Use a rolling pin to crush the cookies.

Puppy Chow

No gross cookbook for kids would be complete without this classic: Chex cereal coated with melted chocolate and peanut butter and dusted in powdered sugar.

▶ *Difficulty: Medium*   ▶ *Makes 10 servings*

2 cups semi-sweet chocolate chips
½ cup (1 stick) butter or margarine
⅓ cup peanut butter
9 cups Corn or Rice Chex cereal
2 to 4 cups powdered sugar

1. Put the chocolate chips, butter, and peanut butter in a microwaveable bowl. Melt the ingredients together in the microwave, following the directions for the microwave. Stop the microwave about halfway through the melting time and stir the mixture at least once. Make sure everything is completely melted.
2. Stir the melted ingredients to blend together.
3. Pour the cereal into a very large bowl.
4. Slowly pour the chocolate mixture over the cereal. Gently fold (turn over) the cereal until it is all completely coated with the chocolate mixture.
5. Put the powdered sugar into a large, clean paper bag.
6. Dump the cereal into the bag. Shake until all the cereal is covered. Add more sugar if needed.

This crunchy concoction could easily pass for puppy chow—minus the stench and taste of liver and lamb meat.

FREAKY FOOD FACT:
Smeared Science
The microwave oven was invented by a scientist after he walked by a radar tube and a chocolate bar in his pocket melted.

Spurting Spider Cake

When you slice into this black cake filled with lime Jell-O, the green "guts" spurt out all over the place. Yuck!

▶ *Difficulty: Hard*   ▶ *Serves 4*

1 (3-ounce) box green Jell-O (lime)	Blue food coloring
1 box yellow cake mix	8 black licorice sticks
1 can prepared chocolate frosting	2 large red gumballs or gum drops

1. Prepare the Jell-O according to the directions on the box. Put in the refrigerator and chill until the gelatin sets completely.
2. Prepare the cake batter according to the directions. Pour into two 9-inch round cake pans that have been greased and floured. Bake according to box instructions. Remove from the oven and let cool to room temperature. Spoon the frosting into a bowl. Stir in blue food coloring until the frosting turns black.
3. Remove the set Jell-O from the refrigerator. Use a spoon to churn it up so that it looks like green guts.
4. Remove the cakes from the pans. Put a few dabs of frosting on a baking sheet. Cut a 5-inch circle out of the center of the cake. Set the small circle aside for the spider's head.
5. Put a few dabs of frosting under the cake to hold it in place. Fill the hole in the cake with Jell-O. Put the uncut layer of cake on top of the filled layer. This is the spider's body.
6. Spread a 3-inch swab of frosting along the edge of the larger cake. Place the smaller cake against the frosting. Spread frosting over the entire cake. To make the legs: bend the licorice in a rainbow shape; stick one end near the top of the cake and then drape the stick downward. Put the gumball eyes on the spider's face.

What is brown, hairy, and wears sunglasses?

A coconut on summer vacation!

To make a tarantula, use coconut-pecan frosting (the kind used for German chocolate cake) instead of chocolate frosting.

Bloody Bug Pops

These homemade popsicles are made with yogurt and berries, blended together in a mushy mess.

▸ **Difficulty:** *Medium* ▸ **Makes 8 pops**

½ cup red berry juice (cranberry, raspberry, cherry—your choice)
1 envelope unflavored gelatin
1 cup vanilla yogurt
1 cup fresh or frozen blueberries
8 small (3-ounce) paper cups
Aluminum foil
8 Popsicle sticks or plastic spoons

1. Pour the berry juice into a saucepan. Add the gelatin.
2. Warm the juice mixture on the stove over low heat, stirring constantly until the gelatin dissolves completely.
3. Pour the juice mixture into a blender. Add the yogurt and blueberries. Blend for about 2 minutes.
4. Pour the blended juice into the paper cups.
5. Cover the top of each cup with foil. Poke a wooden stick (or the handle end of a plastic spoon) in the middle of each paper cup, about 2 inches deep or far enough so that it stays in place.
6. Put the cups on a cookie sheet (or plastic tray). Put in the freezer for about 3 hours, or until frozen all the way through.

When it's time to eat or serve the pops, remove from the freezer and let stand at room temperature for about a minute. Then peel off the paper cup and the foil, and lick and slurp your frozen bloody bug juice.

FREAKY FOOD FACT:
The First Bugsicle
The Popsicle was invented in 1905 by an eleven-year-old boy named Frank Epperson. He accidentally left a cup of soda pop outside with a stir stick in it. When he went to retrieve his drink hours later, it had frozen (no doubt with a bug or two in it). When he grew up, Frank Epperson patented his concoction and called it the "Epsicle." The name was later changed to "Popsicle."

Giant Snails

Cinnamon rolls never tasted so great and looked so creepy crawly!

▸ *Difficulty: Medium*   ▸ *Makes 4 servings*

Cooking oil spray
¼ cup finely chopped walnuts or pecans (optional)
3 tablespoons sugar

½ teaspoon ground cinnamon
Waxed paper
1 package (8) refrigerated breadsticks
4 chocolate chips

1. Preheat the oven to 375 degrees. Spray the cookie sheet with cooking oil.
2. In a mixing bowl, stir together the nuts, sugar, and cinnamon. Pour into the pie pan and spread evenly over the bottom.
3. Lay a large sheet of waxed paper on the counter (or table).
4. Remove two rolled-up breadsticks from the package and put on the waxed paper. Unroll 1 of the breadsticks. Press one end of the unrolled breadstick onto the end of the rolled up breadstick. To make the snail's head, take the other end of the unrolled breadstick and roll the top of it under in the other direction.
5. Lift the snail carefully and put it in the pie pan. Gently flatten the snail with the palm of your hand.
6. Remove the snail from the pie pan and place it sugared side up on the cookie sheet. (If the head separates from the body, just press them back together after you put them on the sheet.) Place a chocolate chip eye on the head.
7. Repeat steps 4, 5, and 6 until you've made all four snails.
8. Bake for 15 minutes, or until the bread crust is golden.

Say this tongue twister as fast as you can as many times as you can:

Ben's bun is better buttered, he muttered.
Ben's bun is better buttered, he muttered.
Ben's bun is better buttered, he muttered.

Serve warm or cool. Enjoy your giant sea snails warm and slithery, with melted butter on top.

Mud Pie

Here's the real deal: a mud pie you can actually eat (without worrying about getting pinworms) because it's made with wafers, ice cream, and nuts—rather than dirt, water, and gravel.

▶ *Difficulty: Easy*   ▶ *Makes 8 servings (1 pie)*

1 quart coffee or mocha ice cream, softened
1 premade packaged chocolate pastry crust (9-inch)
Aluminum foil
1½ cups chocolate fudge sauce
½ cup whipped cream
¼ cup chopped nuts (optional)

FREAKY FOOD FACT:
Hot 'n Cold!
People in Tokyo, Japan, eat horseradish ice cream.

1. Spoon the ice cream into the pastry crust and spread evenly with a rubber spatula.
2. Cover with foil and place in the freezer until the ice cream is firm, at least 1 hour.
3. Remove the ice-cream pie from the freezer. Spread fudge sauce over the top. Return to the freezer for 10 hours (or overnight).
4. Just before serving, top with whipped cream and chopped nuts.

If you don't like gravel (chopped nuts) on your mud pie, you can sprinkle dirt (crushed chocolate wafers) on top instead.

A boy was spending the day at his grandparent's house while his mom went shopping with his grandma. When his grandpa left the room to go to the bathroom, the boy gobbled down a bowl of peanuts that was sitting on the coffee table. Later that afternoon, as the boy and his grandpa played checkers together, the boy started to feel guilty. He told his grandpa how sorry he was for eating the peanuts without asking permission. "Oh, that's okay. I never eat the peanuts anyway," his grandpa said. "Since I lost my teeth, all I can do is suck the chocolate off the M&Ms."

Store leftover petrified rabbit turds in plastic bag or container that seals.

Petrified Rabbit Poop

Bet you can't eat just one handful of these caramelized peanuts, which look and crunch just like petrified bunny turds!

▸ **Difficulty:** *Medium*   ▸ *Makes 4 servings*

Aluminum foil
Cooking oil spray
1 egg white
1 teaspoon cold water
16 ounces shelled peanuts
1 cup brown sugar, packed
¼ teaspoon salt

1. Preheat the oven to 225 degrees. Line a cookie sheet with foil and spray with cooking oil.
2. Separate the egg white from the yolk. (You might need an adult's help to do this.) You won't need the yolk for this recipe.
3. In a large bowl, combine the egg white and water. Beat with mixer (or whisk) until frothy (not stiff).
4. Stir in the peanuts until they're completely coated with egg goo.
5. Spread the peanuts over the cookie sheet.
6. In a separate bowl, combine the brown sugar and salt. Pour over the peanuts.
7. Bake for 1 hour, stirring and turning over every 15 minutes.

Armpit Hair

If they didn't smell and taste so yummy, eating these chewy clumps of chocolate-covered Shredded Wheat armpit hairs could make your stomach heave.

▸ *Difficulty: Medium* ▸ *Serves 8 to 10*

3 large Shredded Wheat cereal bundles
3 tablespoons honey
1 tablespoon brown sugar
1 (6-ounce) bag chocolate chips
2 tablespoons butter or margarine
Waxed paper

1. In a rectangular baking pan (9×13-inch), unravel the Shredded Wheat into long strands, so they look like armpit hairs. Set aside.
2. In a medium-size microwaveable bowl, combine the honey, brown sugar, chocolate chips, and butter. Heat on low in the microwave, stirring every 1 to 2 minutes, until melted.
3. Pour the chocolate mixture over the Shredded Wheat. Use a rubber spatula to gently turn over the cereal until it is coated with the gooey chocolate mixture.
4. Line the bottom of a cookie sheet (or flat tray) with waxed paper. Spoon the chocolate-coated Shredded Wheat onto the waxed paper, making 8 to 10 clumps of equal sizes.
5. Use a fork to gently rake the wheat strands (hairs) in one direction.
6. Put the "hairy" candy in the refrigerator for 30 to 45 minutes before serving.

FREAKY FOOD FACT:
True or False?
Eating chocolate causes acne.

False. That's just an old wives' tale. Contrary to popular belief, the sugar and small amount of caffeine in chocolate don't make you hyper, either. But if you eat too much, the high fat content of chocolate can give you diarrhea.

🐚 *Make sure to store any leftover clumps of armpit hair in the refrigerator.*

Moo Patties

These look like the poop piles found in a field of calves.

▸ *Difficulty: Hard* ▸ *Makes about 2 dozen cookies*

1 (3-ounce) package lime Jell-O
1 cup hot water
1 cup sweetened shredded coconut
1 cup (2 sticks) butter, softened
¼ cup sugar
⅔ cup brown sugar, packed
2 eggs
2 tablespoons milk

2 teaspoons vanilla
1¾ cup flour
1 teaspoon baking soda
1 teaspoon salt
2½ cup quick-cooking oats
  (oatmeal)
1 cup chopped walnuts
1 cup raisins (or currants)

1. Preheat oven to 375 degrees.
2. Mix Jell-O and hot water in a bowl. Stir until the gelatin is completely dissolved. Stir the coconut into the Jell-O. Set aside.
3. In a large bowl, combine the butter, sugar, and brown sugar. Beat until creamy. Add the eggs, milk, and vanilla to the sugar mixture. Beat until blended together. Set aside.
5. In a small bowl, combine the flour, baking soda, and salt.
6. Add the flour mixture to the wet mixture. Stir to combine. Stir the oats, nuts, and raisins into the cookie dough.
8. Pour the coconut into a colander and let the Jell-O drain from the coconut. Spread the coconut on two paper towels. Put two more paper towels on top. Press down with the palm of your hand to squeeze out the extra liquid.
9. Spoon rounded tablespoons of dough on an ungreased cookie sheet. The patties will spread during baking, so space them 1½ to 2 inches apart. Bake 9 minutes, until golden brown (the coconut will be green). Allow the patties to cool on the cookie sheet for 1 minute before moving them to a wire rack.

Two flies were sitting on a pile of poo. One fly passed gas. The other fly said, "Hey, do you mind? I'm eating here!"

After chomping down one of these chewy cow patties, you'll want to bellow, "Moooo-ore!"

Tongue on a Stick

Here's a fun way to totally gross out your whole neighborhood: Walk down the street licking one of these meringue tongues on a stick!

▶ *Difficulty: Hard*　▶ *Makes 12 servings*

6 egg whites
1 cup sugar
Red food coloring

Parchment paper
12 Popsicle sticks
Pink or red cake crystals

CHEF'S SECRET:
To Separate Egg Whites
Hold a raw egg in one hand, with the narrow end pointing up. With your other hand, use a fork to poke a small hole in the pointy end of the egg. Turn the egg upside down over a small bowl, and gently shake and twist the egg until the clear part (the egg white) all comes out of the hole and just until the yolk reaches the hole.

1. Put the oven rack on the lowest level. Preheat the oven to 200 degrees.
2. In a large bowl, separate the egg whites from the yolks. Make sure no yolk falls into the bowl. (You might need an adult's help to do this.) You won't need the yolks for this recipe. With an electric mixer, beat the egg whites rapidly until soft peaks start to form. Slowly stir in the sugar, one spoonful at a time. Continue to beat until the mixture forms stiff and shiny peaks. Gently stir 2 or 3 drops of red food coloring into the meringue.
3. Line the bottom of a cookie sheet with parchment paper.
4. Spoon about 3 tablespoons of meringue onto the parchment paper. Use the curved part of the spoon to shape the meringue into the shape and size of a tongue. Repeat until you've used up all the meringue.
5. Gently press a Popsicle stick into the center of each tongue, leaving about a 2-inch handle sticking out of the wider end of the tongue.
6. Sprinkle the cake crystals over the tongues. Bake for 2½ to 3 hours, until the tongues are completely dry to the touch. Allow to cool completely before carefully removing the tongues from the parchment paper with a spatula.

To create the grossest tongues you'll ever love to eat, use a pastry brush to spread a thin layer of "mucous" (marshmallow topping, melted in the microwave) on each baked and cooled tongue, and then sprinkle with "hair" (chocolate cake sprinkles).

Eat Dirt!

Complete this color-by-letters puzzle to uncover a gritty, grubby, yummy dessert in this chapter.

Color each space with the letters in P-O-O-P brown.
Color each space with the letters in B-A-R-F blue.
Color each space with the letters in G-U-T-S red.
Color each space with the letters in M-I-L-D-E-W yellow.

Chapter 27

Burps
and Slurps

Slug Spit

On hot summer days when slugs hide in the shade, you can cool off by slurping on a frosty glass of slimy, tangy slug spit (banana-lime slush).

▶ *Difficulty: Easy* ▶ *Serves 2*

13½ ounces limeade (or other green citrus fruit drink)
1 (¼-ounce) envelope unflavored gelatin
1 banana, sliced
Green food coloring
Yellow food coloring
6 large ice cubes

1. Pour ¼ cup limeade in small saucepan. Sprinkle the gelatin over the juice. Let stand 1 minute.
2. Stir the gelatin into the fruit drink. Heat over low heat, stirring constantly, until gelatin dissolves. Remove from heat.
3. Peel and slice the banana.
4. Put the banana slices and the rest of the fruit drink in a blender. Cover and mix until smooth.
5. Add the gelatin mix and the green and yellow food coloring. Cover and mix 1 minute.
6. Add the ice cubes to the blender, cover, and blend on high speed for 1 to 2 minutes until slushy.

🍴 *Pour the slug spit into glasses and serve immediately. Slurp slowly, so you don't get brain freeze!*

Bloody Hairy

The toasted coconut floating in this raspberry-lemonade spritzer feels like hair in your mouth. Disgusting!

▶ *Difficulty: Medium* ▶ *Serves 6*

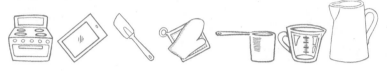

spritzer fruit juice mixed with carbonated (bubbly) water or flavored soda, such as ginger ale

1 cup shredded coconut
3 cups raspberries (fresh or frozen)
6 ounces lemonade (fresh or from frozen concentrate)
1 quart ginger ale

1. Preheat oven to 350 degrees.
2. Spread the coconut on the bottom of an ungreased cookie sheet.
3. Toast the coconut in the oven 5 to 10 minutes, until golden brown. Stir and flip over the coconut two times while it's toasting. Remove from pan and let cool.
4. Rinse and drain the raspberries. Put them in a bowl and mash them with a fork.
5. Put the smashed raspberries, lemonade, and ginger ale in a large pitcher. Stir to mix.
6. Put a handful of toasted coconut in the bottom of each glass.
7. Slowly pour the berry spritzer over the coconut.

What do you call a cat that has eaten a lemon?

A sour puss!

When you pour the bloody pulp (bubbly raspberry lemonade) into a glass, the hair (toasted coconut) will rise to the top with the foam.

Septic Soda

This chocolate frappe with bits of dried poop (chocolate chips) floating in it is grotesquely good to the last gulp!

▸ **Difficulty: Easy**   ▸ **Serves 4**

1 quart chocolate chip ice cream, softened
¾ cup chocolate syrup
1 liter (1 quart) club soda
4 small Tootsie Rolls (optional)

1. Let the ice cream sit on the counter at room temperature for a few minutes, until it is soft enough to scoop easily.
2. Fill tall glasses about half full with ice cream.
3. Pour 3 tablespoons of chocolate syrup in each glass.
4. Slowly pour the soda into each glass and fill almost to the top, leaving about 1 inch from the rim.
5. Stir well with a spoon.
6. Serve immediately with spoons (iced-tea spoons are best) so you and your guests can scoop out all the chunks of "poop" (chocolate chips).

You can use vanilla, chocolate, or mint chocolate chip ice cream for your septic soda. We especially like the revolting mildew-green color of the mint flavor. Septic soda is even more disgusting with a turd (unwrapped mini Tootsie Roll) pressed onto the rim of each glass.

CHEF'S SECRET:
Got Milk Skitters?
For people who are lactose intolerant—meaning they often get diarrhea from dairy products—adding chocolate to milk can make it easier to digest.

Jungle Rot

This strawberry-kiwi smoothie feels, looks, and smells like the goop that squishes out of rotting fruit when you walk through a tropical forest.

▸ **Difficulty:** *Medium*   ▸ **Makes 2 servings**

1 kiwi
6 large strawberries, fresh or frozen
½ cup blueberries, fresh or frozen
1 banana
½ cup frozen vanilla yogurt
¾ cup pineapple juice

WORDS to KNOW

smoothie a cold drink made with fruit, fruit juice or milk, and either yogurt, ice cream, or sherbet all blended together into a smooth liquid; sometimes other ingredients, such as seeds, nuts, and spices, are added.

1. Wash and drain the kiwi, strawberries, and blueberries.
2. Peel the kiwi. Use a blunt knife to cut the kiwi into small pieces.
3. Use a blunt knife to cut the strawberries in half.
4. Peel the banana. Slice it with a blunt knife.
5. Put all the ingredients in a blender. Cover and blend until smooth and slightly frothy.

For 100 percent authentic jungle rot, use a pomegranate instead of strawberries. Pomegranates have a tough outer skin, so ask an adult to cut it open for you. Then, just scoop out the insides, which look like red fish eggs.

What is invisible and smells like a banana?

A monkey fart!

Putrid Punch

This midnight-black fruit punch with gummy-bug ice cubes is a fun way to gross out your friends' parties!

▶ *Difficulty: Easy* ▶ *Serves 16 to 20*

32 to 64 gummy bugs (or raisins)
1 package unsweetened grape Kool-Aid
1 package unsweetened orange Kool-Aid
2 cups sugar
3 quarts cold water
1 quart ginger ale

Step One: Make the Frozen Flies

1. Fill two large ice-cube trays half full with water. Put them in the freezer for several hours, until frozen.
2. Put one or two gummy bugs (or raisins) in each cube.
3. Fill the ice-cube trays the rest of the way with water.
4. Put them in the freezer for several hours, until frozen.

Step Two: Make the Putrid Punch

1. In a large punch bowl (or pitcher), mix together the Kool-Aid mixes, sugar, and water.
2. Slowly stir in the ginger ale.
3. Add the gummy-bug ice cubes.

Instead of freezing gummy bugs in the ice cubes, make frozen eyeballs by putting half a green grape with a raisin stuck in the center in each ice cube.

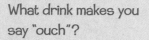

What drink makes you say "ouch"?

Punch!

FREAKY FOOD FACT:
Which of these fruits do American kids like best? Write "1" next to the one you guess is the most favorite, "2" next to the second favorite, and so on.

_____Grapes

_____Apples

_____Bananas

_____Berries

_____Peaches

1. apples 2. bananas 3. grapes 4. peaches 5. berries

Bottoms Up!

Katy, Joe, and Ivan always clink together their glasses and yell "Bottoms up!" before chugging their favorite drinks in one long gulp. The letters that make up the names of the main flavor in each of their favorite drinks are hidden on their shirts. Rearrange the letters from each shirt to find out who likes which flavor the very best.

The main ingredient in Katy's favorite drink is __ __ __ __.

The main ingredient in Joe's favorite drink is __ __ __ __ __ __ __ __.

The main ingredient in Ivan's favorite drink is __ __ __ __ __ __ __ __.

Frozen Flotsam

Make sure you have a teaspoon ready to slurp the gnat-covered flotsam (ice cream with chocolate sprinkles) from this frosty root beer float. Yum!

▶ **Difficulty: Easy** ▶ **Serves 1**

6 ounces root beer
1 scoop vanilla ice cream
1 teaspoon chocolate cake sprinkles

1. Slowly pour the root beer into a frosted or chilled mug. Fill it part way, leaving about 1 inch from the top. Let stand until the foam goes down.
2. Put a large scoop of ice cream into the mug.
3. Sprinkle the chocolate sprinkles over the top of the ice cream.

If you don't want to frost the mug or a tall glass, put it in the refrigerator for 5–10 minutes to chill it before adding the sewer water (root beer), flotsam (ice cream), and gnats (chocolate sprinkles).

Where in school are you most likely to catch a cold?

In the cough-eteria!

CHEF'S SECRET:
To Frost a Mug
Run cool water from the faucet over the outside and inside of a glass or ceramic mug. Put the wet mug in the freezer for 5 to 10 minutes.

Steaming Coyote Pee

This simple recipe for hot apple cider with cinnamon sticks is the most fun when you tell people it's fresh coyote pee stirred with bark from the tree the coyote peed on.

▶ *Difficulty: Easy*   ▶ *Makes 1 serving*

1 cup apple cider   1 cinnamon stick

1. Pour the apple cider into a microwave-safe mug or cup.
2. Warm the cider in the microwave for about 1 minute, until hot but not bubbling. Let the hot cider sit in the microwave for 10 seconds before removing.
3. Put a cinnamon stick in the cup and serve.

Hot 'n Chunky Hershey Squirts

This hot chocolate with melting butterscotch chips and mini marshmallows looks a lot like diarrhea. Enjoy!

▶ *Difficulty: Easy*   ▶ *Serves 1*

1 cup milk
2 heaping tablespoons semi-sweet
  cocoa powder

1 tablespoon butterscotch chips
1 tablespoon mini marshmallows

1. Fill a large microwave-safe mug or cup almost full with milk, leaving about 1 inch from the rim.
2. Heat the milk in the microwave for about 1 minute, until hot but not boiling or curdling. Let the hot chocolate sit in the microwave for 10 seconds before removing.
3. Stir in the butterscotch chips. Top with marshmallows.

🐚🌀 You can leave the cinnamon stick in the mug while you sip the hot pee or you can remove it before you drink.

FREAKY FOOD FACT:
Curds Away!
What type of milk never curdles?
A. Cow milk
B. Goat milk
C. Camel milk
D. Human milk

C. Camel milk!

🐚🌀 You can substitute water and instant hot chocolate mix for the milk and cocoa powder if you'd like, or you can use chocolate syrup instead of cocoa powder.

Gag Me with a Spoonerism

A spoonerism is when the letters or syllables in words or phrases get flip-flopped and form a silly phrase. For example, "This is the pun fart" is a spoonerism for "This is the fun part."

The word "spoonerism" is named after William Archibald Spooner, a professor in England more than seventy years ago who was famous for accidentally goofing up his words—for instance, saying, "Having tasted two worms," when he meant to say, "Having wasted two terms." Try to figure out the real words for these spoonerisms. (Hint: They're all food terms.)

1. dot hog   ___ ___
2. brown fudgie   _____ _____
3. chilled grease   _____ _____
4. chork pops   _____ _____
5. chalk hock a lot ___ _____
6. sea poop   ___ _____
7. toot farts   _____ _____
8. belly jeans   _____ _____
9. snail tracks   _____ _____
10. nasal hut   _____

Chapter 28

Gross Gags and Fun Stuff

Fake Barf

You can actually eat this fake barf—if you can stomach the thought of it.

▸ *Difficulty: Hard*   ▸ *Makes 1 blob of barf*

¼ cup applesauce
1 envelope (¼ ounce) unflavored gelatin
⅛ teaspoon cocoa powder
½ cup uncooked oatmeal
Raisin bran cereal (about ½ cup)
Handful of raisins
Cooking oil spray

1. Warm the applesauce in the frying pan over low heat, stirring constantly, just until heated through.
2. Stir in the gelatin and cocoa powder. Remove from heat.
3. Sprinkle a handful of oatmeal over the applesauce mixture. Stir it in just enough to mix the ingredients. The mixture should be lumpy and sticky.
4. Stir a handful of raisin bran into the oatmeal mixture, just enough to mix it in.
5. Add more oatmeal and raisin bran, a little at a time, until the mixture has the look and consistency of vomit.
6. Spray a dinner plate with cooking oil.
7. Spread the oatmeal mixture on the plate. Use a spoon or your hands to mold it into the shape of a pile of puke.
8. Scatter a small handful of raisins on the gooey gunk.
9. Let the barf sit for a few hours to cool and to set.

 When you're ready to put the fake barf somewhere for one of your family members to discover, use a spatula to remove it from the plate.

What's worse than finding a worm in your half-eaten apple?

Finding half a worm!

Nasty Nibbles

Do you know this little ditty? *Everybody's doing it, doing it, doing it / Picking their nose and chewing it, chewing it / Thinking it's candy, when it's not / It's s-n-o-t, snot, snot, snot!* Well, maybe not everybody eats snot, but some people do. Guess what? That's not the only yucky stuff people eat that is not meant to be eaten. Write the letter that goes with the number to find out the other disgusting things some people eat.

Nasty Nibbles

Do you know this little ditty? *Everybody's doing it, doing it, doing it / Picking their nose and chewing it, chewing it / Thinking it's candy, when it's not / It's s-n-o-t, snot, snot, snot!* Well, maybe not everybody eats snot, but some people do. Guess what? That's not the only yucky stuff people eat that is not meant to be eaten. Write the letter that goes with the number to find out the other disgusting things some people eat.

1 = a
2 = b
3 = c
4 = d
5 = e
6 = f
7 = g
8 = h
9 = i
10 = j
11 = k
12 = l
13 = m
14 = n
15 = o
16 = p

Fake Boogers and Snot

You can smear this edible nose blow on your hand in secret, pretend sneeze in front of your family or friends, and then lick the fake boogers and snot off your hand.

▸ *Difficulty: Easy*   ▸ *Makes about 8 fake nose blows*

½ cup water
3 (¼-ounce) envelopes unflavored gelatin
⅓ to ½ cup light corn syrup
A few white raisins

1. Put the water in a microwave-safe cup or mug. Heat just until it starts to boil.
2. Sprinkle the gelatin into the hot water. Stir with a fork to dissolve the gelatin. Let it set for a few minutes, until it sets to a loose gel.
3. Add enough corn syrup to make 1 cup. Stir with a fork to mix.
4. Add a small handful of white raisins.
5. If the goop thickens too much, add hot water by the teaspoon until it's loose enough to lift with a fork.

Use immediately, lifting the booger-covered snot out of the cup with a fork.

PLAY IT SAFE:

Keep paper towels, oven mitts, wooden spoons, cans of spray cooking oil, and anything else that might be flammable off the stovetop at all times.

FREAKY FOOD FACT:
Record-Breaking Nose Blow

The world's record for the longest strand of spaghetti blown out of a person's nose is 7½ feet. Don't try this at home, or at school, or in restaurants, or at Grandma's, or anywhere!

Fake Slime

This slimy green gunk is not edible. Make it for fun and gags only—not for eating!

▶ *Difficulty: Medium*   ▶ *Makes about 2½ cups*

⅛ cup borax laundry booster
2 cups plus ¼ cup water
¼ cup white glue (such as Elmer's)
1 or 2 drops green food coloring

1. In a small saucepan, mix together the borax and 2 cups of water.
2. Stirring constantly, heat over a medium burner until the borax dissolves completely. Remove from heat and set aside to cool.
3. In a small cup, mix together the glue and the remaining ¼ cup of water.
4. Put a plastic food storage bag that seals inside a large plastic drinking glass. Fold the open sides of the bag over the rim of the glass.
5. Pour (or scrape) the glue mixture into the bag.
6. Stir the food coloring into the borax mixture.
7. Pour the borax mixture into the plastic bag.
8. Close the bag, squeezing out as much air as possible.
9. Knead the mixture in the closed bag until it forms into slime. Squeeze the slime into a plastic container with a tight-fitting lid. This makes it easier to use and to store any leftovers. An empty, clean, and dry margarine tub works well for this.

Make sure not to get the slime on furniture, carpet, clothing, or walls because the food coloring will stain.

WORDS to KNOW

knead to repeatedly fold, press, and turn a mixture of ingredients, called "dough" or "batter," until it is smooth and pliable like putty

Fake Wounds

It's fun to show off your fake wound to friends—and to freak out your mom! Just remember: These are not edible.

▸ *Difficulty: Hard*   ▸ *Makes 1 fake wound*

1 tablespoon (finger full) petroleum jelly
3 or 4 drops red food coloring
2 to 3 pinches cocoa powder
1 white tissue

1. Put a tablespoon of petroleum jelly into a small bowl.
2. Stir in 3 drops of food coloring. If it isn't red enough, add another drop of food coloring.
3. Stir in a pinch of cocoa powder to darken the red to the color of real blood.
4. Rip off a small rectangle of tissue, about 3 inches by 2 inches.
5. Place the rectangle of tissue on your arm or wherever you want your wound to be.
6. Cover the tissue with the blood-red petroleum jelly.
7. Use your fingers to shape the petroleum jelly to look like a wound site—a small mound that's slightly higher in the center.
8. Smear the blood-red petroleum jelly on the center of the wound.
9. Sprinkle cocoa on the edges of the wound and use your finger to rub in the cocoa a little.

If you want to cover yourself with several oozing wounds, just use a bigger bowl and double, triple, or even quadruple the recipe.

What do you get if you cross a snake with a pie?

A pie-thon!

Finger Paint

This inedible (but nontoxic) finger paint gives you double the fun: First, when you stick your fingers in the slimy goop and spread it on the page, and again when you see the repulsed looks on your family's faces when you show them the yucky pictures you drew!

▶ *Difficulty: Medium*   ▶ *Makes 5 small jars of finger paint*

1 cup cold water, divided into ¾ cup and ¼ cup
½ cup cornstarch
1 (3-ounce) envelope unflavored gelatin
½ cup Ivory soap flakes or laundry detergent
Food coloring, 5 colors

1. Put ¼ cup of cold water in a small bowl. Add the gelatin to water in the bowl. Let stand for several minutes.
2. Put ¾ cup of cold water in a saucepan. Add the cornstarch to the saucepan. Stir with a fork until the cornstarch is dissolved.
3. Cook the cornstarch and water over medium heat, stirring constantly, until it is clear and starts to boil. Remove from heat.
4. Add the softened gelatin to the hot starchy water. Stir gently and slowly to fold in. Add the soap and stir until dissolved. Let cool.
5. Divide the cooled water mixture into 5 small jars or plastic bowls.
6. Put a different color of food coloring in each jar and stir to mix. Start with 2 drops and then add more drops one at a time until you get the color you want.
7. Store leftover finger paint in glass or plastic containers with tight-fitting lids. Note: Finger paint will stain fabric, plastic, and other materials.

FREAKY FOOD FACT:
Legume Ka-Boom!
Peanuts are used to manufacture dynamite.

You can mix different colors together to create your own gross colors of finger paint—for example, *Poop Brown* (red and green), *Snot Green* (green and yellow), and *Rot-Gut Black* (red, green, blue).

Smelly Play Dough

You can make this play dough with any flavor of Kool-Aid and shape it into gross stuff like pig's brains, elephant dung, pimple faces, and pointy-tongued lizards.

▶ *Difficulty: Hard*   ▶ *Makes 1 tub of play dough*

1 cup cold water
1 tablespoon vegetable oil
2 packages of same flavor of unsweetened Kool-Aid (or similar drink mix)
¼ cup salt
1 cup flour
5 teaspoons cream of tartar

1. In a medium saucepan, combine water, oil, Kool-Aid, and salt.
2. Cook over medium heat and stir until the salt dissolves.
3. Add the flour and cream of tartar in the saucepan all at once.
4. Continue cooking and stirring for a few minutes, until the dough is mixed very well and forms a ball. Remove from the heat immediately (as soon as it forms a ball).
5. Dump onto an ungreased cookie sheet. Let the dough cool enough for you to handle it comfortably.
6. While the dough is still warm, knead it for a few minutes, until it is smooth and pliable.
7. Let the dough finish cooling completely, to room temperature, before shaping it into hideously gross stuff.

Instead of using two packages of the same flavor of Kool-Aid, you can experiment with combining different flavors to come up with play dough with disgusting colors and sickening smells.

CHEF'S SECRET:
Save It for a Rainy Day
Store your play dough in a resealable plastic bag or in a plastic container with a lid (such as a clean margarine tub) to keep it fresh and pliable.

Slimed!

If you can find your way from the sponge to the end before their mom slips and falls on it, maybe Megan and Todd won't get in deep doo-doo for having a slime fight in the house! On your sponge, get slimed, and go!

Raunchy Food Trivia

As you solve this crossword you'll discover a bunch of fun and funky things about food that are sure to gross you out!

Down

1. Pork rinds are made from this part of a hog. (Clue: Rhymes with "chin.")
2. This can happen if your stomach "turns" when you eat or smell rotten food.
3. The common name for curdled soy bean (a.k.a. "bean crud"), which is a source of protein for vegetarians.
4. A red, heart-shaped fruit with seeds on its skin that look like zits, often eaten with shortcake and whipped cream.
5. Indians of the rainforest in Brazil eat omelets made from the eggs of this big, hairy creature.
6. This deep-fried delicacy is popular in France, but Kermit says his are made for hopping.
7. These sandwiches are made with marshmallow, chocolate, and graham crackers.
9. "Lubberwort" is another name for _____ food. (Clue: Rhymes with "gunk.")
10. Before the Civil War, people in the South called these "monkey nuts" and "goober peas."
13. These grow in bunches on a vine and are red, green, or purple when ripe. When these fruits are dried and shriveled up, they're called "raisins."
14. This small, red, bitter fruit is nicknamed "bounce berry" because it bounces if dropped on the ground. (Clue: Often served on Thanksgiving.)
17. A dry, yellowish-white cheese that "farts" while it is aging, causing holes to form in the cheese when the gas bubbles up and bursts.
19. It takes 4 tons of dried up grapes to produce 1 ton of these chewy fruits.
21. Animal intestines give these deli meats their turd-like shape. (Clue: They're usually served in buns or mixed with baked beans.)
22. Inuits (Eskimos) eat a special dish they call "stinky tail," which is made from the fermented tail of this buck-toothed, paddle-tailed, water-loving, dam-building animal.
24. A kind of jam you don't want to eat, because it usually smells like dirty feet.

Across

2. This main ingredient in PB&J sandwiches is also good for removing chewing gum from hair and clothes.
4. Herring is a small and _____ fish. (Clue: You might need to hold your nose to eat it.)
5. Fungi that are sniffed out by pigs. It's also the name of a fancy chocolate candy with a creamy center.
8. The letters of this canned meat product stand for shoulder, pork, ham. It's also the name of e-mail you don't want.
10. "Chitlins" (or "chitterlings") are a Southern dish made with onions, hot peppers, vinegar, and the intestines of this animal. (Clue: Oink!)
11. A yellow fruit that can be split and that monkeys love.
12. These are hatched by chickens, and they smell like sulfur when they're rotten.
13. An ingredient commonly found in Italian food that has the nickname "stinky rose."
15. This often happens when you eat a lot of spicy food or beans.
16. "Escargot" is a fancy word for these disgusting critters, cooked in garlic and oil or butter. (Clue: They slither on the ground and leave a trail of slime behind them.)
18. This often happens when you drink soda really fast.
20. "Calamari" is a fancy name for this cooked sea creature. (Clue: Rhymes with "skid," as in the skid marks on underwear.)
23. Eighty percent of the people in the world eat these types of small, crawling, and flying critters.
25. Seventy out of 100 people pick their noses, and 3 out of those 70 nose-pickers eat these.
26. This is what you get when you eat way too many prunes. (Clue: There's a song about it in Chapter 5.)

Gastronomical Glossary

Several important cooking terms are explained in Chapter 20. You'll also find several terms explained in the Words to Know boxes scattered throughout the book. To make it easy as pie to look up the meaning of all the words you'll need to know while preparing the recipes in this book, they're all here in one place and in alphabetical order. By the way, gastronomical means "having to do with good eating," and a glossary is a mini dictionary that defines special words used in a book.

al dente—an Italian word that means "to the tooth;" cooking pasta until it is tender but still firm and gives a slight resistance when you bite into it

Alfredo sauce—a white sauce made of butter, cream, and Parmesan cheese, served over pasta

au gratin—covered with bread crumbs and/or butter and grated cheese and browned in the oven

bake—to cook something inside the oven, using the heat from the bottom of the oven

baking pan—a glass or metal pan used for cooking food in the oven; can be square or rectangular and is usually shallow (not very deep)

batter—a soft and wet mixture of ingredients, such as sugar, eggs, flour, spices, butter, and milk, that is used to cook or bake many different things, including cakes, cookies, the coating on fried foods, muffins, and pancakes

beat—to mix ingredients together fast and hard with an electric mixer, fork, spoon, or whisk

blend—to mix ingredients together to form a smooth batter, dough, or liquid

blender—an electric appliance used for blending, chopping, grinding, and mixing foods; it has a glass or metal pitcher with a tight-fitting lid attached to it

boil—to heat a liquid or to cook solid food in a liquid until the liquid bubbles; some recipes call for a "full boil," which means the liquid is bubbly all over, while other recipes say to heat the liquid until it "starts" to boil, which means only until small bubbles begin to form

boil over—when boiling liquid rises above the top edge of the pot and falls over the sides of the pot

blunt knife—a knife with a dull edge, rather than a sharp edge, such as a butter knife; some blunt knives have a serrated edge, which helps in cutting bread and many other solid foods

broil—to cook food under the broiler part of the oven where the heat comes from the top; a broiler is either part of an oven or is its own separate unit

brown—to cook food on the stovetop or to bake in the oven until the food turns brown and crispy on the outside

can opener—an electric appliance or a manual tool used to open metal cans containing food

caramelize—heating sugar or food covered in a sugary ingredient (such as brown sugar or maple syrup) until it melts and turns the color and constancy of caramel candy

Gastronomical Glossary

casserole dish—a large glass dish with sides that is used to make casseroles and baked foods in the oven; available in round, oval, square, and rectangular shapes and in different sizes (usually 1-quart or 2-quart), and they often have lids

chill—to put ingredients, mixtures, or prepared food in a refrigerator until it is cold

chop—to cut food into small pieces with a blender, knife, or food processor

colander—a large bowl with holes in it used to drain water or liquid from foods such as vegetables, boiled potatoes, and cooked pasta; can be metal or plastic, and usually has a small handle on each side

confectioners' sugar—sugar that has been ground to a fine powder and mixed with cornstarch, which causes the food being prepared to thicken (such as with cake frosting)

cookie sheet—a flat metal sheet used for baking cookies and many other solid foods; sometimes called a "baking sheet"

cooking oil spray—a vegetable oil that comes in a spray can, used to grease pots and other cooking ware; also sometimes sprayed directly on foods to help brown them during baking or broiling.

cooking spoon—a large spoon (made of metal, hard plastic, or wood) with a long handle; some cooking spoons have slats or holes in them

cool—to let food sit at room temperature until it is no longer hot

core—to remove the center of a fruit or vegetable containing the seeds, leaving the outer skin and enough flesh for the fruit to maintain its shape; the center of a vegetable or fruit (such as an apple)

cream—to mix wet and dry ingredients together (such as butter, eggs, sugar, and flour) until they form a smooth and creamy mixture

cutting board—a flat board made of wood, hard plastic, or glass used to cut food on

delicacy—a special food that a group of people really like

dice—to cut food into very small, even-sized, square-shaped pieces

drain—to pour off the liquid in which food is stored or cooked, usually by pouring the food into a colander

drizzle—to sprinkle a liquid ingredient, such as chocolate sauce or melted butter, over a food

dry mixture—a combination of certain dry ingredients in a recipe—such as flour, baking soda, baking powder, salt, and dried herbs and spices

Dutch oven—a large, heavy pot with a tight-fitting lid that is shaped like a dome

edible—can be eaten

electric mixer—an electric appliance used for mixing ingredients

entrée—the main course of a meal, such as spaghetti with meat balls

fold—to combine ingredients by gently and repeatedly turning the mixture over just until the different foods are mixed together

fondue—bite-sized foods (bread, meat, poultry, fish, fruit, or vegetables) skewered on a long, thin metal fork and dipped in melted cheese, melted chocolate, hot oil, broth, or a sauce

frappe—a blended drink that is frozen or partially frozen so that it's slushy and has foam on top

fry—to cook food in fat or oil in a skillet over medium to high heat

gel—to allow a liquid to set or firm up (congeal) to the consistency of jelly

glass measuring cup—a glass cup with a handle, a spout, and measurements printed on the side of the cup, used to measure liquids; comes in 1-cup, 2-cup, and 4-cup sizes

grate—to shred food into very tiny pieces with a shredder, blender, or food processor

grease—to spray or spread a thin layer of butter, margarine, shortening, or oil on a baking pan or dish to prevent food from sticking

griddle—a flat, square pan used to grill pancakes, French toast, sandwiches, hamburgers, and other food

ice-cream scoop—a hard plastic or metal tool shaped like either a giant spoon or a round ball, used to scoop ice cream and sherbet out of the carton; can also be used to scoop cookie batter, sour cream, and other foods

knead—to repeatedly fold, punch, press, and turn dough or batter to work air into it and to make it the right consistency—for example, to make bread dough smooth and pliable, like silly putty

knife—a tool with a handle and a flat, sharp edge, used for cutting, slicing, or carving food; available in many sizes, and some have serrated edges

ladle—a deep, rounded spoon with a long handle used to scoop sauces, soups, and other liquids out of a pot, serving dish, or other container

level—a measuring cup or spoon filled with a dry ingredient that is then flattened with a blunt knife so that the top of an ingredient is not overflowing or "rounded"

measuring cups—metal or plastic cups of many different sizes (⅛ cup, ¼ cup, ⅓ cup, ¾ cup, and 1 cup) used to measure dry ingredients, usually nested so the smaller ones fit inside the larger ones to form a single stack of cups

microwave oven—an electrical appliance that looks like a small oven but is used to warm, cook, melt, and boil food; cooks food very quickly using electromagnetic waves (microwaves)

mince—to cut food into tiny pieces using a knife, grater, or food processor

mix—to stir together two or more ingredients to combine them

mixing bowls—deep bowls of varying widths and made of glass or metal, used to blend, mix, or whip ingredients together.

muffin tins—a baking pan with small, rounded cups used for baking cupcakes and muffins, usually made of metal and sometimes out of glass

new potatoes—very small potatoes that are harvested early, before they can grow large; sometimes called "young" or "baby" potatoes, they have a thinner skin and their flesh is sweeter and firmer than mature potatoes

oven—an electric or gas appliance used for baking and broiling food

oven mitts—large, thick mittens made of fire-resistant material, used to handle hot pots and pans, cooking utensils, and other cookware

parchment paper—strong, see-through paper that can withstand heat and is used to wrap foods in to seal in juices and flavors while baking

pastry brush—a small brush used to spread melted butter and sauces over food

pie plate—a shallow dish made of glass or metal, used for baking pies and other baked goods; sometimes called a "pie tin" or "pie pan"

peel—to remove skin from fruits and vegetables

pitcher—A large glass, plastic, or metal container with a handle and a spout used for serving water or cold drinks

pitted—when the seed in the center of the fruit is removed—such as with apricots, avocados, peaches, and olives

pizza cutter—a tool with a handle on one end and a thin, sharp wheel at the other end used to cut pizza, cookie dough, bread dough, and other mushy foods

plate—a small, flat dish used to serve individual helpings of food

platter—a large, flat dish used to serve food "family style," from which individual servings are dished out at the table

potato masher—a tool used to mash cooked potatoes or soft foods, such as avocados, until they are smooth

pot holders—thick, fire-resistant material, usually in the shape of a square, used to handle hot pots and pans, cooking utensils, and other cookware

preheat—to turn on a cooking appliance (such as an oven, an electric skillet, or an electric crock pot), set it to the desired temperature, and wait until it reaches that temperature before putting the food in to cook; oil and liquids are also sometimes preheated in a pan on a stovetop burner

puree—to mix and mash food until it is the consistency of baby food (or baby poop)

rolling pin—a roller made of wood, plastic, or marble with handles on each end, used to flatten dough such as for piecrust, biscuits, and cookies

rounded—a measuring cup or spoon filled until the ingredient makes a slight mound on top, rather than being "level"

rubber spatula—a tool with a flat rubber tip and a long handle, used to remove batter or liquids from a blender, food processor, or mixing bowl and to spread or level foods, such as icing on a cake and brownie batter in a pan

saucepan—a pot with a long handle used to cook food on a stovetop; come in several sizes, often with form-fitting lids

sauté—to cook food on a low to medium temperature in a skillet with a small amount of butter, margarine, or oil

serrated knife—a sharp knife that has an edge with a row of small notches that are similar to the teeth on a saw

serving bowls—different sizes and shapes of bowls, usually made of glass but sometimes made of plastic or wood, used to serve food "family style" by dishing out individual helpings at the table.

set—to let prepared food, such as brownies and pudding, sit or cool without stirring until it congeals (firms up) to the desired consistency

shish kabob—cubes of marinated meat and sometimes vegetables cooked on a skewer (stick) over hot coals or broiled

shred—to cut food into small, thin strips, using a shredder, blender, or food processor

simmer—to cook food over low heat, allowing it to bubble gently but not boil fully

skewer—a long, thin stick made of wood or metal, used to cook shish kabobs

skillet—a shallow pan used for frying, stir-frying, and sautéing food in hot fat or oil

slice—to cut food into thin slices of about the same size, such as with bread

smoothie—a cold drink made with fruit, fruit juice or milk, and either yogurt, ice cream, or sherbet all blended together into a smooth liquid; sometimes other ingredients such as seeds, nuts, and spices are added

spatula—a tool with a flat metal shovel on one end and a long handle on the other, used to flip, lift, turn, and remove foods (such as cookies, eggs, grilled cheese sandwiches, hamburgers, and pancakes) from pots, pans, and other cookware

spritzer—fruit juice mixed with carbonated (bubbly) water or flavored soda, such as ginger ale

steam—to cook food over boiling water so the steam (not the water) cooks the food

stir—to turn food in a circular motion with a spoon

stir-fry—to cook food in a small amount of oil in a wok or skillet over high heat while stirring continuously

stock—a liquid broth made from slowly cooking meat, bones, and/or vegetables in water over low heat; also called "soup stock" or "soup base"

stove—an electric or gas appliance with burners for cooking food, also called a "range" (A stove or range may have only a stovetop and no oven, or it can be a stovetop and oven combined.)

taco—a small tortilla that is folded, filled with ingredients (such as meat, cheese, lettuce), and prepared soft (warmed) or crisp (fried)

thicken—to heat and stir a combination of water, milk, broth, and sometimes butter or margarine with a thickening agent such as flour or cornstarch until the mixture turns from liquid to a heavy sauce, such as gravy, or a soft solid, such as pudding

toast—to cook food, such as bread, coconut, and nuts, in a toaster or oven until the surface turns crispy and golden brown

toaster—an electric appliance with two or four slots, used to toast bread, English muffins, and bagels

tongs—a metal tool with a long handle and rounded pinchers at the other end (for grabbing food)

tortilla—a flat, round, thin bread made from wheat flour or cornmeal; usually filled or topped with other ingredients and served flat (quesadilla), wrapped (burrito), rolled up (enchilada), or folded (taco)

utensils—a variety of hand-held tools used to prepare and cook food

vegetable peeler—a tool with a handle on one end and a sharp implement that looks like a long keyhole on the other, used to scrape the skin off of apples, carrots, cucumbers, pears, potatoes, zucchini, and other vegetables; sometimes called a "potato peeler"

wet mixture—a combination of certain wet ingredients in a recipe—such as butter, shortening, oil, water, milk, eggs, sugar, brown sugar, syrup, and liquid extracts

whip—to beat food rapidly with a blender, egg-beater, electric mixer, food processor, fork, or whisk.

whisk—a tool used to combine ingredients and to beat foods rapidly

wok—a wide and deep pan with a rounded bottom used to stir-fry food in a small amount of very hot oil

wooden spoons—long-handled spoons made out of wood and in many different sizes, used for mixing and stirring all types of food

Puzzle Answers

page 274 • Appliance Monsters

page 277 • Tool Mess!

page 290 • Trouble at the Table
Tina told Tony not to taste toenails at the table.

page 302 • Can You Say Flatulence?

page 307 •
Race to the Latrine

Puzzle Answers

page 318 • Barf-A-Rhyme

scarf	barf	duke	puke
comet	vomit	shelf	ralph
twirl	hurl	use hunch	lose lunch
snow	blow	fetch	retch
woodchuck	upchuck	chin up	throw up
sleeve	heave	hesitate	regurgitate

page 325 • Eewwww! Who Eats This Stuff?

Baked rooster combs . . . . Italy
Beef blood pudding . . . . Norway
Bird's nest soup . . . . China
Blubber . . . . The Arctic
Boiled fish eyes . . . . The Philippines
Broiled beetle grubs . . . . Japan
Deep-fried monkey toes . . . . . . Indonesia
Fried squirrel brain . . . . United States (Southern)
Raw turtle eggs . . . . Nicaragua
Roasted bat . . . . Samoa
Salted, sun-dried grasshoppers . . . Mexico
Sautéed camel's feet . . . . France
Spoiled yak milk . . . . Tibet
Warm cow urine . . . . Kenya
White ant pie . . . . Tanzania

page 330 • Funky Fridge

page 345 • Slurp-ghetti

page 350 • Find and Sing

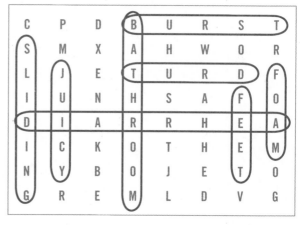

page 361 • Bug-Eating Veggie Ogress

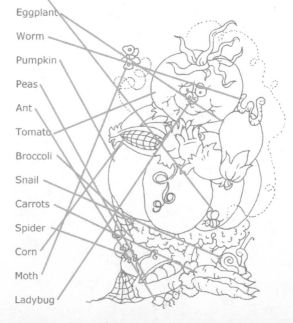

Bee
Eggplant
Worm
Pumpkin
Peas
Ant
Tomato
Broccoli
Snail
Carrots
Spider
Corn
Moth
Ladybug

Puzzle Answers

page 366 • Poo-ey!

vinegar	moldy bread
Brussels sprouts	rotten eggs
blue cheese	spoiled milk
tuna fish	rancid meat

page 380 • Eat Dirt!

page 387 • Bottoms Up!

Kate = lime, Joe = raspberry, Ivan = chocolate.

page 390 • Gag Me with a Spoonerism

1. dot hog . . . . hot dog
2. brown fudgie . . . . fudge brownie
3. chilled grease . . . grilled cheese
4. chork pops . . . . . pork chops
5. chalk hock a lot . . hot chocolate
6. sea poop . . . . pea soup
7. toot farts . . . . fruit tarts
8. belly jeans . . . . . . jelly beans
9. snail tracks . . . . . trail snacks
10. nasal hut . . . . hazelnut

page 399 • Slimed!

page 393 •

Nasty Nibbles

(A) boogers
(B) fingernails
(C) scabs
(D) dead skin
(E) hair
(F) snot
(G) toe jam
(H) ear wax
(I) blood
(J) navel lint

page 400 • Raunchy Food Trivia